DIFFERENTIAL EQUATIONS

ABOUT THE AUTHOR

Kaj L. Nielsen received the degrees of B.S. from the University of Michigan, M.A. from Syracuse University, and Ph.D. from the University of Illinois. He has held teaching positions at Syracuse, Illinois, Brown, and Louisiana State University. He has been associated with a number of industries as a research engineer and scientist. He is at present Professor of Mathematics at Butler University. Dr. Nielsen has written numerous articles based upon original research in mathematics and published in leading mathematical and engineering journals. He is the author or coauthor of *College Mathematics*, *Plane and Spherical Trigonometry*, *Logarithmic and Trigonometric Tables*, and *Problems in Plane Geometry*, all in the College Outline Series, of *Mathematics for Practical Use*, in the Everyday Handbook Series, and of three other mathematical books.

COLLEGE
OUTLINE
SERIES

DIFFERENTIAL
EQUATIONS

KAJ L. NIELSEN
PROFESSOR OF MATHEMATICS
BUTLER UNIVERSITY

BARNES & NOBLE, INC.
PUBLISHERS · BOOKSELLERS
SINCE 1873 · NEW YORK

This book is an original work (Number 72) in the original College Outline Series. It was written by a distinguished educator, carefully edited, and produced in the United States of America in accordance with the highest standards of publishing.

TO
CARLENE

PREFACE

This book presents the fundamentals of a course in elementary differential equations. It includes the basic treatment of both ordinary and partial differential equations. Although the main purpose of the outline is to furnish supplementary reading for students enrolled in this course of study, it is complete in itself and may be read with profit by those who are beginning the study of differential equations. The techniques for obtaining solutions to differential equations as well as the basic ideas and theory behind these techniques have been developed so that the book can furnish an excellent review for people who have completed this course of study some time ago. Since the theory of existence of solutions and related concepts are dependent upon a greater mathematical maturity than is usually required for the study of elementary differential equations, it is the author's firm belief that such proofs should not form a part of this course.

Each technique has been illustrated with many examples. Neatness and systematic manner of solving the problems have been stressed, for these should be products of the study of mathematics. Logical thinking and elimination of errors can be achieved by the adaptation of systematic procedures.

The techniques for obtaining solutions of differential equations are developed in a logical sequence much in the same manner as those for algebraic equations. Starting with the simpler equations defined by the order and degree, the development proceeds to the more complex equations and techniques. Since many differential equations defy solution in closed form, a chapter on numerical techniques has been included as an introduction for the scientists and engineers who may have computing equipment available.

Differential equations form one of the most powerful tools for the solution of scientific and engineering problems. With the completion of this course the student has reached a certain maturity which should enable him to analyze elementary scientific problems. Consequently, a chapter (XIV) has been included which is intended to serve as an example of elementary scientific analysis. It is also hoped that this chapter may provide interesting reading.

A thorough knowledge of any branch of mathematics cannot be obtained without solving problems. Consequently, a few typical exercises have been placed at the end of each chapter. The student is urged to work all the exercises. Answers are furnished to those that require answers, so that the reader may check his work. A set of examinations, with answers, forms a part of this book, and it is hoped that they may aid the student in preparing for any examination or in testing his own mastery of the subject.

The author gratefully acknowledges his indebtedness to the many friends who contributed to the manuscript. Particular mention is due Robert V. Esperti, who furnished the idea for the material of Chapter XIV, Professor C. O. Oakley, who read the original manuscript and whose suggestions greatly improved the book, and the staff of Barnes & Noble, Inc., who contributed to the finished product.

TABLE OF CONTENTS

TABULATED BIBLIOGRAPHY
AND
QUICK REFERENCE TABLE
TO STANDARD TEXTBOOKS

TABULATED BIBLIOGRAPHY
OF STANDARD TEXTBOOKS

This *College Outline* is keyed to standard textbooks in two ways.

1. If you are studying one of the following textbooks, consult the cross references here listed to find which pages of the *Outline* summarize the appropriate chapter of your text. (Roman numerals refer to the textbook chapters, Arabic figures to the corresponding *Outline* pages.)

2. If you are using the *Outline* as your basis for study and need a fuller treatment of a topic, consult the pages of any of the standard textbooks as indicated in the Quick Reference Table on pages xviii–xxi.

Agnew, *Differential Equations,* 1960, McGraw-Hill.
> I (21–31); II (1–20); III (48–53); IV (58–69); V (32–57); VI (87–106); VII (156–174); VIII (175–184); IX (none); X (122–126); XI (108–117); XII (185–212); XIII (1–14); XIV (208–209); XV (none); XVI (none).

Bear, *Differential Equations,* 1962, Addison-Wesley.
> I (21–30, 32–57, 63); II (36–62); III (87–106); IV (87–106); V (none); VI (175); VII (141–154).

Coddington, *An Introduction to Ordinary Differential Equations,* 1961, Prentice-Hall.
> 0 (1–20); I (21–27); II (87–106); III (156–158); IV (163–174); V (none); VI (none).

Ford, *Differential Equations,* 1955, McGraw-Hill.
> I (21–30, 71–86); II (32–57); III (87–106); IV (87–106); V (none); VI (141–154); VII (none); VIII (108–121, 175–184); IX (141–154); X (185–198); XI (200–212).

Fort, *Differential Equations,* 1960, Holt, Rinehart, Winston.
> I (21–30); II (32–57); III (none); IV (23–25); V (71–86); VI (58–69); VII (87–106); VIII (87–106); IX (156–174); X (131–139); XI (none); XII (141–154); XIII (208–212); XIV (185–212).

Golomb, Shanks, *Elements of Ordinary Differential Equations,* 1950, McGraw-Hill.
> I (1–19); II (21–30); III (32–57); IV (87–93); V (91–106); VI (108–121); VII (none); VIII (156–174).

Greenspan, *Theory and Solution of Ordinary Differential Equations,* 1960, Macmillan.

I (1–30); II (32–57); III (87–106); IV (108–121); V (none); VI (141–154); VII (156–174); VIII (175–184); IX (none).

Kaplan, *Ordinary Differential Equations,* 1958, Addison-Wesley.

I (1–30); II (32–64, 71–86); III (none); IV (87–106); V (122–139); VI (141–154); VII (none); VIII (none); IX (58–69); X (156–174); XI (175–184); XII (none); XIII (none).

Kells, *Elementary Differential Equations,* 1960, McGraw-Hill.

I (21–30); II (71–86, 122–139); III (32–57); IV (122–139); V (58–69); VI (87–106); VII (none); VIII (122–139); IX (none); X (71–86, 125–139); XI (none); XII (156–174); XIII (175–184); XIV (185–198, 200–212); XV (214–241).

Leighton, *An Introduction to the Theory of Differential Equations,* 1951, McGraw-Hill.

I (21–30); II (32–57); III (71–86); IV (87–88); V (87–117); VI (122–139); VII (156–174); VIII (141–154); IX (none); X (none); XI (none).

Leininger, *Differential Equations,* 1962, Harper.

I (21–30); II (1–19); III (1–19); IV (32–57); V (122–139); VI (87–106); VII (175–184); VIII (none); IX (156–174); X (122–139).

Martin, Reissner, *Elementary Differential Equations,* 1961, Addison-Wesley.

I (21–30); II (32–57); III (87–106, 156–158); IV (87–106, 158–174); V (141–154); VI (175–184); VII (none); VIII (185–212).

Moore, *Introduction to Differential Equations,* 1962, Allyn and Bacon.

I (21–30, 32–57); II (175–184); III (71–86, 122–139); IV (141–154); V (87–106, 156–174); VI (none); VII (122–139).

Morris, Brown, *Differential Equations,* 1952, Prentice-Hall.

I (21–30); II (32–57); III (58–69); IV (87–106); V (175–

184); VI (156–174); VII (none); VIII (185–198); IX (none); X (200–212).

Murphy, *Ordinary Differential Equations and Their Solutions,* 1960, Van Nostrand.
A (21–30); A_1 (32–57); A_2 (58–69); B_1 (87–106); B_2 (none); C_1 (87–106, 156–174); C_2 (none); Part II (Everywhere).

Nelson, Folley, Coral, *Differential Equations,* 1960, Heath.
I (21–30); II (32–57); III (71–86); IV (87–106); V (175–184); VI (none); VII (58–69); VIII (156–174); IX (none); X (185–212).

Rainville, *A Short Course in Differential Equations,* 1958, Macmillan.
I (21–30); II (32–57); III (122–126); IV (53–57); V (71–86); VI (none); VII (87–91); VIII (87–95); IX (95–106); X (108–121); XI (87–106); XII (122–139); XIII (121–154); XIV (137–139); XV (none); XVI (58–69); XVII (none).

Rainville, *Elementary Differential Equations,* 1958, Macmillan.
I (21–30); II (32–57); III (122–126); IV (53–57); V (71–86); VI (none); VII (87–91); VIII (87–96); IX (95–106); X (108–121); XI (87–106); XII (122–139); XIII (121–154); XIV (137–139); XV (none); XVI (58–69); XVII (none); XVIII (156–174); XIX (163–174); XX (none); XXI (none); XXII (185–198); XXIII (none); XXIV (none); XXV (none).

Reddick, Kibbey, *Differential Equations,* 1956, Wiley.
I (21–30); II (32–57); III (87–106); IV (none); V (141–154); VI (87–106); VII (156–174); VIII (185–212).

Spiegel, *Applied Differential Equations,* 1958, Prentice-Hall.
I (21–30); II (32–57); III (71–86); IV (122–139); V (87–106); VI (122–139); VII (141–154); VIII (156–174); IX (175–184); X (185–212); XI (209–212).

Steen, *Differential Equations Applied in Science and Engineering,* 1957, Van Nostrand.
I (1–19); II (21–57); III (87–95); IV (95–106); V (156–174); VI (185–188); VII (185–198); VIII (200–212).

All figures

Chapter in This Outline	Topic	Agnew	Bear	Coddington	Ford
I	Foundations	20, 417	48, 59	1	
II	Definitions and Fundamentals	1, 130	1	33	1
III	First Order D.E. of First Degree	31, 65 130	1	39	4, 33
IV	First Order D.E. of Higher Degree	103			24
V	Geometric Applications	125	8, 46 161	192	20
VI	Linear Equations with Constant Coefficients	153	58, 83	49	60, 84
VII	Operational Methods	216, 381	194	49, 94	197
VIII	Applications	Many Places		Many Places	6, 26 131, 144
IX	Systems of Equations	243, 332	161	229	120
X	Solution in Power Series	251	53	103	150
XI	Numerical Methods	293	156		109, 174 208
XII	Partial D.E. of First Order	406			225
XIII	Partial D.E. of Higher Order				251
XIV	Elementary Scientific Analyses				

TO STANDARD TEXTBOOKS

refer to pages.

Fort	Golomb Shanks	Green-span	Kaplan	Kells	Leigh-ton	Lein-inger
	1	1		1		11, 32
1, 38	19	5	1	2	1	1
13	42	8	33	11, 33	10	70
69			326	70		
52	62		6, 62	15	28	
88, 107	90, 143	16, 34	112, 494	83	35, 47	112
116	162, 191	34	120, 155	83, 97	56	
62, 128	66, 110 126, 222		178, 206 64, 259	135	29, 60	98, 248
145	200	102	218	124	99	
120	279	112	344, 520	202	75	228
	31, 85	127	400	229	112	
165				248		
174				248		
		135		263	117, 132	

All figures

Chapter in This Outline	Topic	Martin Reissner	Moore	Morris Brown	Murphy
I	Foundations		1		
II	Definitions and Fundamentals	1	1	1	7
III	First Order D.E. of First Degree	45	5	21	7
IV	First Order D.E. of Higher Degree			57	58
V	Geometric Applications	5	36, 77		
VI	Linear Equations with Constant Coefficients	101, 145	121	69	82, 190
VII	Operational Methods	170		86	
VIII	Applications	16	201		
IX	Systems of Equations	179	107	101	
X	Solution in Power Series	66, 126 165	147	143	46, 96 200
XI	Numerical Methods	203		124	54
XII	Partial D.E. of First Order	254		210, 231	
XIII	Partial D.E. of Higher Order	265		259	
XIV	Elementary Scientific Analyses				

TO STANDARD TEXTBOOKS (cont.)

refer to pages.

Nelson Folley Coral	Rainville (Short)	Rainville	Reddick Kibbey	Spiegel	Steen
					5
1	1	1	1	1	33
18	16, 57	16, 57	22	25	33, 89
168	227	227			79
49	80	80	85	83	51
72	98, 115 164	98, 115 164	103, 220	142	89, 147
91	147	147		171	89
60, 115	48, 179 203	48, 179 203	61, 162	59, 183	127
112	198	198	192	217	171
180		256, 272 310, 323	246	249	182
131		356		278	
234		365	267	289	201, 214
215					239
162		305			

GREEK ALPHABET

Letters		Names	Letters		Names	Letters		Names
A	α	Alpha	I	ι	Iota	P	ρ	Rho
B	β	Beta	K	κ	Kappa	Σ	σ	Sigma
Γ	γ	Gamma	Λ	λ	Lambda	T	τ	Tau
Δ	δ	Delta	M	μ	Mu	Υ	υ	Upsilon
E	ε	Epsilon	N	ν	Nu	Φ	φ	Phi
Z	ζ	Zeta	Ξ	ξ	Xi	X	χ	Chi
H	η	Eta	O	o	Omicron	Ψ	ψ	Psi
Θ	θ	Theta	Π	π	Pi	Ω	ω	Omega

SYMBOLS

$=$, is equal to;

$\equiv$, is identical to;

$\neq$, is not equal to;

$\doteq$, is approximately equal to;

$<$, is less than;

$>$, is greater than;

$\leq$, is less than or equal to;

$\geq$, is greater than or equal to;

ln, natural logarithm;

log, common logarithm;

$\frac{d}{dx}( )$, derivative of;

$D_x y$, derivative of;

D, differential operator;

$\frac{\partial}{\partial x}( )$, partial derivative of;

Σ, sum of;

$\cdots$, and so on;

P_1, P sub 1;

$n \rightarrow \infty$, n approaches infinity;

$\sqrt{n}$, square root of n;

$\angle ABC$, angle with vertex at B;

$\triangle ABC$, triangle ABC;

$\cong$, is congruent to;

Δx, increment of x;

$f(x)$, value of function at x;

$\int$, integral of;

$\dot{x}$, derivative with respect to t;

dx, differential;

Π, product of;

$\therefore$, therefore.

I

FOUNDATIONS

1. Introduction. The creation of a system of mathematics is the formation of a logical structure. Each subject matter in mathematics is developed by a step-by-step procedure using building blocks which have been clearly constructed from elementary definitions and concepts. Beginning with arithmetic and proceeding through courses in algebra, geometry, trigonometry, analytic geometry, and the calculus, the student should have discovered that each course forms a prerequisite for the courses that follow in a logical order. Since mathematics builds upon itself, it is necessary to have a thorough understanding of each and all of the prerequisites if it is desired to master a new subject.

This book will discuss the subject of elementary differential equations. In order to understand the discussion and master the subject it is necessary to possess a thorough knowledge of the calculus and all the subjects which form a prerequisite for the calculus. It is logical to begin with a short review of some of the topics, but it is also recommended that the student consult books dealing with the respective subject matters.*

Of all the tools furnished by mathematics for solving the problems of engineering and science, the subject of differential equations provides some of the most powerful. We shall therefore be interested in many of the applications as well as the systematic solutions of these equations. It is not difficult for the student to find numerous references to the role of differential equations in the development of many theories of modern science nor is it necessary to develop a motivation for study at this level

---

* See Kaj L. Nielsen, *College Mathematics* (New York: Barnes & Noble, Inc., 1958) and C. O. Oakley, *The Calculus* (New York: Barnes & Noble, Inc., 1957).

of mathematical maturity. It is the purpose of this book to present the subject in a clear, logical manner so that the student may pursue his quest for knowledge without unnecessary difficulty.

2. Elementary Definitions. We shall begin with some elementary definitions and concepts from the calculus.

I. Limit of a variable. A constant A is said to be the **limit** of a variable Z, if for every positive number ϵ, $|Z - A| < \epsilon$.

II. Limiting value of a function. The limiting value of a function f, as x approaches a, equals K,

$$\lim_{x \to a} f(x) = K,$$

if for every positive number ϵ there exists a positive number δ such that

$$|f(x) - K| < \epsilon$$

for every x (in the domain of f) satisfying the inequality

$$0 < |x - a| < \delta.$$

If x approaches a through values greater than a, and the limit exists, we have a right-hand limit,

$$\lim_{x \to a+} f(x) = f(a+).$$

Similarly we have a left-hand limit,

$$\lim_{x \to a-} f(x) = f(a-).$$

III. Continuous function. A function f is said to be **continuous for $x = a$** if

$$\lim_{x \to a} f(x) = f(a).$$

A function f is said to be **continuous in an interval** when it is continuous for all values of x in this interval.

A function f is said to be **piecewise continuous** in the interval $a < x < b$ if the interval can be divided into a finite number of subintervals by $n + 1$ points

$$[a = x_0] < x_1 < x_2 < \cdots < x_{n-1} < [x_n = b]$$

such that f is continuous in each of the subintervals $(x_{i-1} < x < x_i)$ and the right-hand and left-hand limits, $f(x_i+)$ and $f(x_i-)$, exist at each x_i. The concept is illustrated in Fig. 1.

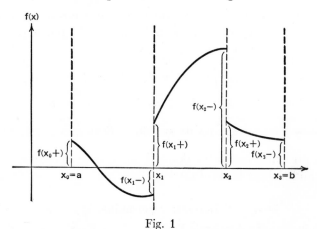

Fig. 1

IV. Derivatives and integrals. The value of a derivative of f at x is defined by the limit

$$\lim_{\Delta x \to 0} \frac{f(x + \Delta x) - f(x)}{\Delta x} = f'(x) = \frac{d}{dx} f(x) = D_x f(x).$$

Note that there are many symbols used to express a derivative. The student may also be familiar with the notation

$$y' = \frac{dy}{dx} = p \text{ when } y = f(x);$$

$$\dot{x} = \frac{dx}{dt} \text{ when } x = f(t).$$

Higher order derivatives are defined as derivatives of derivatives; thus

$$\frac{d}{dx} (y') = \frac{d^2y}{dx^2} = D_x^2 y = y'',$$

$$\frac{d}{dx} (y'') = \frac{d^3y}{dx^3} = D_x^3 y = y'''.$$

A function F is said to be an **indefinite integral** of $f(x)$ if

$$\frac{d}{dx} F(x) = f(x),$$

and symbolically we write

$$F(x) = \int f(x)dx.$$

Since the derivative of a constant is zero, it is possible to add to $F(x)$ an arbitrary constant c and still satisfy the hypothesis. Thus for the indefinite integral we write

$$\int f(x)dx = F(x) + c.$$

The definite integral may be defined symbolically by

$$\int_a^b f(x)dx = F(b) - F(a).$$

We present a list of the derivatives of some elementary functions and a short table of integrals.*

Derivative Formulas

Formulas for the Algebraic Forms.

I. $\quad\dfrac{dc}{dx} = 0.$

II. $\quad\dfrac{dx}{dx} = 1.$

III. $\quad\dfrac{d}{dx}(u + v - w) = \dfrac{du}{dx} + \dfrac{dv}{dx} - \dfrac{dw}{dx}.$

IV. $\quad\dfrac{d}{dx}(cv) = c\dfrac{dv}{dx}.$

V. $\quad\dfrac{d}{dx}(uv) = u\dfrac{dv}{dx} + v\dfrac{du}{dx}.$

VI. $\quad\dfrac{d}{dx}(v^n) = nv^{n-1}\dfrac{dv}{dx}.$

VIa. $\quad\dfrac{d}{dx}(x^n) = nx^{n-1}.$

VII. $\quad\dfrac{d}{dx}\left(\dfrac{u}{v}\right) = \dfrac{v\dfrac{du}{dx} - u\dfrac{dv}{dx}}{v^2}.$

---

* For more extensive tables see any book on mathematical tables, e.g., C. D. Hodgman, *Mathematical Tables* (Cleveland: Chemical Rubber Publishing Co., 1957).

VIIa. $\dfrac{d}{dx}\left(\dfrac{u}{c}\right) = \dfrac{1}{c}\dfrac{du}{dx}.$

VIII. $\dfrac{dy}{dx} = \dfrac{dy}{dv}\cdot\dfrac{dv}{dx}$, where $y = f(v)$.

IX. $\dfrac{dy}{dx} = \dfrac{1}{\dfrac{dx}{dy}}$, where $y = f(x)$.

Formulas for Transcendental Functions.*

X. $\dfrac{d}{dx}(\ln v) = \dfrac{1}{v}\dfrac{dv}{dx}.$

Xa. $\dfrac{d}{dx}(\log_{10} v) = \dfrac{\log_{10} e}{v}\dfrac{dv}{dx}.$

XI. $\dfrac{d}{dx}(a^v) = a^v \ln a \dfrac{dv}{dx}.$

XIa. $\dfrac{d}{dx}(e^v) = e^v \dfrac{dv}{dx}.$

XII. $\dfrac{d}{dx}(u^v) = vu^{v-1}\dfrac{du}{dx} + u^v \ln u \dfrac{dv}{dx}.$

XIII. $\dfrac{d}{dx}(\sin v) = \cos v \dfrac{dv}{dx}.$

XIV. $\dfrac{d}{dx}(\cos v) = -\sin v \dfrac{dv}{dx}.$

XV. $\dfrac{d}{dx}(\tan v) = \sec^2 v \dfrac{dv}{dx}.$

XVI. $\dfrac{d}{dx}(\cot v) = -\csc^2 v \dfrac{dv}{dx}.$

XVII. $\dfrac{d}{dx}(\sec v) = \sec v \tan v \dfrac{dv}{dx}.$

XVIII. $\dfrac{d}{dx}(\csc v) = -\csc v \cot v \dfrac{dv}{dx}.$

---

* In all formulas involving log x we shall assume $x > 0$, and all angles are measured in radians.

XIX. $\dfrac{d}{dx} (\arc\sin v) = \dfrac{1}{\sqrt{1 - v^2}}\left(\dfrac{dv}{dx}\right).$

XX. $\dfrac{d}{dx} (\arc\cos v) = -\dfrac{1}{\sqrt{1 - v^2}}\left(\dfrac{dv}{dx}\right).$

XXI. $\dfrac{d}{dx} (\arc\tan v) = \dfrac{1}{1 + v^2}\left(\dfrac{dv}{dx}\right).$

XXII. $\dfrac{d}{dx} (\arc\cot v) = -\dfrac{1}{1 + v^2}\left(\dfrac{dv}{dx}\right).$

XXIII. $\dfrac{d}{dx} (\arc\sec v) = \dfrac{1}{v\sqrt{v^2 - 1}}\left(\dfrac{dv}{dx}\right).$

XXIV. $\dfrac{d}{dx} (\arc\csc v) = -\dfrac{1}{v\sqrt{v^2 - 1}}\left(\dfrac{dv}{dx}\right).$

Elementary Forms of the Indefinite Integral *

(1) $\displaystyle\int (du + dv - dw) = \int du + \int dv - \int dw.$

(2) $\displaystyle\int a\,du = a\int du.$

(3) $\displaystyle\int dx = x + c.$

(4) $\displaystyle\int u^n\,du = \dfrac{u^{n+1}}{n + 1} + c, \quad (n \neq -1).$

(5) $\displaystyle\int \dfrac{du}{u} = \ln u + c.$

(6) $\displaystyle\int a^u\,du = \dfrac{a^u}{\ln a} + c.$

(7) $\displaystyle\int e^u\,du = e^u + c.$

(8) $\displaystyle\int \sin u\,du = -\cos u + c.$

(9) $\displaystyle\int \cos u\,du = \sin u + c.$

(10) $\displaystyle\int \sec^2 u\,du = \tan u + c.$

(11) $\displaystyle\int \csc^2 u\,du = -\cot u + c.$

(12) $\displaystyle\int \sec u \tan u\,du = \sec u + c.$

---

* In all the formulas involving log x we shall assume $x > 0$.

(13) $\int \csc u \cot u \, du = -\csc u + c.$

(14) $\int \tan u \, du = \ln \sec u + c.$

(15) $\int \cot u \, du = \ln \sin u + c.$

(16) $\int \sec u \, du = \ln (\sec u + \tan u) + c.$

(17) $\int \csc u \, du = \ln (\csc u - \cot u) + c.$

(18) $\int \dfrac{du}{u^2 + a^2} = \dfrac{1}{a} \arctan \dfrac{u}{a} + c.$

(19) $\int \dfrac{du}{u^2 - a^2} = \dfrac{1}{2a} \ln \dfrac{u - a}{u + a} + c.$

(20) $\int \dfrac{du}{a^2 - u^2} = \dfrac{1}{2a} \ln \dfrac{a + u}{a - u} + c.$

(21) $\int \dfrac{du}{\sqrt{a^2 - u^2}} = \arcsin \dfrac{u}{a} + c.$

(22) $\int \sqrt{a^2 - u^2} \, du = \dfrac{u}{2} \sqrt{a^2 - u^2} + \dfrac{a^2}{2} \arcsin \dfrac{u}{a} + c.$

(23) $\int u \, dv = uv - \int v \, du.$

(24) $\int e^{ax} \sin nx \, dx = \dfrac{e^{ax}}{a^2 + n^2} (a \sin nx - n \cos nx) + c.$

(25) $\int e^{ax} \cos nx \, dx = \dfrac{e^{ax}}{a^2 + n^2} (n \sin nx + a \cos nx) + c.$

(26) $\int x^m e^{ax} \, dx = \dfrac{1}{a} \left[x^m e^{ax} - m \int x^{m-1} e^{ax} \, dx \right] + c, \quad (m > 0).$

V. Series. If a function f possesses derivatives of all orders in an interval containing $x = a$, it may be represented by a *Taylor Series*

$$f(x) = f(a) + f'(a)(x - a) + f''(a) \frac{(x - a)^2}{2!} + \cdots$$
$$+ f^{(n)}(a) \frac{(x - a)^n}{n!} + \cdots,$$

where $f^{(n)}(a)$ is the value of the nth derivative of $f(x)$ at $x = a$.

If $a = 0$ we have the well-known *Maclaurin Series*

$$f(x) = f(0) + f'(0)x + f''(0) \frac{x^2}{2!} + \cdots + f^{(n)}(0) \frac{x^n}{n!} + \cdots.$$

The series expansion of some elementary functions will be listed for quick reference.

Table of Series

1. $\sin x = x - \dfrac{x^3}{3!} + \dfrac{x^5}{5!} - \dfrac{x^7}{7!} + \cdots$

$$= \sum_{n=0}^{\infty} (-1)^n \frac{x^{2n+1}}{(2n+1)!}, \quad [x^2 < \infty].$$

2. $\cos x = 1 - \dfrac{x^2}{2!} + \dfrac{x^4}{4!} - \dfrac{x^6}{6!} + \cdots$

$$= \sum_{n=0}^{\infty} (-1)^n \frac{x^{2n}}{(2n)!}, \quad [x^2 < \infty].$$

3.* $\tan x = x + \frac{1}{3}x^3 + \frac{2}{15}x^5 + \frac{17}{315}x^7 + \frac{62}{2835}x^9 + \cdots$

$$= \sum_{n=1}^{\infty} \frac{2^{2n}(2^{2n}-1)}{(2n)!} B_n x^{2n-1}, \quad \left[x^2 < \frac{\pi^2}{4}\right].$$

4. $\text{arc } \tan x = x - \frac{1}{3}x^3 + \frac{1}{5}x^5 - \frac{1}{7}x^7 + \cdots$

$$= \sum_{n=0}^{\infty} (-1)^n \frac{x^{2n+1}}{2n+1}, \quad [x^2 < 1].$$

5. $e^x = 1 + x + \dfrac{x^2}{2!} + \dfrac{x^3}{3!} + \dfrac{x^4}{4!} + \cdots = \sum_{n=0}^{\infty} \dfrac{x^n}{n!}, \quad [x^2 < \infty].$

If we let x be ix in the series for e^x, we obtain

$$e^{ix} = 1 + (ix) + \frac{(ix)^2}{2!} + \frac{(ix)^3}{3!} + \frac{(ix)^4}{4!} + \cdots$$

$$= \left(1 - \frac{x^2}{2!} + \frac{x^4}{4!} - \cdots\right) + i\left(x - \frac{x^3}{3!} + \frac{x^5}{5!} - \cdots\right)$$

$$= \cos x + i \sin x.$$

The following additional formulas, which may be obtained from operation on power series, will prove helpful.

1. $e^{(a+bi)x} = e^{ax}(\cos bx + i \sin bx)$.
2. $e^{(a-bi)x} = e^{ax}(\cos bx - i \sin bx)$.
3. $\sin x = \dfrac{e^{ix} - e^{-ix}}{2i}$.

---

* B_n are Bernoulli's numbers. See E. P. Adams, *Smithsonian Mathematical Formulae* (Washington: Smithsonian Institute, 1957), Section 6.902.

4. $\cos x = \dfrac{e^{ix} + e^{-ix}}{2}$.

5. $e^{2\pi i} = 1$ and $e^{\pi i} = -1$.

6. $e^{ax} \cos bx = \operatorname{Re} e^{(a+bi)x}$,

where Re means the real part of the complex number.

7. $e^{ax} \sin bx = \operatorname{Im} e^{(a+bi)x}$,

where Im means the imaginary part of the complex number.

VI. Families of curves. If an equation relating two variables contains an arbitrary constant c, it defines a family of curves, one curve for each value assigned to c. For example,

$$xy = c$$

defines a family of equilateral hyperbolas. See Fig. 2.

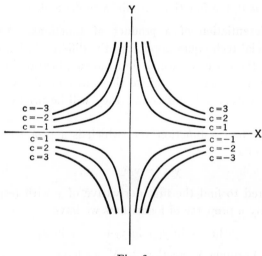

Fig. 2

VII. Linear dependence. The quantities $y_1, \cdots, y_n$ are said to be **linearly dependent** if there exist numbers $c_1, \cdots, c_n$, *not all zero*, such that

$$c_1 y_1 + \cdots + c_n y_n = 0.$$

If no numbers c_i exist, then $y_1, \cdots, y_n$ are said to be **linearly independent**.

Illustrations.

1. Show that x and x^2 are linearly independent.

Solution. In order for

$$c_1 x + c_2 x^2 = 0$$

to be satisfied for all values of x we must have $c_1 = 0$ and $c_2 = 0$.

2. Show that $\sin x$, $\cos x$, and $\sin(x + \alpha)$ are linearly dependent.

Solution. Since

$$c_1 \sin x + c_2 \cos x + c_3 \sin (x + \alpha)$$
$$= c_1 \sin x + c_2 \cos x + c_3(\sin x \cos \alpha + \cos x \sin \alpha)$$
$$= (c_1 + c_3 \cos \alpha) \sin x + (c_2 + c_3 \sin \alpha) \cos x$$
$$= 0$$

can be satisfied for all values of x if

$$c_1 = -c_3 \cos \alpha \quad \text{and} \quad c_2 = -c_3 \sin \alpha$$

with $c_3 \neq 0$, the functions are linearly dependent.

VIII. Differentiation of a product of functions. Among the many special techniques applied to the differentiation of special functions, there are two which find wide application in the study of differential equations. Since they are not always discussed in an elementary calculus course they will be briefly developed here.

Consider first a function $y(x)$ which is a product of several functions of x,

$$y(x) = y_1 y_2 \cdots y_n.$$

It is desired to find the first derivative of y with respect to x, i.e., y'. By a property of logarithms we have

$$\ln y = \ln y_1 + \ln y_2 + \cdots + \ln y_n$$

and from Formula X, Section 2, IV, we have

$$\frac{y'}{y} = \frac{y_1'}{y_1} + \frac{y_2'}{y_2} + \cdots + \frac{y_n'}{y_n}.$$

Solving this equation for y' results in

$$y' = y \left[\frac{y_1'}{y_1} + \frac{y_2'}{y_2} + \cdots + \frac{y_n'}{y_n} \right].$$

An application of this formula to a simple binomial raised to a power,

$$y = (ax + b)^n,$$

yields

$$y' = y\left(\frac{na}{ax + b}\right),$$

which reduces to the usual expression

$$y' = na(ax + b)^{n-1}.$$

Some examples will illustrate the value of this formula.

Illustrations.   Find $D_x y$.

1. $y = \dfrac{x^3(x + 1)^2}{(2x + 3)^2(5x - 2)^5}.$

Solution.

$$y' = y\left[\frac{3}{x} + \frac{2}{x + 1} - \frac{4}{2x + 3} - \frac{25}{5x - 2}\right].$$

2. $y = \dfrac{x + n}{x(x + 1)(x + 2)\cdots(x + n - 1)}.$

Solution.

$$y' = y\left[\frac{1}{x + n} - \frac{1}{x} - \frac{1}{x + 1} - \frac{1}{x + 2} - \cdots - \frac{1}{x + n - 1}\right].$$

3. $y = \dfrac{x}{[(x + 1)(x + 2)\cdots(x + n)]^2}.$

Solution.

$$y' = y\left[\frac{1}{x} - 2\left(\frac{1}{x + 1} + \frac{1}{x + 2} + \cdots + \frac{1}{x + n}\right)\right].$$

The second special formula which we shall use is Leibnitz'
formula for the **nth derivative of a product of two functions**

$$y = uv$$

where u and v are functions of an independent variable x.   The
formula is

$$\frac{d^n(uv)}{dx} = u\frac{d^n v}{dx} + \frac{n}{1!}\frac{du}{dx}\frac{d^{n-1}v}{dx^{n-1}} + \frac{n(n - 1)}{2!}\frac{d^2u}{dx^2}\frac{d^{n-2}v}{dx^{n-2}}$$

$$+ \frac{n(n - 1)(n - 2)}{3!}\frac{d^3u}{dx^3}\frac{d^{n-3}v}{dx^{n-3}} + \cdots + v\frac{d^n u}{dx^n}$$

$$= \sum_{i=0}^{n} C_{n,i}u^{(n-i)}v^{(i)}$$

where $C_{n,i}$ is the binomial coefficient:

$$C_{n,i} = \frac{n!}{i!(n-i)!}.$$

Illustration.　Find $D_x^4 y$ for

$$y = x^3 e^{2x}.$$

Solution.　The binomial coefficients with $n = 4$ are 1, 4, 6, 4, 1.
Then

$$
\begin{aligned}
y^{(iv)} &= (x^3)^{(iv)}(e^{2x}) + 4(x^3)'''(e^{2x})' + 6(x^3)''(e^{2x})'' \\
&\qquad\qquad + 4(x^3)'(e^{2x})''' + x^3(e^{2x})^{(iv)} \\
&= 0 + 4(6)(2e^{2x}) + 6(6x)(4e^{2x}) + 4(3x^2)(8e^{2x}) + x^3(16e^{2x}) \\
&= 16e^{2x}(3 + 9x + 6x^2 + x^3).
\end{aligned}
$$

IX. Velocity and acceleration.　Let a particle move along a
plane curve C in the (x,y)-plane and let its location, $P(x,y)$, be
dependent upon time t.　The *velocity* V of the particle at a point
of its path is directed along the tangent to the path at that point.

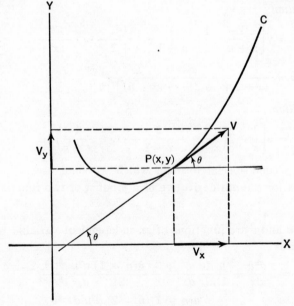

Fig. 3

Let θ be the angle from the positive X-axis to the tangent at the
point $P(x,y)$.　See Fig. 3.　We recall from the calculus the following relations with $\dot{x} = D_t x$:

$$V_x = \dot{x} = V \cos \theta,$$
$$V_y = \dot{y} = V \sin \theta,$$
$$V = \sqrt{\dot{x}^2 + \dot{y}^2} = \left| \frac{dS}{dt} \right|,$$
$$\theta = \text{Arc tan } \frac{V_y}{V_x} = \text{Arc tan } \frac{dy}{dx}, \quad (V_x > 0),$$
$$\theta = \pi + \text{Arc tan } \frac{V_y}{V_x} = \pi + \text{Arc tan } \frac{dy}{dx}, \quad (V_x < 0).$$

The *acceleration a* is analyzed in a similar manner. See Fig. 4. We recall the following relations:

$$a_x = \dot{V}_x = \ddot{x} = a \cos \varphi,$$
$$a_y = \dot{V}_y = \ddot{y} = a \sin \varphi,$$

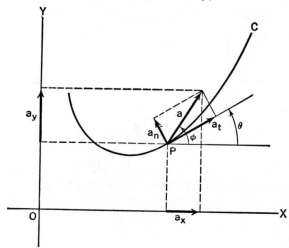

Fig. 4

$$a = \sqrt{a_x^2 + a_y^2} = \sqrt{\ddot{x}^2 + \ddot{y}^2},$$
$$\varphi = \text{Arc tan } \frac{a_y}{a_x} = \text{Arc tan } \frac{\ddot{y}}{\ddot{x}}, \quad (a_x > 0),$$
$$\varphi = \pi + \text{Arc tan } \frac{a_y}{a_x} = \pi + \text{Arc tan } \frac{\ddot{y}}{\ddot{x}}, \quad (a_x < 0),$$
$$a_t = a \cos (\varphi - \theta) = a_x \cos \theta + a_y \sin \theta = \dot{V},$$
$$| a_n | = a | \sin (\varphi - \theta) | = | a_y \cos \theta - a_x \sin \theta | \doteq K V^2,$$

where a_t is the *tangential* component, a_n is the *normal* component, and K is the *curvature* of C at the point P.

Again consider a point P which is moving along a curve C with its position dependent upon t. Let β be the angle from the positive X-axis to the radius OP. See Fig. 5. The instantaneous rate of change of the angle β with respect to time is called the *angular velocity of* OP and is usually denoted by ω.

$$\omega = \dot{\beta}.$$

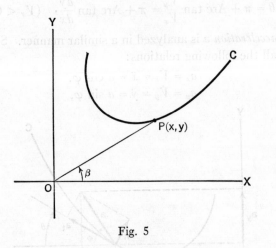

Fig. 5

The instantaneous rate of change of ω with respect to t is called the *angular acceleration* of OP and is denoted by α,

$$\alpha = \frac{d\omega}{dt} = \ddot{\beta}.$$

3. Physical Laws. Although most situations in nature cannot be exactly expressed by mathematics, they frequently can be approximated to a high degree of accuracy. The approximations are obtained by mathematical "models" usually consisting of a combination of equations and formulas which describe the situation as accurately as experimentation and reasoning will permit. As science is developed, many of these models take the form of physical "laws." Since this is not a physics book, these laws will be accepted without further proof and employed in our study of the applications of differential equations. We shall merely list a few of them which find extensive application. For a rigorous discussion of these laws the student should consult a book on physics.

I. Newton's basic laws. Sir Isaac Newton (1642–1727) is credited with the formulation of three basic laws of dynamics. Literally translated, they state:

(1) A particle remains in a state of rest or of uniform motion along a straight line until it is compelled to change this state by applied forces.

(2) The change of motion of a particle is directly proportional to the applied force, is inversely proportional to the mass, and takes place in the direction of the line along which the force is applied.

(3) Action is always equal to reaction; that is, the mutual interactions of two bodies are equal and opposite.

The application of these laws to modern dynamics has changed the wording to easy mathematical formulation and we shall state the forms which are most commonly exhibited.

If a particle of mass m moves in a straight line with acceleration a under the influence of a resultant force F, then the force is proportional to the mass times acceleration. If the units of measure are consistent (see table below), the constant of proportionality is 1 and we write

$$F = ma.$$

The consistent units are:

Distance s or x	Time t	Mass m	Force F
Foot	Second	Slug	Pound
Foot	Second	Pound	Poundal
Centimeter	Second	Gram	Dyne

If all the particles of a body have plane motion with respect to the same plane, then the sum of the components in any direction of all the external forces acting on the body is equal to the product of the acceleration of the center of gravity of the body and the mass of the body; symbolically,

$$\sum F_d = ma_d.$$

If a rigid body has plane motion, the torque of the external forces acting on it about an axis through the center of gravity of the body and perpendicular to the plane of its motion is equal to the product of the moment of inertia of the body with respect to the same axis and the angular acceleration of the body; symbolically,

$$T_q = I_g\alpha.$$

II. Newton's law of cooling. The cooling of a body is proportional to the difference between the temperature of the body and that of the surrounding air; symbolically,

$$\dot{T} = -kT$$

where T is the difference of the temperatures and $\dot{T} = \dfrac{dT}{dt}$, the time derivative.

III. The snowball law. If a quantity varies at a rate which is proportional to its size, it is said to obey the *snowball law;* symbolically,

$$\dot{A} = kA$$

where A is the amount of the quantity and $\dot{A}$ is the time rate of change of A. The constant of proportionality k may be a positive or a negative quantity. There are many examples of this law in science: money invested with the interest compounded continuously, the law of cooling, the decomposition of radioactive matter, mixtures and solutions, and many others.

IV. Hooke's law. The stress set up within an elastic body is proportional to the strain to which the body is subjected by an applied load, or more simply, the deformation of a body is proportional to the restoring force. When this law is applied to springs it is usually symbolized in terms of the displacement,

$$-kx = m\dot{v},$$

where x is the displacement from rest caused by a mass m, and k is the spring constant.

V. Kirchhoff's network laws. We shall state two laws which apply to electric circuits.

At any point in an electric circuit where two or more conductors are joined, the sum of the currents directed toward the junction equals the sum of the currents directed away from the junction. If we call the currents toward the junction positive, and those away from the junction negative, then

$$\sum i = 0.$$

If we consider the rise of a potential to be positive and the drop of a potential negative, then around any closed path in an electric circuit the algebraic sum of the potential differences equals zero.

VI. Law of universal gravitation. Each particle of matter attracts every other particle of matter with a force which is directly proportional to the product of their masses and inversely proportional to the square of the distance between them; symbolically,

$$F = k\,\frac{m_1 m_2}{d^2}.$$

Application of this law to the attraction which the earth exerts upon objects near it leads to the familiar gravitational force mg, where g is acceleration due to gravity.

Note. In the construction of mathematical models to represent physical situations it is essential to be rigorous in the assignment of algebraic signs. In the formulation of the physical laws minus signs were sometimes explicitly indicated and at other times were absorbed in the constant of proportionality. It is advised that, in the solution of problems, diagrams be drawn with directions clearly indicated and all symbols be rigorously defined.

4. Physical Units. In discussing physical problems it is necessary to have consistent units of measurement. In general we employ "standard" units and will summarize those which are needed for applied problems.

I. Mechanical units.

Quantity	Symbol	English Units	Mks Units
Displacement	s or x	foot	meter
Time	t	seconds	seconds
Linear velocity	v	ft./sec.	meter/sec.
Linear acceleration	a	ft./sec.^{2}	meter/sec.^{2}
Angular velocity	ω	rad./sec.	rad./sec.
Angular acceleration	α	rad./sec.^{2}	rad./sec.^{2}
Mass	m	slug	kilogram
Force	F	pound	newton
Work	W	foot-pound	joule
Moment of inertia	I	slug-ft.^{2}	kg.-meter^2

II. Electrical units.

Quantity	Symbol	English Units	Mks Units
Current	i	ampere	ampere
Resistance	R	ohm	ohm
Capacitance	C	farad	farad
Inductance	L	henry	henry
Charge	q	coulomb	coulomb
Electromotive force	e or E	volt	volt

In applying mathematical formulas to the solution of problems which arise from the physical sciences, it is essential that uniform dimensions be used. Formulas should always be checked for their dimensional accuracy by using ratios and considering the expressions for the dimensions as algebraic quantities. The equations should be dimensionally balanced, and the check will frequently indicate any errors in the construction of the mathematical model.

Illustrations.

1. If x is given in feet, m in slugs, v in feet/second, and t in seconds, prove that the formula $kx = m\dfrac{dv}{dt}$ is accurate when the spring constant k is given in pounds/foot.

Solution. Since, by definition, slug = lb.-sec.²/ft. and the rate of change of velocity is ft./sec.², we have

$$\frac{\text{lb.}}{\text{ft.}} \times \text{ft.} = \frac{\text{lb.-sec.}^2}{\text{ft.}} \times \frac{\text{ft.}}{\text{sec.}^2}$$

or

$$\text{lb.} = \text{lb.}$$

2. Prove that the formula is not correct if the spring constant k is given in pounds/inch and the other dimensions remain the same.

Solution.

$$\frac{\text{lb.}}{\text{in.}} \times \text{ft.} = \frac{\text{lb.-sec.}^2}{\text{ft.}} \times \frac{\text{ft.}}{\text{sec.}^2}$$

or

$$\frac{1 \text{ ft.}}{1 \text{ in.}} = 1,$$

which is not true.

The same procedure may be used to change dimensions.

Illustration. How many feet/second does an automobile travel if its speed is 50 miles/hour?

Solution.

$$x \frac{\text{ft.}}{\text{sec.}} = \frac{50 \text{ mi.}}{\text{hr.}} = \frac{50 \text{ mi.}}{1 \text{ hr.}} \times \frac{1 \text{ hr.}}{3600 \text{ sec.}} \times \frac{5280 \text{ ft.}}{1 \text{ mi.}}$$

$$= \frac{220 \text{ ft.}}{3 \text{ sec.}} = 73\tfrac{1}{3} \text{ ft./sec.}$$

5. Exercise I.

1. Find $D_x y$.
   - (a) $b^2 x^2 - a^2 y^2 = a^2 b^2$.
   - (b) $y = e^{ax} \left(\dfrac{a \sin nx - n \cos nx}{a^2 + n^2} \right)$.
   - (c) $y = 2x^2 - x + 3 \ln 2x^2$.
   - (d) $Ax^2 + Bxy + Cy^2 + Dx + Ey + F = 0$.
   - (e) $y = 2(x^{\frac{1}{2}} + x^{-\frac{1}{2}}) \arctan \sqrt{x}$.

2. Integrate
   - (a) $\displaystyle\int x^3 e^{3x} \, dx$.

(b) $\int e^{2x} \sin 2ax \, dx$.

(c) $\int x(4x^2 - 3) \sin x^2 \, dx$.

3. Evaluate

(a) $\int_0^{\pi} \sin x \, dx$.

(b) $\int_{-1}^{3} 3x^2 \, dx$.

(c) $\int_0^x e^{(x-t)} e^{3t} \, dt$.

4. Test the function $y = 3x^{-2}$ for continuity in the interval $-1 \leq x \leq 3$.

5. Expand $y = e^{ix}$ in a Maclaurin Series.

6. Plot the family of curves

$$y - c = 4ax^2$$

for $c = 0, 1, 2, 3, 4$.

7. A mathematical model for the drag on a projectile is

$$D = K_D \rho \, d^2 v^2$$

where the drag D is given in (mass)(ft.)/sec.^{2}; the air density ρ in (mass)/ft.^{3}; the diameter d of the projectile in ft.; and the projectile velocity v relative to the air in ft./sec. Prove that the drag coefficient K_D is dimensionless.

8. A particle is projected upward with a velocity of 64.4 ft./sec. from the top of a tower 80.5 ft. high. Find the maximum height it will go and the time it will take to strike the ground. (Use $g = 32.2$ ft./sec.)

9. A ship A is 50 miles due north of a ship B and is sailing south at the rate of 15 mi./hr. The ship B is sailing east at the rate of 20 mi./hr. Find the minimum distance between the ships.

10. A horizontal force of 5 pounds is exerted upon a 100 pound body which is resting upon a smooth (frictionless) horizontal surface. What is the velocity of the body at the end of 5 seconds and what is the distance traveled?

II

DEFINITIONS AND FUNDAMENTALS

6. Definitions. We begin the detailed study of differential equations by defining our terminology. In general, a **differential equation** *is an equation containing differentials or derivatives.* If only one independent variable is involved, the derivatives and differentials are *total* derivatives and *total* differentials and the equation is called an **ordinary differential equation.** If more than one independent variable is involved, there exist partial derivatives and the equation is called a **partial differential equation.** The following are examples of ordinary differential equations:

$$(1) \qquad \frac{dy}{dx} = x^3 + 5,$$

$$(2) \qquad (D_x^3 y)^2 + 3x \, D_x^2 y \, D_x y + ax(D_x y)^3 = 0,$$

$$(3) \qquad (x^2 + y^2)dx - 3y \, dy = 0,$$

$$(4) \qquad D_x u + D_x v = ux + vx.$$

The following are examples of partial differential equations:

$$(5) \qquad \frac{\partial v}{\partial x} = xy,$$

$$(6) \qquad \frac{\partial^2 u}{\partial x^2} + \frac{\partial^2 u}{\partial y^2} + \frac{\partial^2 u}{\partial z^2} = 0,$$

$$(7) \qquad \frac{\partial^2 u}{\partial x \, \partial y} = au.$$

There are many ways to write differential equations, some of which were illustrated above. Note that they can be written in terms of derivatives such as (1), (2), and (4) or in terms of differentials such as (3). Another form is given by the expression

$$(8) \qquad f(x,y,y',y'') = 0,$$

which indicates an equation involving the independent variable x, the dependent variable y, and the first and second derivatives of y. Still another expression is given by the equation

$$(9) \qquad \sum_{i=0}^{n} a_i(x)y^{(n-i)} = f(x).$$

The **order** *of a differential equation is the order of the highest-ordered derivative involved in its expression.* Referring to the examples above it can be seen that equations (1), (3), and (4) are first order differential equations and (2) is a third order differential equation.

The **degree** *of an ordinary differential equation is the algebraic degree of its highest-ordered derivative.* Again referring to the above examples it should be clear that equations (1), (3), and (4) are of the first degree and equation (2) is of the second degree. For greater clarity we emphasize that there is a difference between

$$(10) \qquad \left(\frac{dy}{dx}\right)^2 \equiv (D_x y)^2,$$

and

$$(11) \qquad \frac{d^2 y}{dx^2} \equiv D_x^2 y.$$

The expressions in (10) indicate *the first derivative squared* (i.e., equation is of the first order and second degree), whereas the expressions in (11) indicate *the second derivative* (i.e., equation is of the second order and first degree).

In order to determine the degree of a differential equation, the equation must first be cleared of any fractional power. For example,

$$(D_x^2 y)^{\frac{2}{3}} = [y + D_x y]^{\frac{1}{2}}$$

is analyzed after raising both sides to the sixth power to obtain

$$(D_x^2 y)^4 = [y + D_x y]^3,$$

and we see that it is a second order differential equation of the fourth degree.

A **linear differential equation** *is one in which the dependent variable and any of its derivatives appear to no degree higher than the first.* The general form is given by

$$(12) \qquad a_0(x)D_x^n y + a_1(x)D_x^{n-1} y + \cdots + a_n(x)y = f(x).$$

We close this section by again pointing out that a differential equation may be expressed either in terms of derivatives or in terms of differentials. Thus

$$(x^2 + y)\frac{dy}{dx} - x = 3$$

and

$$(x^2 + y)dy - x\,dx = 3dx$$

define the same differential equation.

7. Solution of a Differential Equation. *A solution of an ordinary* **differential equation** *in two variables is a functional relation between the two variables which satisfies the differential equation.* Thus, by a solution we mean exactly the same as the normal definition of "solution" for any mathematical equation. The only thing which may be new to the student is that the solution is now expressed as a functional relation instead of as a number or an algebraic expression. If the solution of a differential equation in x and y has the form

$$y = f(x),$$

there will result an identity when $f(x)$ and its derivatives are substituted for y and the derivatives of y in the given differential equation. In such cases $f(x)$ is called an **integral,** or a **primitive,** of the differential equation.

Illustration 1. Show that $y = 2x^3 + Ax + B$ is a solution of $y'' = 12x$.

Solution. Since

$$y = 2x^3 + Ax + B,$$

we have

$$y' = 6x^2 + A,$$

and

$$y'' = 12x.$$

Substituting these values into the given differential equation we have

$$12x = 12x,$$

which is an identity.

The solution of a differential equation may also be given in an implicit form

$$F(x,y) = 0,$$

and by the solution is meant all the functions $f_i(x)$, $(i = 1, \cdots, n)$, which can be obtained by solving $F(x,y) = 0$ explicitly in terms of x, and which are integrals of the given differential equation.

Illustration 2. Show that $x^2 + y^2 = r^2$ is a solution of the differential equation $x\,dx + y\,dy = 0$.

Solution. Rewrite the differential equation in the form

$$x + yy' = 0.$$

Differentiate the proposed solution implicitly to obtain

$$2x + 2yy' = 0.$$

Solve for y',

$$y' = -\frac{x}{y},$$

and substitute into the differential equation to obtain

$$x + y\left(-\frac{x}{y}\right) = x - x = 0,$$

thus satisfying the equation.

It is possible to have more than one solution of a given differential equation. For example, in illustration 1 above we can show that $y = 2x^3$ is also a solution. It is also clear that an arbitrary constant could be added and still a different solution, $y = 2x^3 + B$, would be obtained. This situation leads to further terminology.

A **particular solution** *of a differential equation is any relation which satisfies the equation.*

The **general solution** *of an* n*th order differential equation is a relation which contains* n *linearly independent arbitrary constants and satisfies the differential equation.* If the functional relation defines an n-parameter family of curves, then the general solution is this family of curves and each curve satisfies the differential equation. Many times there will exist solutions which are not members of the above-mentioned family; however, in most applications of differential equations it is sufficient to obtain a general solution and, from it, particular integrals.

8. Finding a Differential Equation from a Given Primitive.
Although the prime problem in the study of differential equations
is the finding of the general solution to a given differential equation, the converse problem is also interesting. This is, of course,
the problem of finding a differential equation which will be
satisfied by a given primitive. The problem is solved by repeated
differentiation and elimination of the arbitrary constants. We
shall illustrate by an example.

Illustration. Find the differential equation which has

$$y = c_1 e^x + c_2 e^{-x} + 3x$$

as the general solution.

Solution. Differentiate the given expression twice.

(1) $$y = c_1 e^x + c_2 e^{-x} + 3x,$$
(2) $$y' = c_1 e^x - c_2 e^{-x} + 3,$$
(3) $$y'' = c_1 e^x + c_2 e^{-x}.$$

Eliminate c_1 and c_2 by subtracting (3) from (1) to obtain

(4) $$y - y'' = 3x.$$

Equation (4) is the desired differential equation.

The arbitrary constants can also be eliminated by the use of
determinants.* From the system of linear equations in c_i obtained by differentiation of the given solution i times, form a
determinant of the coefficients of c_i and the constant terms of
this system. Set the resulting determinant equal to zero and
expand.

Illustration. Find the differential equation which has

$$y = c_1 e^{2x} + c_2 e^{-3x} + \sin x$$

as the general solution.

Solution. Differentiate twice.

(1) $$y = c_1 e^{2x} + c_2 e^{-3x} + \sin x,$$
(2) $$y' = 2c_1 e^{2x} - 3c_2 e^{-3x} + \cos x,$$
(3) $$y'' = 4c_1 e^{2x} + 9c_2 e^{-3x} - \sin x.$$

---

* For a review of determinants see Kaj L. Nielsen, *College Mathematics* (New
York: Barnes & Noble, Inc., 1958), p. 241.

Set the determinant of the coefficients of c_1 and c_2 and the constant terms equal to zero:

$$\begin{vmatrix} y - \sin x & e^{2x} & e^{-3x} \\ y' - \cos x & 2e^{2x} & -3e^{-3x} \\ y'' + \sin x & 4e^{2x} & 9e^{-3x} \end{vmatrix} = 0.$$

Simplify:

$$e^{2x}e^{-3x} \begin{vmatrix} y - \sin x & 1 & 1 \\ y' - \cos x & 2 & -3 \\ y'' + \sin x & 4 & 9 \end{vmatrix} = 0,$$

$$e^{-x}[-5y'' - 5y' + 30y - 35 \sin x + 5 \cos x] = 0,$$

or

$$y'' + y' - 6y + 7 \sin x - \cos x = 0$$

is the desired differential equation.

9. Direction Fields. Let us consider a first order differential equation of the first degree. It can be written in the form

$$\frac{dy}{dx} = f(x,y).$$

We recall from the calculus that if we evaluate the derivative y' at a point $P_0(x_0,y_0)$ we obtain the slope of the tangent line to the curve $y = F(x)$ at that point. Furthermore, the *direction of a curve* at any point is defined as the direction of the tangent line to the curve at that point. Thus, by evaluating the derivative at a point $P_0(x_0,y_0)$,

$$\frac{dy}{dx}\bigg|_0 = f(x_0,y_0),$$

we find at (x_0,y_0) the direction of the curve $y = F(x)$ which satisfies the differential equation $y' = f(x,y)$. These directions can be found at each point in the plane for which the derivative exists. The totality of these directions is called a *direction field*. The direction field may be used to sketch the family of curves which satisfies the given differential equation without finding the explicit functional relation.

Illustration. Find the direction field for the family of curves satisfying the differential equation

$$\frac{dy}{dx} = x.$$

Solution. Calculate the table of values.

x	0	$\pm\frac{1}{2}$	± 1	$\pm\frac{3}{2}$	± 2
y'	0	$\pm\frac{1}{2}$	± 1	$\pm\frac{3}{2}$	± 2

Since y is not involved in $f(x,y) = x$, this table indicates the direction of the tangent line at all values of y for each calculated x. Let us therefore choose values of y to be -1, 0, 1, 2, and 3. Next draw a small line segment through a given point with the indicated slope, i.e., at (1,1) with slope 1, at (1,2) with slope 1, etc. Fig. 6 shows the lines for the above values of x. Fig. 6 also shows the sketch of the function $y = F(x)$

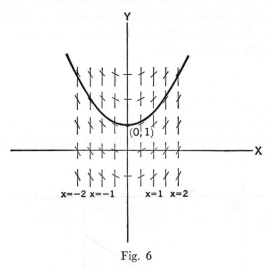

Fig. 6

which goes through the point (0,1). It appears to be a parabola, and if we rewrite the differential equation in the form

$$dy = x \, dx,$$

and integrate both sides to obtain

$$y = \tfrac{1}{2}x^2 + c,$$

we see that the solution $y = F(x)$ is a family of parabolas.

10. Existence of Solutions. In our previous discussions we have assumed that for each differential equation it is possible to obtain the general solution. It is the job of a mathematician to establish this as a fact and not as an assumption if such be the case. This is accomplished by the statement and proof of *existence theorems*. Frequently the proof of existence theorems reaches into other branches of mathematics which may be further advanced than the particular subject matter under discussion. In other words, the student has not yet reached the mathematical maturity which permits him to comprehend the proof. Such is the case for the theorems which assure the existence of general solutions for differential equations. We shall concern ourselves only with the statement of the theorems and assume their validity.

In most current books the existence theorem for a first order and first degree differential equation is stated in slightly different forms. We shall exhibit the two most common ones. Consider the differential equation

$$\frac{dy}{dx} = f(x,y).$$

The function $f(x,y)$ is defined in some region R of the (x,y)-plane; for example, the rectangle $a < x < b$ and $c < y < d$ which could be the whole plane if we permit a, b, c, and d to include $\pm \infty$. See Fig. 7.

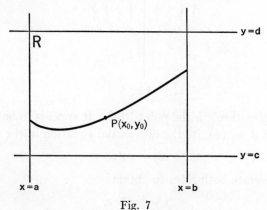

Fig. 7

Theorem. *If* $f(x,y)$ *can be developed by Taylor's theorem as a series in* $x - x_0$ *and* $y - y_0$, *absolutely convergent in* R, *there exists a unique solution,* $y = y(x)$, *which satisfies the initial condition* $y_0 = y(x_0)$.

Theorem. *If for the differential equation*

$$\frac{dy}{dx} = f(x,y),$$

f(x,y) *and* $\dfrac{\partial f}{\partial y}$ *are continuous in the region* R, *then there exists a unique function* y = F(x) *which satisfies the given differential equation and takes on the value* y_0 *when* x = x_0.

The choice of y_0 is arbitrary within R, and thus for the first order equation there is one arbitrary constant.

The severe restrictions placed on $f(x,y)$ by the hypothesis are *sufficient* conditions. They are not *necessary* conditions, and it is possible that a solution will exist even though these conditions are not satisfied.

Consider the differential equation

$$\frac{dy}{dx} = -\frac{x}{y}.$$

The function $f(x,y) = -\dfrac{x}{y}$ is continuous and $\dfrac{\partial f}{\partial y} = \dfrac{x}{y^2}$ exists everywhere, except at $y = 0$ where neither is defined. Now if we rewrite the equation in the form

$$y\,dy = -x\,dx$$

and integrate both sides, we obtain

$$\tfrac{1}{2}y^2 = -\tfrac{1}{2}x^2 + c$$

or

$$y^2 + x^2 = r^2$$

where $r^2 = 2c$, the arbitrary constant. The solution is the equation of a circle with the center at the origin and, for chosen values of the parameter r, will give a continuous unique curve in the (x,y)-plane. However, by the statement of the theorem we see that through each point (x_0,y_0), $y_0 \neq 0$, there passes a unique semicircle

$$y = \sqrt{r^2 - x^2} \quad \text{or} \quad y = -\sqrt{r^2 - x^2}$$

which satisfies the differential equation. However, through a point $(x_0,0)$ there pass *both* semicircles.

A more dramatic example is given by the equation

$$\frac{dy}{dx} = \frac{y}{x}.$$

A solution of this equation is $y = cx$, which is the family of lines through the origin. Through any point (x_0, y_0) in the plane except $(0,0)$, a unique line will pass. However, *all* the lines, not a unique one, pass through the point $(0,0)$.

It is also the job of mathematicians to develop the techniques which are necessary to find an actual solution. We shall now turn our attention to the systematic development of these techniques and will assume that all the differential equations under discussion satisfy the conditions for existence of solutions unless otherwise indicated.

11. Exercise II.

1. State the order and degree of the following differential equations:

   (a) $x^2\, dy + y\, dx = 0$.

   (b) $(D_x y)^3 = 3x^2 - 1$.

   (c) $\left[D_x^2 y\right]^{\frac{1}{2}} = \left[x - D_x y\right]^{\frac{1}{3}}$.

   (d) $\left(\dfrac{d^3 y}{dx^3}\right)^4 - \left(\dfrac{d^2 y}{dx^2}\right)^5 + x = 0$.

   (e) $x^4 \dfrac{dy}{dx} - x^2 \dfrac{d^2 y}{dx^2} = y^4 \dfrac{d^3 y}{dx^3}$.

2. Prove that each equation is a solution of the expressed differential equation.

Solution	Differential Equation
(a) $y = cx^2 - x$.	$xy' = 2y + x$.
(b) $x^2 + y^2 = r^2$.	$x\, dx + y\, dy = 0$.
(c) $y = A \sin x + B \cos x$.	$y'' + y = 0$.
(d) $y = c_1 e^{2x} + c_2 e^{-3x} + x e^{2x}$.	$y'' + y' = 6y + 5e^{2x}$.
(e) $y = (2x + c)e^{-x}$.	$\dfrac{dy}{dx} + y = 2e^{-x}$.

3. Find the differential equations for which the following are primitives:

   (a) $y = x^3 + c$.

   (b) $y = c_1 e^x + c_2 e^{-x} + x$.

   (c) $y = c_1 \ln x$.

   (d) $x^2 - y^2 = 1$.

   (e) $y = c_1 x^3 + c_2 x^2 + c_3 x + c_4$.

4. Find the direction field for the equation

$$\frac{dy}{dx} = -\frac{x}{4y},$$

and sketch the curve which passes through the point (1,1).

III

FIRST ORDER DIFFERENTIAL EQUATIONS OF THE FIRST DEGREE

12. Introduction. The systematic development of the techniques for solving differential equations logically begins with the equation which is of the first order and first degree. In this chapter we shall develop seven techniques and summarize their usage.

13. Variables Separable. The simplest technique is the one applied to a differential equation which can be reduced to the form

$$M(x)dx + N(y)dy = 0,$$

where M is a function of x *alone* and N is a function of y *alone*. In this form the variables have been separated; whenever this is possible the differential equation is known as a **variables separable** type. The general solution is obtained by direct integration

$$\int M(x)dx + \int N(y)dy = c,$$

where c is an arbitrary constant.

Illustration. Find the general solution of

$$\frac{dy}{dx} = 3x^2.$$

Solution. Rewrite the equation in the form

$$dy = 3x^2 \, dx.$$

By an integration we obtain

$$\int dy = \int 3x^2 \, dx + c$$

or

$$y = x^3 + c.$$

It has already been pointed out (Section 7) that the general solution of a first order differential equation contains one arbitrary constant. The form of this arbitrary constant may vary; for example, we could write c, $\ln c$, e^c, arc sin c, etc. The form which is usually chosen is the one which will yield the simplest form for the solution.

Illustration. Find the general solution of

$$xy(1 + y^2)dx - (1 + x^2)dy = 0.$$

Solution. Separate the variables by dividing the equation by $y(1 + y^2)(1 + x^2)$ to obtain

$$\frac{x \, dx}{1 + x^2} - \frac{dy}{y(1 + y^2)} = 0.$$

By integration we obtain

$$\frac{1}{2} \ln (1 + x^2) - \frac{1}{2} \ln \frac{y^2}{1 + y^2} = \text{constant}.$$

If we choose the constant to be $\frac{1}{2} \ln c$, we can multiply the equation by 2 and apply the properties of logarithms to obtain

$$\ln (1 + x^2) - \ln \frac{y^2}{1 + y^2} = \ln c$$

or

$$\ln \frac{(1 + x^2)(1 + y^2)}{y^2} = \ln c.$$

Since two numbers that have the same logarithms are equal, we have

$$\frac{(1 + x^2)(1 + y^2)}{y^2} = c$$

or

$$(1 + x^2)(1 + y^2) = cy^2.$$

The form of the general solution of a differential equation is somewhat arbitrary, and it is sometimes difficult to specify which is the simplest. In the above illustration the last five equations are all expressions of the same function $F(x,y) = 0$ which satisfies the given differential equation; however, the last one is considered the simplest since it will yield the geometric properties and other characteristics of the family of curves more readily than any of the others.

Illustration. Find the general solution, and the particular curve passing through the point (0,0), of the differential equation

$$e^x \cos y \, dx + (1 + e^x) \sin y \, dy = 0.$$

Solution. Separate the variables:

$$\frac{e^x \, dx}{1 + e^x} + \tan y \, dy = 0.$$

Integrate to obtain

$$\ln (1 + e^x) - \ln \cos y = \ln c.$$

or

$$1 + e^x = c \cos y,$$

which is the general solution. Substituting the point (0,0) into this solution yields

$$1 + 1 = (c)(1) \quad \text{so that} \quad c = 2.$$

The particular solution through (0,0) is, therefore,

$$1 + e^x = 2 \cos y.$$

Remark. The transformation of a given differential equation into one which has the variables separated may involve division by the variables and functions of the variables. This fact necessitates a slight pause for some reflection. Division is a mathematical operation which may lead to trouble, for this operation is restricted; namely, division by zero is undefined and, in general, is not permitted. Nevertheless, in this section and throughout the entire book we shall divide by variables and functions which may be zero. Most of the time we are primarily concerned with the development and application of techniques for obtaining solutions, and the student is concerned with the learning of these techniques and applications. Under these circumstances, it is advisable to ignore this troublesome fact. If, however, it is desired to perform a complete analysis of a problem, which should always be the case in problems arising from actual situations, the solutions must be investigated at those values of the variables for which a division by zero may have been performed. A complete analysis may run something along the lines of the following illustration:

Illustration. Find the general solution of

$$x \, dy - (y + 1)dx = 0.$$

Solution. Separate the variables by dividing the equation by $x(y + 1)$ to obtain

$$\frac{dy}{y + 1} - \frac{dx}{x} = 0.$$

By an integration we obtain

$$\ln (y + 1) - \ln x = \ln c$$

or

$$y + 1 = cx.$$

The divisor, $x(y + 1)$, will be zero at $x = 0$ and $y = -1$. Let us investigate the solution at these points. At $x = 0$, the solution is $y + 1 = 0$, and at $y = -1$, the solution is $cx = 0$. If we substitute each condition into the given differential equation, we find that it is satisfied, and the solution is valid at this point. [Notice that both conditions yield the same point, $(0,-1)$.] Consequently, the division did not cause a false solution at the values for which the divisor became zero.

14. Exercise III.

  1. Find the general solution.

   (a) $\dfrac{dy}{dx} = \dfrac{x}{y}.$

   (b) $3x^2 - 2y^3 \, D_x y = 0.$

   (c) $(1 + y + y^2)dx + x(x^2 - 4)dy = 0.$

   (d) $\sin \theta \, d\rho + \rho \cos \theta \, d\theta = 0.$

   (e) $x^3 \, dy - x^3 \, dx = dx.$

  2. Find the particular solution satisfied by the given conditions.

   (a) $x \, dx + y \, dy = 0;$ $y = 2$ when $x = 1.$

   (b) $d\rho = \rho \tan \theta \, d\theta;$ $\rho = 1$ when $\theta = 0.$

   (c) $e^x \sec y \, dx + (1 + e^x) \sec y \tan y \, dy = 0;$ $y = 60°$ when $x = 3.$

15. Homogeneous Equations. An expression of the nth degree in x and y is said to be **homogeneous of degree n** if, when x and y are replaced by tx and ty, the result will be the original expression multiplied by t^n; symbolically,

$$f(tx,ty) = t^n f(x,y).$$

Illustrations. Show that the following expressions are homogeneous, and determine the degree.

1. $x^2 + xy - y^2$.

Solution. Replace x and y by tx and ty to obtain

$$t^2 x^2 + (tx)(ty) - t^2 y^2 = t^2(x^2 + xy - y^2).$$

The degree is 2.

2. $\sqrt{x^2 - y^2} + x \sin \dfrac{x}{y}$.

Solution.

$$\sqrt{t^2 x^2 - t^2 y^2} + tx \sin \frac{tx}{ty} = t\left[\sqrt{x^2 - y^2} + x \sin \frac{x}{y} \right].$$

The degree is 1.

We note the fact that *any polynomial in* x *and* y, *all terms of which are of the same degree in* x *and* y, *is homogeneous.*

If in a homogeneous function, $K(x,y)$, of degree n, we let $t = \dfrac{1}{x}$ and replace x by tx and y by ty, we obtain

$$K(tx,ty) = K\left(\frac{x}{x},\frac{y}{x}\right) = K\left(1,\frac{y}{x}\right)$$

and

$$K(x,y) = x^n K\left(1,\frac{y}{x}\right) = x^n K(v),$$

where $v = \dfrac{y}{x}$. This property permits us to change a homogeneous expression in two variables by "factoring out" one variable and thereby obtain an expression in a "single" variable which is the quotient of the two variables; for example,

$$x^2 + y^2 = x^2\left[1 + \frac{y^2}{x^2}\right] = x^2[1 + v^2].$$

Consider the differential equation

$$M(x,y)dx + N(x,y)dy = 0.$$

It i   if M and N are homo-
gen x and y.   The technique
for   a substitution $y = vx$ or
x :   theorem:

ential equation of the first
ed to the type of variables
$/$x *or* x = vy.

quation

$(x,y)dy = 0$

ous functions of degree n.   By

$$x^n M\left(1,\frac{y}{x}\right),$$

$$= x^n N\left(1,\frac{y}{x}\right).$$

$$= vx$$

$$y = v\,dx + x\,dv$$

on to obtain

$$+ x^n g(v)\big[v\,dx + x\,dv\big] = 0.$$

Dividing by   lecting terms, we have

$$\big[f(v) + v\,g(v)\big]dx + x\,g(v)dv = 0,$$

or

$$\frac{dx}{x} + \frac{g(v)dv}{f(v) + v\,g(v)} = 0,$$

and the variables x and v have been separated.   The proof for
$x = vy$ is similar.

Illustration.   Find the general solution of

$$2xy\,dx - (x^2 - y^2)dy = 0.$$

Solution.   A check reveals that the equation is homogeneous.
Let

$$y = vx$$

and

$$dy = v\,dx + x\,dv,$$

and substitute into the differential equation to obtain

$$2x(vx)dx - (x^2 - v^2x^2)(v\,dx + x\,dv) = 0$$

or

$$x^2(v + v^3)dx + x^3(v^2 - 1)dv = 0.$$

Dividing by $x^3(v + v^3)$ separates the variables:

$$\frac{dx}{x} + \frac{(v^2 - 1)dv}{v(1 + v^2)} = 0.$$

An integration yields

$$\ln x - \ln v + \ln (v^2 + 1) = \ln c$$

or

$$x(v^2 + 1) = cv.$$

Returning to the original variables by substituting $v = \dfrac{y}{x}$, we obtain

$$y^2 + x^2 = cy.$$

16. Exercise IV.

1. Find the general solution.
   (a) $(x - y)dy = (y - x)dx$.
   (b) $y\,dx = x\,dy - \sqrt{x^2 + y^2}\,dx$.
   (c) $(x^3 - y^3)dx + xy^2\,dy = 0$.
   (d) $dy = \left(\dfrac{y}{x} - \csc^2\dfrac{y}{x}\right)dx$.
   (e) $(3x^2 + 2xy + 4y^2)dx + (20x^2 + 6xy + y^2)dy = 0$.

2. Find the particular solution satisfied by the given conditions.
   (a) $(x + y)dy = y\,dx$; $y = 1$ when $x = 0$.
   (b) $(x^2 + 2xy - 2y^2)dx + (y^2 + 2xy - 2x^2)dy = 0$; $\quad y = 3$ when $x = 0$.

3. Prove that

$$(x + y)^{a+b}(x - y)^{a-b} = k$$

is the solution of $(ax - by)dx + (bx - ay)dy = 0$.

17. Exact Differential Equations.

It may be recalled from calculus that a total differential of a function $u(x,y)$ is given by

$$du(x,y) = \frac{\partial u}{\partial x}\,dx + \frac{\partial u}{\partial y}\,dy.$$

Any expression that is exactly the total differential of some function of x and y is called an *exact differential*. Consider now the differential equation

$$M(x,y)dx + N(x,y)dy = 0.$$

If there exists a function $u(x,y)$ such that

$$\frac{\partial u}{\partial x} = M(x,y)$$

and

$$\frac{\partial u}{\partial y} = N(x,y),$$

then the differential equation is said to be **exact**. In order to test a given differential equation for exactness, we need the following theorem:

Theorem. *A necessary and sufficient condition that*

(1) $$M(x,y)dx + N(x,y)dy = 0$$

be exact is that

(2) $$\frac{\partial M}{\partial y} \equiv \frac{\partial N}{\partial x}.$$

Proof. If equation (1) is exact, there exists, by definition, a function $u(x,y)$ such that

$$\frac{\partial u}{\partial x} = M \quad \text{and} \quad \frac{\partial u}{\partial y} = N.$$

Since

$$\frac{\partial^2 u}{\partial x\, \partial y} \equiv \frac{\partial^2 u}{\partial y\, \partial x},$$

it follows that

$$\frac{\partial M}{\partial y} = \frac{\partial^2 u}{\partial x\, \partial y} = \frac{\partial^2 u}{\partial y\, \partial x} = \frac{\partial N}{\partial x},$$

and equation (2) holds, thus proving that equation (2) is necessary. To establish the sufficiency of equation (2), let us construct the function $u(x,y)$. Consider

$$u(x,y) = \int^x M(x,y)dx + C(y),$$

where $\int^x$ denotes an integration with respect to x holding y

constant, and $C(y)$ is the arbitrary "constant" of integration, which can be a function of y since the integration is with respect to x. Let us now find the partial derivatives of u with respect to x and y, noting that they should be equal to M and N, respectively, for equation (1) to be exact.

$$\text{(3)} \qquad \frac{\partial u}{\partial x} = \frac{\partial}{\partial x} \int^x M(x,y)dx + \frac{\partial}{\partial x} C(y)$$

$$= M(x,y).$$

$$\text{(4)} \qquad \frac{\partial u}{\partial y} = \frac{\partial}{\partial y} \int^x M(x,y)dx + \frac{\partial}{\partial y} C(y).$$

Since the partial derivative of u with respect to y should equal $N(x,y)$, we desire to determine $C(y)$ so that this is true. Since $C(y)$ is a function of y only,

$$\frac{\partial C}{\partial y} = \frac{dC}{dy}.$$

Setting equation (4) equal to $N(x,y)$ and solving for $D_y C$, we obtain

$$\frac{dC}{dy} = N(x,y) - \frac{\partial}{\partial y} \int^x M(x,y)dx,$$

and (Cy) may be found by an integration, providing the right-hand side is independent of x, or, symbolically, if

$$\frac{\partial}{\partial x}\left[N(x,y) - \frac{\partial}{\partial y} \int^x M(x,y)dx \right] = 0.$$

Performing the differentiation, we obtain

$$\frac{\partial}{\partial x} N(x,y) - \frac{\partial}{\partial y} M(x,y) = 0,$$

which is true when equation (2) holds, thus proving that this condition is also sufficient.

For an exact differential equation

$$0 = M \, dx + N \, dy = du,$$

the solution can be obtained by an integration

$$\int du = 0$$

or

$$u(x,y) = c.$$

The technique, therefore, reduces to one of finding $u(x,y)$, and the construction of such a function in the sufficiency proof of the theorem developed this technique.

Illustration.   Show that

$$2xy\, dx + (1 + x^2)dy = 0$$

is exact, and find the general solution.

Solution.

$$M = 2xy$$

and

$$N = 1 + x^2.$$
$$\frac{\partial M}{\partial y} = 2x = \frac{\partial N}{\partial x}; \quad \therefore \quad \text{exact.}$$

Let

$$u(x,y) = \int^x 2xy\, dx + C(y) = x^2 y + C(y).$$

Since $\dfrac{\partial u}{\partial y} = N$, we have

$$\frac{\partial}{\partial y}\left[x^2 y + C(y)\right] = x^2 + \frac{d}{dy}\,C(y) = 1 + x^2.$$

Solving for $D_y C$, we obtain

$$\frac{dC}{dy} = 1$$

and

$$C = y.$$

We do not add a constant of integration here as C is *any* function such that $u_y = N$. The function $u(x,y)$ is now completely determined:

$$u(x,y) = x^2 y + C(y) = x^2 y + y,$$

and the solution is

$$x^2 y + y = c.$$

Although the differential equation in the above illustration could be solved by separating the variables, it is not true that all exact differential equations can be solved by this method. However, the converse is true. That is, all equations in which

the variables can be separated are exact. This can easily be
seen if the differential equation is transferred to the form

$$M(x)dx + N(y)dy = 0.$$

Then

$$\frac{\partial M}{\partial y} = 0 = \frac{\partial N}{\partial x},$$

and the condition for exactness is satisfied. Let us consider
another example of an exact differential equation.

Illustration. Show that

$$(3xy^4 + x)dx + (6x^2y^3 - 2y^2 + 7)dy = 0$$

is exact, and find the solution.

Solution. Equation is exact since

$$\frac{\partial M}{\partial y} = 12xy^3 = \frac{\partial N}{\partial x}.$$

Let

$$u(x,y) = \int^x (3xy^4 + x)dx + C(y)$$
$$= \tfrac{3}{2}x^2y^4 + \tfrac{1}{2}x^2 + C(y).$$

Then

$$\frac{dC}{dy} = 6x^2y^3 - 2y^2 + 7 - 6x^2y^3$$
$$= -2y^2 + 7$$

and

$$C(y) = -\tfrac{2}{3}y^3 + 7y.$$

The solution is

$$u(x,y) = \tfrac{3}{2}x^2y^4 + \tfrac{1}{2}x^2 - \tfrac{2}{3}y^3 + 7y = c.$$

18. Exercise V.

1. Find the general solution.
   (a) $(2x^2 + 5xy^2)dx + (5x^2y - 2y^4)dy = 0.$
   (b) $(ax^2 + 2bxy + cy^2)dx + (bx^2 + 2cxy + y^2)dy = 0.$
   (c) $\sec^2 x \tan y\, dx + \sec^2 y \tan x\, dy = 0.$
   (d) $(x^2 + ye^{2y})dx + (2xy + x)e^{2y}\, dy = 0.$
   (e) $(\sin x + \sin y)dx + (x \cos y + \cos y)dy = 0.$

2. Find the particular integral passing through the given
   point.

(a) $(4x - 2y + 3)dx + (5y - 2x + 7)dy = 0$; $(1,2)$.

(b) $(2x \sin y + 2x + 3y \cos x)dx + (x^2 \cos y + 3 \sin x)dy$;
$\left(\dfrac{\pi}{2}, 0\right)$.

(c) $(ye^{2x} - 3xe^{2y})dx + (\frac{1}{2}e^{2x} - 3x^2e^{2y} - e^y)dy = 0$; $(1,0)$.

19. Integrating Factors.   The differential equation

(1) $$M(x,y)dx + N(x,y)dy = 0$$

can always be transformed into an exact differential equation by
multiplying it by a suitable expression, $\mu(x,y)$.   The expression
$\mu(x,y)$ which makes the equation exact is called an **integrating
factor.**   It follows from the existence theorem that there exists
a solution which we can write in the form

(2) $$u(x,y) = c.$$

Then the equations

(3) $$du = \frac{\partial u}{\partial x}\,dx + \frac{\partial u}{\partial y}\,dy = 0$$

and

(4) $$M\,dx + N\,dy = 0$$

both hold along an integral curve of the family.   If we solve both
equations for the derivative of y with respect to x, we obtain

(5) $$\frac{dy}{dx} = -\frac{M}{N} = -\frac{\partial u/\partial x}{\partial u/\partial y}.$$

Further simplification yields

(6) $$\frac{1}{M}\frac{\partial u}{\partial x} = \frac{1}{N}\frac{\partial u}{\partial y} = \mu(x,y)$$

as we let $\mu(x,y)$ equal the common ratio.   We can now solve
equations (6) to obtain

(7) $$\frac{\partial u}{\partial x} = \mu M \quad \text{and} \quad \frac{\partial u}{\partial y} = \mu N,$$

and substituting into equation (3) we get

(8) $$du = \frac{\partial u}{\partial x}\,dx + \frac{\partial u}{\partial y}\,dy = \mu(M\,dx + N\,dy) = 0.$$

Thus the integrating factor μ makes equation (1) exact. The integrating factor is by no means unique; in fact, there exist infinitely many integrating factors.

Although equation (1) can be solved by finding an integrating factor, reducing the equation to an exact differential equation, and then employing the technique for exact equations, this procedure is used only for simple examples. The difficulty lies in finding an appropriate integrating factor. Some suggestions may be made, but in practice much depends upon the skill of the user. As an aid, let us recall some exact differentials:

I. $$x\,dy + y\,dx = d(xy).$$

II. $$x\,dx \pm y\,dy = d\left[\tfrac{1}{2}(x^2 \pm y^2)\right].$$

III. $$\frac{x\,dy - y\,dx}{x^2} = d\left(\frac{y}{x}\right).$$

IV. $$\frac{x\,dy - y\,dx}{y^2} = d\left(-\frac{x}{y}\right).$$

V. $$\frac{x\,dy - y\,dx}{xy} = d\left(\ln\frac{y}{x}\right).$$

VI. $$\frac{x\,dy - y\,dx}{x^2 + y^2} = d\left(\arctan\frac{y}{x}\right).$$

VII. $$\frac{x\,dy - y\,dx}{x^2 - y^2} = d\left(\frac{1}{2}\ln\frac{x+y}{x-y}\right).$$

VIII. $$\frac{x\,dy - y\,dx}{(x-y)^2} = d\left[\frac{1}{2}\left(\frac{x+y}{x-y}\right)\right].$$

IX. $$\frac{x\,dy - y\,dx}{x\sqrt{x^2 - y^2}} = d\left(\arcsin\frac{y}{x}\right).$$

X. $$\frac{y\,dx - x\,dy}{(x+y)^2} = d\left[\frac{1}{2}\left(\frac{x-y}{x+y}\right)\right].$$

XI. $$\frac{x\,dy + y\,dx}{x^2 y^2} = d\left(-\frac{1}{xy}\right).$$

XII. $$\frac{dx + dy}{x + y} = d[\ln(x+y)].$$

The fact that these are exact differentials can be seen by expanding the right-hand side. Should the numerator of the left side of any of the above expressions occur in a differential equation, then the integrating factor to be used is $\mu = \dfrac{1}{D}$, where D is one of the above denominators, and the solution can be obtained by a simple integration. Let us consider some examples.

Illustrations. Find an integrating factor and solve.

1. $$x \, dy + y \, dx = x^2 y^2 \, dx.$$

Solution. The differential XI suggests the integrating factor $\mu = x^{-2} y^{-2}$. Multiply by μ to obtain

$$\frac{1}{x^2 y^2} \left[x \, dy + y \, dx \right] = dx$$

or

$$d\left(-\frac{1}{xy} \right) = dx.$$

A simple integration yields

$$\int d\left(-\frac{1}{xy} \right) = \int dx + c,$$

from which we write the solution

$$-\frac{1}{xy} = x + c$$

or

$$x^2 y + cxy + 1 = 0.$$

2. $$x^2 y \, dy - xy^2 \, dx - x^3 y^2 \, dx = 0.$$

Solution.

Factor: $xy(x \, dy - y \, dx) - x^3 y^2 \, dx = 0.$

Multiply by $x^{-2} y^{-2}$: $\dfrac{x \, dy - y \, dx}{xy} - x \, dx = 0.$

By V: $d\left(\ln \dfrac{y}{x} \right) - x \, dx = 0.$

Integrate: $\ln \dfrac{y}{x} - \dfrac{1}{2} x^2 = c.$

3. $$x \, dy - y \, dx = x^3 y (x \, dy + y \, dx).$$

Solution.

Multiply by x^{-2}: $\quad \dfrac{x\,dy - y\,dx}{x^2} = xy(x\,dy + y\,dx).$

By III and I: $\quad d\left(\dfrac{y}{x}\right) = xy\,d(xy).$

Integrate: $\quad \dfrac{y}{x} = \dfrac{1}{2}\,x^2y^2 + k$

or
$$2y = x^3y^2 + cx.$$

4. Show that $x^m y^n$ is an integrating factor for
$$(ay + bx^iy^j)dx + (cx + rx^{i+1}y^{j-1})dy = 0,$$

providing $bc - ad \neq 0$, $c \neq a$, and $d(i+1) \neq bj$, simultaneously.

Solution. An integrating factor transforms a differential equation into one which is exact. Consequently, *after multiplying by $x^m y^n$*, we should have
$$\frac{\partial M}{\partial y} \equiv \frac{\partial N}{\partial x}$$

or
$$a(n+1)x^my^n + b(n+j)x^{m+i}y^{n+j-1}$$
$$\equiv c(m+1)x^my^n + r(m+i+1)x^{m+i}y^{n+j-1}.$$

For this to be an identity in x and y, the coefficients of the like powered terms must be equal; thus we have
$$\begin{cases} a(n+1) = c(m+1), \\ b(n+j) = r(m+i+1) \end{cases}$$

or
$$\begin{cases} an - cm = c - a, \\ bn - rm = r(i+1) - bj, \end{cases}$$

which can be solved for m and n, providing the stated conditions of the problem are satisfied. Consequently, there exist values for m and n such that $x^m y^n$ is an integrating factor for the given differential equation.

5. Find an integrating factor of the form $x^m y^n$ and solve
$$(2y + 3x^2y^3)dx + (3x + 5x^3y^2)dy = 0.$$

Solution.   Multiply by $x^m y^n$:

$$(2x^m y^{n+1} + 3x^{m+2}y^{n+3})dx + (3x^{m+1}y^n + 5x^{m+3}y^{n+2})dy = 0.$$

Equate $M_y = N_x$:

$$2(n+1)x^m y^n + 3(n+3)x^{m+2}y^{n+2}$$
$$\equiv 3(m+1)x^m y^n + 5(m+3)x^{m+2}y^{n+2}.$$

Then

$$\begin{cases} 2(n+1) = 3(m+1), \\ 3(n+3) = 5(m+3). \end{cases}$$

Solving for m and n, we obtain

$$m = -9 \quad \text{and} \quad n = -13.$$

The equation

$$(2x^{-9}y^{-12} + 3x^{-7}y^{-10})dx + (3x^{-8}y^{-13} + 5x^{-6}y^{-11})dy = 0$$

is exact, and

$$u(x,y) = \int^x (2x^{-9}y^{-12} + 3x^{-7}y^{-10})dx$$
$$= -\tfrac{1}{4}x^{-8}y^{-12} - \tfrac{1}{2}x^{-6}y^{-10} + C(y).$$

Since $u_y = N(x,y)$, we have

$$3x^{-8}y^{-13} + 5x^{-6}y^{-11} + \frac{dC}{dy} = 3x^{-8}y^{-13} + 5x^{-6}y^{-11},$$

which yields

$$C(y) = K.$$

The solution is

$$u(x,y) = x^{-8}y^{-12} + 2x^{-6}y^{-10} = c$$

or

$$2x^2 y^2 - cx^8 y^{12} + 1 = 0.$$

20. Exercise VI.

1. Find the general solution.
   (a) $x\,dy - y\,dx = x^2 y\,dy.$
   (b) $x^3\,dy - x^2 y\,dx = x^5 y\,dx.$
   (c) $(x^2 + y^2)(x\,dy + y\,dx) = xy(x\,dy - y\,dx).$
   (d) $3y\,dx + 2x\,dy + 4xy^2\,dx + 3x^2 y\,dy = 0.$
   (e) $x\,dy - y\,dx = x^2\sqrt{x^2 - y^2}\,dx.$

2. Find the integral curves through the given points.

(a) $x\,dy + y\,dx = 3x^2\,dx$; (2,1).

(b) $x^2\,D_x y - xy = x^2 - y^2$; (1,0).

(c) $y\,dx = (2x^2 y^3 - x)dy$; (1,1).

21. Linear Equations of the First Order. A differential equation in which the dependent variable and its derivatives enter to the first degree only is said to be **linear**. The general form of a *first order linear* differential equation is given by

$$(1) \qquad \frac{dy}{dx} + yP(x) = Q(x).$$

If $Q(x) = 0$, the equation is said to be *homogeneous*.* Let us consider the solution of it. We may separate the variables to obtain

$$\frac{dy}{y} = -P(x)dx.$$

Integrating we get

$$\ln y = -\int P(x)dx + \ln k.$$

Simplifying:

$$y = ke^{-\int P(x)dx},$$

or

$$ye^{\int P(x)dx} = k.$$

Consequently, the left-hand side of equation (1) can be made an exact differential

$$du = d(ye^{\int P(x)dx})$$

by multiplying it by the integrating factor

$$\mu(x) = e^{\int P(x)dx}$$

which is a function of x only. Thus equation (1) is changed to

$$(2) \qquad \mu(x)[dy + yP(x)dx] = \mu(x)Q(x)dx,$$

and the right-hand side is a function of x only, so that the solution may be obtained by an integration:

---

* The word *homogeneous* is used here in the equational sense, which is not to be confused with the functional sense discussed in Section 15. The equation with $Q(x) = 0$ is also called the *reduced linear equation*.

$$\int d(y\mu) = y\mu = \int \mu(x)Q(x)dx + c.$$

Let us illustrate the procedure by examples.

Illustrations. Find the general solution for each of the following linear differential equations:

1. $$y' + 2xy = x.$$

Solution. In this problem $P(x) = 2x$, and the integrating factor is

$$\mu(x) = e^{\int 2x\, dx} = e^{x^2}.$$

Multiply by the integrating factor to obtain

$$e^{x^2}[dy + 2xy\, dx] = e^{x^2}x\, dx.$$

Now the left-hand side is the exact differential

$$e^{x^2}[dy + 2xy\, dx] = d[ye^{x^2}],$$

and an integration yields

$$ye^{x^2} = \int e^{x^2}x\, dx$$
$$= \tfrac{1}{2}e^{x^2} + c,$$

which may be rewritten

$$e^{x^2}(2y - 1) = k.$$

2. $$x^2 y' + xy = x^4 + x^2.$$

Solution. Divide by x^2:

$$y' + \frac{1}{x}\, y = x^2 + 1.$$

Since $P(x) = x^{-1}$, we have

$$\mu(x) = e^{\int dx/x} = e^{\ln x} = x.$$

Multiply by x: $d(yx) = (x^3 + x)dx.$

Integrate: $yx = \tfrac{1}{4}x^4 + \tfrac{1}{2}x^2 + c,$

or

$$4y = x^3 + 2x + kx^{-1}.$$

3. $$dx + 2x\, dy = y\, dy.$$

Solution. Interchange the roles of x and y. Since $P(y) = 2$,

$$\int P(y)dy = 2y \quad \text{and} \quad \mu(y) = e^{2y}.$$

Multiply by $\mu(y)$: $d(xe^{2y}) = ye^{2y} \, dy$.

Integrate: $xe^{2y} = \frac{1}{4}e^{2y}(2y - 1) + c$.

Simplify: $4x = 2y - 1 + ke^{-2y}$.

22. Exercise VII.

1. Prove $e^{\ln x} = x$.
2. Find the general solution.
    (a) $y' + 4y = x^2$.
    (b) $y' + (\sin x)y = 2xe^{\cos x}$.
    (c) $x^2 \, dy + xy \, dx = 8x^2 \cos^2 x \, dx$.
    (d) $dy + 2y \, dx = \sin 3x \, dx$.
    (e) $dx - x \, dy = \ln y \, dy$.

23. Linear Fractional Equations.

A first order, first degree differential equation may be written in the form

(1) $$\frac{dy}{dx} = \frac{M(x,y)}{N(x,y)},$$

and if $M(x,y)$ and $N(x,y)$ are linear functions of x and y, the equation is called a **linear fractional equation.** The general form of M and N are now given by

(2) $M(x,y) = a + bx + cy, \quad N(x,y) = \alpha + \beta x + \gamma y,$

in which we assume that b and β (c and γ) are not both zero at the same time, for if they were, the equation would be one in which the variables were separable immediately.

There are two cases to consider.

Case I. $b\gamma - c\beta \neq 0$. In this case the two straight lines defined by setting equations (2) equal to zero are not parallel and will intersect in a point (h,k). If we translate the origin to this point by the transformations

$$x = X + h \quad \text{and} \quad y = Y + k,$$

we have

$$\frac{dy}{dx} = \frac{dY}{dX},$$

and the differential equation (1) reduces to

(3)
$$\frac{dY}{dX} = \frac{a + b(X + h) + c(Y + k)}{\alpha + \beta(X + h) + \gamma(Y + k)}$$

$$= \frac{a + bh + ck + bX + cY}{\alpha + \beta h + \gamma k + \beta X + \gamma Y}$$

$$= \frac{bX + cY}{\beta X + \gamma Y}$$

by virtue of

$$a + bh + ck = 0 \quad \text{and} \quad \alpha + \beta h + \gamma k = 0,$$

since (h,k) is the point of intersection of the two lines $M(x,y) = 0$ and $N(x,y) = 0$ and must therefore satisfy these equations.

Equation (3) is a homogeneous differential equation and can be solved by the technique developed in Section 15.

Illustration. Find the general solution of

$$(x - 2y + 1)dx + (2x - y - 1)dy = 0.$$

Solution. Find the point (h,k) by solving

$$x - 2y + 1 = 0,$$
$$2x - y - 1 = 0$$

to obtain $x = h = 1$ and $y = k = 1$. The transformation $x = X + 1, y = Y + 1$ yields

$$(X - 2Y)dX + (2X - Y)dY = 0.$$

Note that this equation is obtained from the given differential equation by simply replacing a $(=1)$ and α $(=-1)$ by zero and changing the unknowns to capital letters. The resulting differential equation is homogeneous, so let

$$Y = vX \quad \text{and} \quad dY = v \, dX + X \, dv$$

to obtain

$$\frac{dX}{X} + \frac{(2 - v)dv}{1 - v^2} = 0.$$

An integration yields

$$\ln X + \ln \frac{1 + v}{1 - v} + \frac{1}{2} \ln (1 - v^2) = \ln c$$

or

$$(X + Y)^3 = k(X - Y).$$

Transform back to the original variables by

$$X = x - 1 \quad \text{and} \quad Y = y - 1$$

to obtain

$$(x + y - 2)^3 = c(x - y).$$

Case II. $b\gamma - c\beta = 0$. Since c and γ cannot both be zero, let us assume $c \neq 0$. If we let $bx + cy = v$, then $b\,dx + c\,dy = dv$ or

$$(4) \qquad \frac{dy}{dx} = -\frac{b}{c} + \frac{1}{c}\frac{dv}{dx}.$$

By substituting this into the differential equation (1), we obtain

$$(5) \qquad -\frac{b}{c} + \frac{1}{c}\frac{dv}{dx} = \frac{a + v}{\alpha + \beta x + \gamma y}.$$

Since $b\gamma - c\beta = 0$, we have

$$\frac{\gamma}{c} = \frac{\beta}{b} = k \quad \text{or} \quad \gamma = kc \quad \text{and} \quad \beta = kb,$$

so that

$$\beta x + \gamma y = kbx + kcy = k(bx + cy) = kv,$$

and equation (5) becomes

$$(6) \qquad -\frac{b}{c} + \frac{1}{c}\frac{dv}{dx} = \frac{a + v}{\alpha + kv}.$$

Now the variables are separable and the equation can be solved by a simple integration. If $c = 0$, then $\gamma \neq 0$, and if we make the substitution $\beta x + \gamma y = v$, the result will again be an equation in which the variables are separable.

Illustration. Solve

$$(1 + x + y)dx + (3 + 2x + 2y)dy = 0.$$

Solution. We first note that

$$b\gamma - c\beta = 2 - 2 = 0.$$

Let $x + y = v$, then

$$\frac{dy}{dx} = \frac{dv}{dx} - 1 = -\frac{1 + v}{3 + 2v}.$$

Simplify:
$$\frac{3 + 2v}{2 + v}\, dv = dx.$$

Integrate:
$$2v - \ln\,(v + 2) = x + c.$$

In terms of x, y: $\quad x + 2y - \ln\,(x + y + 2) = c.$

24. Exercise VIII. Find the general solution.
1. $(2 - x - y)dx + (3 + x + y)dy = 0.$
2. $(2 + 3x - 5y)dx + 7dy = 0.$
3. $(4x + 3y + 2)dx + (5x + 4y + 1)dy = 0.$
4. $(x - y - 3)dx + (3x - 3y + 1)dy = 0.$
5. $(2x - y - 1)dx + (3x + 2y - 5)dy = 0.$

25. Substitutions. At this point of our study we have developed six techniques for solving a first order differential equation of the first degree. The seventh technique is one which reduces a given differential equation to one of the previously studied types. The reduction is accomplished by a substitution. We have already used this principle in the case of the homogeneous equation where we let $y = vx$ and reduced the equation to one in which the variables were separable. This procedure is very similar to the finding of an integrating factor in that there is great dependence upon the experience and skill of the user. The most frequently encountered substitution is one which will make the variables separable, such as the substitution used in Case II, Section 23.

The general procedure is:
(a) Determine the substitution equations.
(b) Differentiate the substitution equations.
(c) Eliminate all but two of the unknowns from the given differential equation and the equations obtained in (a) and (b).
(d) Solve the resulting differential equation.
(e) Return to the original variables.

We shall illustrate with some examples.

Illustrations.

1. Solve $(x + y)^2 dy = dx.$

Solution.   Let $x + y = u$; then $dx = du - dy$, and the equation reduces to

$$u^2 \, dy = du - dy$$

or

$$dy = \frac{du}{u^2 + 1}.$$

Integrate to obtain

$$y = \arctan u + c$$
$$= \arctan (x + y) + c.$$

2. Solve $\dfrac{x}{y} (dx + dy) + (x + y)(y \, dx - x \, dy) = 0$.

Solution.   Let $u = x + y$ and $w = \dfrac{x}{y}$. Then

$$dx + dy = du, \quad y \, dx - x \, dy = y^2 \, dw, \quad y = \frac{u}{w + 1}.$$

The differential equation becomes

$$w \, du + uy^2 \, dw = 0$$

or

$$\frac{du}{u^3} + \frac{dw}{w(w + 1)^2} = 0.$$

Integrate to obtain

$$-\frac{1}{2} u^{-2} + \ln \frac{w}{w + 1} + (w + 1)^{-1} = c$$

or

$$-\frac{1}{2(x + y)^2} + \frac{y}{x + y} + \ln \frac{x}{x + y} = c.$$

The equation

$$y' + P(x)y = Q(x)y^n$$

(often called *Bernoulli's equation*) may be reduced to a linear equation by a substitution.   Divide the equation by y^n to obtain

$$y^{-n}y' + P(x)y^{1-n} = Q(x).$$

This suggests the substitution

$$v = y^{1-n}, \quad \frac{dv}{dx} = (1 - n)y^{-n}y',$$

thus changing the equation to

$$\frac{1}{1-n}\frac{dv}{dx} + P(x)v = Q(x),$$

which is a linear equation.

Illustration. Solve

$$y' - \frac{3}{x}y = y^5.$$

Solution. Divide the equation by y^5 to obtain

$$y^{-5}y' - \frac{3}{x}y^{-4} = 1.$$

Let

$$v = y^{-4}, \ v' = -4y^{-5}y'.$$

Then we have

$$-\frac{1}{4}v' - \frac{3}{x}v = 1$$

or

$$v' + \frac{12}{x}v = -4.$$

The integrating factor is x^{12}, and

$$d(vx^{12}) = -4x^{12}\,dx.$$

Integrate to obtain

$$vx^{12} = -4\frac{x^{13}}{13} + c$$

or

$$y^{-4} = -\frac{4}{13}x + cx^{-12}.$$

26. Exercise IX. Solve

1. $xy(x\,dy + y\,dx) = 4x^3\,dx.$
2. $y^3(x\,dx + y\,dy) = (x^2+y^2)^3 dy.$
3. $(1 + e^{-\frac{y}{x}})dy + \left(1 - \frac{y}{x}\right)dx = 0; \ \left(\text{let } z = \frac{y}{x}\right).$
4. $yy' + y^2 \tan x = \cos^2 x.$
5. $xy' - y = y^3.$

27. Summary. The techniques discussed in the previous sections provide us with procedures for solving the first order differential equation of the first degree,

$$(1) \qquad M(x,y)dx + N(x,y)dy = 0,$$

providing it falls into one of the mentioned types. To discover which method of solution to use, test the given equation to determine its type in the following sequence:

I.   Answer these questions:
   (a) Are the variables separable (§ 13)?
   (b) Are M and N homogeneous and of the same degree (§ 15)?
   (c) Is the equation an exact differential equation (§ 17)?
   (d) Is the equation linear (§ 21)?
   (e) Is the equation a linear fractional equation (§ 23)?
II. Search for an integrating factor (§ 19).
III. Make a substitution to reduce the equation to a known type (§25).

This procedure by no means exhausts all the equations of the type

$$M(x,y)dx + N(x,y)dy = 0.$$

A general method of solution may be developed from the fact that if this equation is multiplied by $\mu(x,y)$ and the result yields

$$(2) \qquad \frac{\partial(\mu M)}{\partial y} = \frac{\partial(\mu N)}{\partial x},$$

then the equation is exact. Equation (2) is a partial differential equation and we shall discuss its solution in Section 87 and obtain μ as a function of x and y. This, however, does not necessarily guarantee that the integration can be performed in terms of elementary functions. In such cases, we resort to approximate methods or series for the evaluation of the integral. Fortunately, many of the first order differential equations occurring in scientific problems fall into the above categories.

We shall close this chapter with a group of miscellaneous exercises.

28. Exercise X. Solve the following differential equations and determine the constant of integration when appropriate conditions are given.

1. $y' + 3x^2 y = 3x^2$.
2. $4x^2 y^2\, dy - 3xy^3\, dx = x^2 y^3\, dx + 2x^2\, dy$.
3. $(\sin x + \cos y)dx + \cos x\, dx - \sin y\, dy = 0$.
4. $xy' + y = y^2 x^3 \sin x$.
5. $R\dfrac{dq}{dt} + \dfrac{1}{C} q = E$; $\quad q = 0$ when $t = 0$.
6. $(x^2 y^2 - xy - 2)x\, dy + (x^2 y^2 - 1)y\, dx = 0$; $\quad$ (let $v = xy$).
7. $(3x^2 - 2xy)dx + (4y^3 - x^2)dy = 0$; $\quad y = 1$ when $x = 2$.
8. $(3x^2 + 2xy - 2y^2)dx + (2x^2 + 6xy + y^2)dy$.
9. $(2x - y + 1)dx + (x - 2y - 1)dy = 0$.
10. $(3x + 3y - 2)dx + (2x + 2y + 1)dy = 0$.
11. Prove that if

$$\frac{\partial M}{\partial y} - \frac{\partial N}{\partial x} = N\frac{k}{x},$$

then x^k is an integrating factor of

$$M\, dx + N\, dy = 0.$$

12. Show that if the equation

$$(axy - b)y\, dx + (cxy - d)x\, dy = 0$$

is divided by $xy[(axy - b) - (cxy - d)]$, then it is exact.

IV

FIRST ORDER EQUATIONS OF HIGHER DEGREE

29. Introduction. In this chapter we shall discuss the first order differential equation

$$F(x,y,y') = 0,$$

in which y' is of degree higher than the first. It will be seen that the solutions of these equations yield more than one integral curve passing through the same point (x,y). This will lead us into a discussion of envelopes. We shall consider four types of equations and develop the technique for obtaining the solution of each. Furthermore, we shall make extensive use of the notation

$$p = \frac{dy}{dx}.$$

30. Equations Solvable for p. The first type is the one in which it is possible to solve the given differential equation for p. In other words, it is possible to factor the equation into linear factors of the form

$$[p - f_1(x,y)][p - f_2(x,y)] \cdots [p - f_n(x,y)] = 0.$$

The solution is obtained by setting each linear factor equal to zero and solving the resulting first order differential equations which are of the first degree. We thus obtain n solutions:

$$F_1(x,y,c) = 0, \; F_2(x,y,c) = 0, \cdots, F_n(x,y,c) = 0.$$

This is considered to be the most desirable form of the solution. The product of all the functions

$$\prod_{i=1}^{n} F_i(x,y,c) = 0$$

may also be considered as the general solution since it contains all the curves defined by the individual functions set equal to zero, and no others.

Illustrations. Solve:

1. $$p^2 - p - 6 = 0.$$

Solution. We may factor the given equation to obtain

$$(p - 3)(p + 2) = 0.$$

Set each factor equal to zero:

$$p - 3 = 0; \quad p + 2 = 0.$$

Integrate:

$$(1) \ y = 3x + c \quad \text{and} \quad (2) \ y = -2x + c.$$

The general solution is given by both of these families of straight lines as shown in Fig. 8.

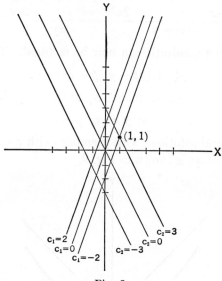

Fig. 8

It should be noted that two lines pass through the same point; for example, the point (1,1) satisfies both lines with $c = -2$ in (1) and $c = 3$ in (2).

2. $(x + 2y)(3x - 2y)p^2 - (4x^2 + 4y^2 - 2xy)p$
$$- (2x - 3y)(2x + y) = 0.$$

Solution. Factor:

$$[(x + 2y)p - (2x + y)][(3x - 2y)p + (2x - 3y)] = 0.$$

Solving each factor which is homogeneous:

$$(x + y)^{-1}(x - y)^{-3} = c; \quad (x + y)^5(x - y)^{-1} = c.$$

These two equations form the general solution.

3. $xp^3 + (x - 2x^2 - y)p^2 - (2x^2 + y - 2xy)p + 2xy = 0.$

Solution.   This is a cubic equation in p; to express it in factored form we recall the Factor Theorem from algebra and use synthetic division. The divisors are in the set

$$\pm \{1, 2, x, y, 2x, 2y, 2xy\}$$

and the same set with the elements divided by x. A division by -1 yields

$$
\begin{array}{ccccc}
x & x - 2x^2 - y & -2x^2 - y + 2xy & 2xy & \underline{|-1} \\
 & -x & 2x^2 + y & -2xy & \\
\hline
x & -2x^2 - y & & 2xy & 0
\end{array}
$$

The resulting quadratic can now be factored. Thus we have

$$(p + 1)(xp - y)(p - 2x) = 0.$$

The solution of each factor set equal to zero yields

$$y + x = c; \quad y = cx; \quad y - x^2 = c$$

as the general solution. One member (with $c = 0$) from each family of curves is shown in Fig. 9.

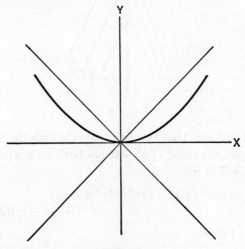

Fig. 9

31. Equations Solvable for y. This method is also called the method of eliminating the dependent variable, which is exactly what is done. If the first order differential equation can be solved for y, it can be written in the form

$$(1) \qquad\qquad y = f(x,p).$$

The total derivative of this equation with respect to x is

$$(2) \qquad\qquad \frac{dy}{dx} = p = \frac{\partial f}{\partial x} + \frac{\partial f}{\partial p}\frac{dp}{dx},$$

an expression involving only x and p. If we can solve equation (2) to obtain

$$(3) \qquad\qquad F(x,p,c) = 0,$$

then we will have two equations, (1) and (3), relating x, y, and p. Considered together, these equations form a pair of parametric equations, with p as the parameter, for the general solution of the original differential equation. The parameter p can be eliminated to obtain a solution in x, y, and an arbitrary constant. This elimination may produce extraneous factors, so such a solution should always be checked by substituting it into the original differential equation.

Illustrations.

1. Solve $\qquad\qquad p^2 + 2xp - 2y = 0.$

Solution. Solve for y to obtain

$$y = \tfrac{1}{2}p^2 + xp.$$

Differentiate with respect to x:

$$\frac{dy}{dx} = p = p\frac{dp}{dx} + x\frac{dp}{dx} + p$$

or

$$(p + x)\frac{dp}{dx} = 0.$$

It now follows that either

$$\frac{dp}{dx} = 0 \quad \text{or} \quad p + x = 0,$$

so that

$$p = c \quad \text{or} \quad p = -x.$$

Eliminating p between the last equations and the solution for y, we have

$$y = \tfrac{1}{2}c^2 + cx$$

and

$$y = \tfrac{1}{2}x^2 - x^2 = -\tfrac{1}{2}x^2,$$

both of which satisfy the original differential equation. We note that the second solution does not contain an arbitrary constant and is therefore not the general solution. Furthermore, since it cannot be obtained from the general solution by a choice of c, it is not a particular integral. Such solutions are called **singular solutions.**

2. Solve $\qquad\qquad p^2x - y = 0.$

Solution. Solve for y: $\quad y = p^2x.$ $\qquad\qquad$ (1)

Differentiate: $\qquad y' = p = p^2 + 2pxp'.$ $\qquad$ (2)

Rearrange: $\qquad \dfrac{2dp}{p-1} + \dfrac{dx}{x} = 0.$ $\qquad\qquad$ (3)

Solve: $\qquad\qquad (p-1)^2x = c.$ $\qquad\qquad$ (4)

Eliminate p between (1) and (4):

$$y - 2\sqrt{yx} + x = c,$$

which is the general solution.

32. Equations Solvable for x. This method is also called the method of eliminating the independent variable. If the first order differential equation can readily be solved for x, it can be written in the form

(1) $\qquad\qquad\qquad x = f(y,p).$

The total derivative of this equation with respect to y is

(2) $\qquad\qquad\qquad \dfrac{dx}{dy} = \dfrac{1}{p} = \dfrac{\partial f}{\partial y} + \dfrac{\partial f}{\partial p}\dfrac{dp}{dy}$

and is an equation involving only y and p. If we can solve this differential equation to obtain

(3) $\qquad\qquad\qquad F(y,p,c) = 0,$

then equations (1) and (3) form the general parametric solution of the original differential equation. Again, we can eliminate p

if desired and obtain the general solution as a relationship among x, y, and a constant of integration.

Illustration. Solve

$$p^2 + 2y - 2x = 0.$$

Solution. Solve for x:

$$x = \tfrac{1}{2}(2y + p^2).$$

Differentiate:

$$\frac{dx}{dy} = \frac{1}{p} = 1 + p\frac{dp}{dy}.$$

Simplify:

$$\frac{p^2}{p-1}\,dp + dy = 0$$

or

$$\left(p + 1 + \frac{1}{p-1}\right)dp + dy = 0.$$

Solve:

$$\tfrac{1}{2}p^2 + p + \ln\,(p-1) + y = c.$$

The parametric form of the general solution of the differential equation becomes

$$\begin{cases} y = c - \tfrac{1}{2}p^2 - p - \ln\,(p-1), \\ x = c - p - \ln\,(p-1). \end{cases}$$

In this case it does not seem to be advantageous to eliminate p.

33. Clairaut's Equation. A differential equation of the form

(1) $$y = px + f(p),$$

where $f(p)$ does not contain x or y explicitly, is already solved for y and the method of Section 31 can be applied directly. This was first done by Alexis Clairaut (1713–1765) and the equation is called *Clairaut's equation.*

Let us differentiate equation (1) with respect to x to obtain

$$p = p + \left[x + \frac{df}{dp}\right]p'$$

or

(2) $$\left[x + \frac{df}{dp}\right]p' = 0.$$

Then either

(3) $$p' = \frac{dp}{dx} = 0$$

or $\left[\text{letting } \dfrac{df}{dp} = f'(p) \right]$

(4) $$x + f'(p) = 0.$$

The solution of equation (3) is

$$p = c, \text{ a constant,}$$

and after substituting this value into equation (1) we obtain

(5) $$y = cx + f(c)$$

as the general solution to Clairaut's equation. Thus to obtain the general solution to Clairaut's equation, it is necessary only to *replace* p *by an arbitrary constant* c. Furthermore, equation (5) is the equation of a family of straight lines, and thus the solution of Clairaut's equation yields the simplest of all families of curves.

We have yet to consider equation (4). If we solve this equation for x to obtain

(6) $$x = -f'(p)$$

and consider this together with equation (1), we get

(7) $$y = f(p) - pf'(p).$$

Equations (6) and (7) yield a set of parametric equations for x and y in terms of the parameter p since $f(p)$ and $f'(p)$ are known. If $f(p)$ is not the value of a linear function of p and not a constant, then equations (6) and (7) form a solution of Clairaut's equation which cannot be obtained from (5) and is therefore a *singular solution*. (See illustration 1, Section 31.)

Illustration. Solve

$$y = px + 2p^2.$$

Solution. Since this is a Clairaut equation, we can write a general solution directly,

$$y = cx + 2c^2.$$

The singular solution is found in parametric form by

$$f'(p) = \frac{df}{dp} = 4p,$$

and by equation (6),

$$x = -4p,$$

so that

$$y = px + 2p^2$$
$$= -4p^2 + 2p^2 = -2p^2.$$

If we eliminate the parameter p, then

$$y = -2p^2 = -2\left(-\frac{x}{4}\right)^2$$

or

$$y = -\tfrac{1}{8}x^2$$

is the closed form of the singular solution.   See Fig. 10.

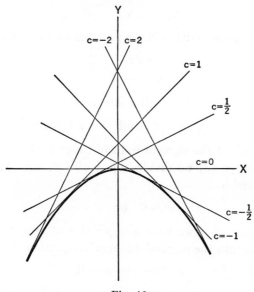

Fig. 10

Note. Any equation of the form $f(y - px, p) = 0$ is a Clairaut equation and $f(y - cx, c) = 0$ is a solution. It is left for the student to check the following example: the general solution of

$$(px - y)^3 = 3p^2 + 2p$$

is given by

$$(cx - y)^3 = 3c^2 + 2c.$$

34. Singular Solutions and Envelopes. It was illustrated previously that it is possible to find a solution of a nonlinear first order differential equation which is not a particular integral of the general solution. We defined such a solution as a *singular solution*. Geometrically, it is a solution such that each point on the curve which it defines is tangent to some element of the one-parameter family which is the general solution of the given differential equation. (Return to Fig. 10.)

The classical example, which is easy to visualize, is given by the solution to the differential equation

$$(1) \qquad y^2 p^2 - a^2 + y^2 = 0.$$

In our solution for p we arrive at

$$(2) \qquad yp = \pm \sqrt{a^2 - y^2},$$

which then can be written in a separation of variables form

$$(3) \qquad \frac{y\,dy}{\pm \sqrt{a^2 - y^2}} = dx,$$

and the solutions obtained after integrating are

$$(4) \qquad x = c - \sqrt{a^2 - y^2} \quad \text{and} \quad x = c + \sqrt{a^2 - y^2},$$

one from each of the signs in front of the radical. However, to obtain equation (3) we divided by $\sqrt{a^2 - y^2}$, and this division is not allowed if

$$(5) \qquad a^2 - y^2 = 0 \quad \text{or} \quad y = \pm a.$$

For this value of y we have $y' = p = 0$, and after substituting these values into the original differential equation (1),

$$a^2(0) - a^2 + a^2 = 0,$$

we find it to be satisfied. Thus $y = \pm a$ is also a solution of the differential equation. Since this solution cannot be obtained from either of equations (4), it is a singular solution according to our definition.

Geometrically, the two functions shown in (4) are semicircles of radius a with centers on the x-axis. The two equations may be combined into the more familiar equation

$$(6) \qquad (x - c)^2 + y^2 = a^2.$$

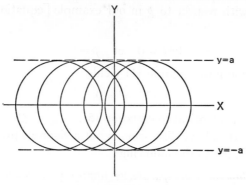

Fig. 11

A few elements of the one-parameter family of curves are shown in Fig. 11. If the singular solution, $y = \pm a$, is plotted on the same figure, it is easily seen that the two straight lines are tangent to the circles.

Definition. *Any curve which at each of its points is tangent to a member of a one-parameter family of curves is called an* **envelope** *of that family.*

Thus the two straight lines, $y = \pm a$, are envelopes of the family of circles, and the points of intersection are determined by a specific value of c.

To continue our discussion, we need two more concepts. Let us take the partial derivative of the solution [equation (6)] of the differential equation [equation (1)] with respect to c and set it equal to zero; i.e.,

(7) $$2(x - c)(-1) = 0 \quad \text{or} \quad x = c.$$

Let us now eliminate c between equations (6) and (7) by substituting (7) into (6). The result is

(8) $$y^2 = a^2 \quad \text{or} \quad y = \pm a,$$

which is identical to equation (5). The result of eliminating c is called the **c-discriminant**. If we take the partial derivative of the original differential equation with respect to p and set it equal to zero, we can then eliminate p. The result of eliminating p between the above-mentioned equation and the given differential equation is called the **p-discriminant**. Taking the partial derivative with respect to p in our example [equation (1)], we obtain

$$(9) \qquad\qquad 2y^2p = 0 \quad \text{or} \quad p = 0.$$

A substitution into equation (1) yields

$$y^2 - a^2 = 0,$$

which again is identical to equation (5).

Although the above discussion is not a rigorous proof, we are, nevertheless, led to the following:

The envelope of a one-parameter family of curves represented by the general solution

$$F(x,y,c) = 0$$

of a differential equation

$$f(x,y,p) = 0$$

satisfies the c-*discriminant and the* p-*discriminant.*

Thus, to find the envelope we find the factors of the c-discriminant or the p-discriminant and substitute them into the given differential equation. If they satisfy the differential equation, they represent the envelope loci; otherwise, they are simply extraneous factors.* Furthermore, if they satisfy the differential equation but cannot be obtained from the general solution as a particular integral, they are also singular solutions.

Illustration. Find the general solution and the singular solution of

$$(1) \qquad\qquad xp^2 - yp + 1 = 0.$$

Solution. Solve for y to obtain a Clairaut's equation

$$(2) \qquad\qquad y = xp + \frac{1}{p}$$

which has the solution

$$(3) \qquad\qquad y = cx + \frac{1}{c} \quad \text{or} \quad c^2x - cy + 1 = 0.$$

---

* Some of the extraneous factors are associated with loci which exhibit interesting geometric properties such as nodal loci, cuspidal loci, and tac-loci. See Section 39.

Take the partial derivative of (3) with respect to c:

(4) $$2cx - y = 0.$$

Eliminating c between (3) and (4) to obtain

(5) $$y^2 = 4x$$

and substituting (5) into (1) shows that (1) is satisfied by (5). Consequently, (5) is the envelope of (3), and since it cannot be obtained from (3) by a choice of c, it is a singular solution. Let us also check the p-discriminant by taking the partial derivative of (1) with respect to p to obtain

(6) $$2xp - y = 0,$$

and by eliminating p between (1) and (6) to obtain

(7) $$y^2 = 4x,$$

which is identical to (5). The family of one-parameter curves and the envelope are shown in Fig. 12.

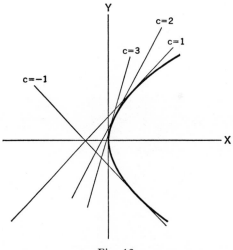

Fig. 12

35. Exercise XI. Find the general solutions and the singular solutions whenever they exist in the following differential equations.

1. $p^2 - 3 = 0$.
2. $p^2 - 4p + 2 = 0$.

3. $xy^2p^2 + (x^3 + xy^2 - y^3)p + x^3 - y^3 = 0.$

4. $p^2 + xp - y = 0.$

5. $2p^3 + 3p^2 = x + y.$

6. $2ax^3y - ax^4p + cp^3 = 0.$

7. $y^2 - 2xyp + p^2x^2 - p^3 = 0.$

8. $x + yp^2 = 0.$

9. $2x + yp(4p^2 + 6) = 0.$

10. $xp^2 + yp - y^4 = 0.$

11. $y = 4xp^2 + 2xp.$

12. $(x^2 - 2xy)p^2 - (3x^2 + 2y)(x - 2y)p + 6xy(x - 2y) = 0.$

13. $y + p^2 = xp + 1.$

14. $yp = -xp^2.$

15. $(y - px)^2 = p.$

16. $y - p^2 = 0.$

17. $x - xp^2 = 0.$

18. $p^3 + yp^2 - x^2p - x^2y = 0.$

19. $y = px + \ln p.$

20. $xp^2 = y.$

V

GEOMETRIC APPLICATIONS

36. Introduction. In the previous chapters we have indicated some geometric results which are obtainable from differential equations. In this chapter we shall pause in our development of techniques for obtaining solutions of differential equations and pursue some applications to the field of geometry. Although some of the basic concepts are familiar to us from our study of the calculus, it is advantageous to review some of the formulas, perhaps add some new ones, and list them for easy reference.

I. Rectangular coordinates. Refer to Fig. 13 and Fig. 14.

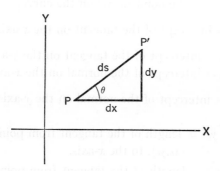

Fig. 13

(1) $\dfrac{dy}{dx} = \tan\theta \equiv$ slope of the tangent to the curve $f(x,y) = 0$
at the point (x,y).

(2) $\quad -\dfrac{dx}{dy} \equiv$ slope of the normal to the curve $f(x,y) = 0$
at the point (x,y).

(3) $ds = \sqrt{dx^2 + dy^2} = \sqrt{1 + y'^2}\,dx \equiv$ element of arc length.

(4) $\sin\theta = \dfrac{dy}{ds}$ and $\cos\theta = \dfrac{dx}{ds}.$

71

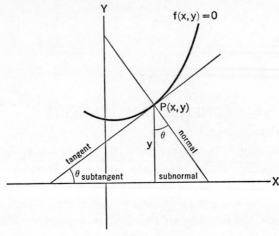

Fig. 14

(5) $y - y_0 = y_0'(x - x_0)$ is the equation of the tangent at the point (x_0, y_0) on the curve.*

(6) $y_0'(y - y_0) + (x - x_0) = 0$ is the equation of the normal at the point (x_0, y_0) on the curve.

(7) $x_0 - \dfrac{y_0}{y_0'} \equiv$ intercept of the tangent on the x-axis.

(8) $y_0 - x_0 y_0' \equiv$ intercept of the tangent on the y-axis.

(9) $x_0 + y_0 y_0' \equiv$ intercept of the normal on the x-axis.

(10) $y_0 + \dfrac{x_0}{y_0'} \equiv$ intercept of the normal on the y-axis.

(11) $\dfrac{y_0}{y_0'} \sqrt{1 + y_0'^2} \equiv$ length of the tangent from point of contact, (x_0, y_0), to the x-axis.

(12) $x_0 \sqrt{1 + y_0'^2} \equiv$ length of the tangent from point of contact, (x_0, y_0), to the y-axis.

(13) $\dfrac{x_0 y_0' - y_0}{y_0'} \sqrt{1 + y_0'^2} \equiv$ length of the tangent intercepted by the coordinate axes.

(14) $\dfrac{y_0}{y_0'} \equiv$ length of the subtangent.

(15) $y_0 \sqrt{1 + y_0'^2} \equiv$ length of the normal from (x_0, y_0) to the x-axis.

* $y_0' = $ value of $\dfrac{dy}{dx}$ at the point (x_0, y_0).

(16) $\dfrac{x_0}{y_0'}\sqrt{1+y_0'^2} \equiv$ length of the normal from (x_0, y_0) to the y-axis.

(17) $\dfrac{x_0 + y_0 y_0'}{y_0'}\sqrt{1+y_0'^2} \equiv$ length of normal intercepted by the coordinate axes.

(18) $y_0 y_0' \equiv$ length of the subnormal.

(19) $\dfrac{x_0 y_0' - y_0}{\sqrt{1+y_0'^2}} \equiv$ distance of the tangent from the origin.

II. Polar coordinates. Refer to Fig. 15 and Fig. 16.

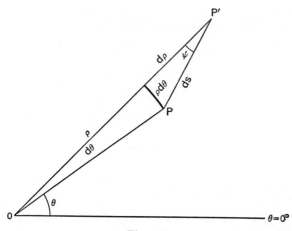

Fig. 15

(20) $\psi \equiv$ angle which the tangent at (ρ_0, θ_0) makes with the radius vector to the point.

(21) $\tau = \theta + \psi \equiv$ angle which the tangent makes with the initial line, $(\theta = 0°)$.

(22) $\tan\psi = \dfrac{\rho_0}{\rho_0'}$ where $\rho_0' \equiv \dfrac{d\rho}{d\theta}$ evaluated at (ρ_0, θ_0).

(23) $ds = \sqrt{d\rho^2 + \rho^2 d\theta^2} = \sqrt{\rho^2 + \rho'^2}\,d\theta \equiv$ element of arc length.

(24) $\rho_0 \tan\psi_0 = \dfrac{\rho_0^2}{\rho_0'} \equiv$ length of the polar subtangent.

(25) $\rho_0 \cot\psi_0 = \rho_0' \equiv$ length of the polar subnormal.

(26) $PT = \dfrac{\rho_0}{\rho_0'}\sqrt{\rho_0'^2 + \rho_0^2}$

(27) $PN = \sqrt{\rho_0'^2 + \rho_0^2}$.

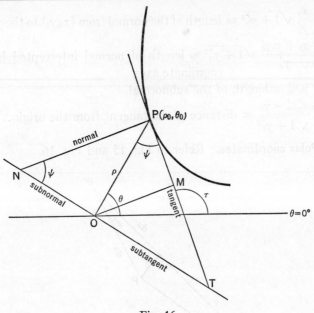

Fig. 16

(28) $OM = \rho_0 \sin \psi = \dfrac{\rho_0^2}{\sqrt{\rho_0^2 + \rho_0'^2}} \equiv$ length of perpendicular from the pole to the tangent.

The formulas listed have been stated in terms of a fixed point (x_0, y_0) or (ρ_0, θ_0) on the given curve. If an arbitrary variable point on the curve is considered, these formulas become functional representations of conditions and in many cases yield defining differential equations.

37. Family of Curves. A differential equation of the first order and first degree,

(1) $$f(x, y, y') = 0,$$

may have

(2) $$F(x, y, c) = 0$$

for the general solution. This general solution represents a family of curves in which a definite integral curve corresponds to each value of c. Since we can assign an infinite number of values to c, equation (2) is said to be a *family of a single infinity of curves.* Equation (1) is the differential equation of the family of curves of equation (2). These two equations are two ways of expressing the equation of a family of a single infinity of curves; one involves an arbitrary constant and the other is a differential equation of the first order. We thus have two ways of obtaining the equation of a family of curves corresponding to a given property: (1) the stated property is such that our knowledge of analytical geometry permits a direct derivation of the equation $F(x,y,c) = 0$; (2) the stated property is such that, when expressed analytically, there results a differential equation, the solution of which yields the desired family of curves.

Illustration 1. Write the equation of all circles which pass through the origin and have their centers on the x-axis.

Solution. The general equation of a circle is

$$(x - h)^2 + (y - k)^2 = r^2.$$

The desired circles must pass through the origin $(0,0)$; therefore

$$h^2 + k^2 = r^2.$$

The centers must lie on the x-axis; therefore, $k = 0$. Thus we have

$$x^2 + y^2 - 2hx + h^2 = r^2.$$

But since $k = 0$,

$$h^2 + k^2 = h^2 = r^2,$$

and we obtain

$$x^2 + y^2 - 2hx = 0$$

as the desired family of circles, with $2h$ as the arbitrary constant.

Illustration 2. Find the family of curves such that the perpendicular distance from the origin to each tangent is equal to the value of x at the point of contact.

Solution. From formula (19), Section 36, for an arbitrary point of contact, we have

$$\frac{xy' - y}{\sqrt{1 + y'^2}} = x$$

which, after clearing of fractions and then squaring, becomes

$$y^2 - x^2 - 2xyy' = 0.$$

This is a homogeneous differential equation, the solution of which is

$$x^2 + y^2 - cx = 0,$$

a family of circles.

The following procedure is recommended for the solution of problems which are stated in geometric terms:

I. Make a rough sketch of the stated facts.
II. Express analytically the given properties; this should give rise to a differential equation.
III. Find a general solution of the equation.
IV. Interpret the result geometrically.
V. If required, find a particular curve by solving for the constant of integration.

Illustration 3.   Find the curves whose subnormals are constants, and draw the one passing through the point (1,1).

Solution.

Make a rough sketch as shown in Figure 17.   By formula (18), Section 36:

$$yy' = k.$$

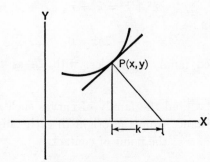

Fig. 17

The general solution of this differential equation is

$$y^2 = 2kx + c,$$

where k is the constant length of the subnormals and c is the constant of integration which specifies the family of curves. The solution yields a family of parabolas for the given constant k. The particular integral passing through the point $(1,1)$ is found by solving for c,

$$1 = 2k + c \quad \text{or} \quad c = 1 - 2k,$$

and substituting this value into the solution to obtain

$$y^2 = 2kx + 1 - 2k.$$

It is important to understand the difference between the two constants, k and c. We emphasize again that k is the given constant length of subnormals and c is the constant of integration. Fig. 18 shows a few of the family of curves for a given value of k ($k = 2$ for the figure), with the particular integral passing through the point $(1,1)$ emphasized.

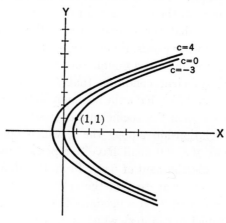

Fig. 18

38. Discriminant. The word *discriminant* has been used in Section 34, and it was also encountered in connection with the study of the quadratic equation. Let us discuss it here in greater detail by considering a polynomial of the nth degree,

$$(1) \qquad f(x) = c_0 x^n + c_1 x^{n-1} + c_2 x^{n-2} + \cdots + c_{n-1} x + c_n.$$

If we expand this function about the point $x = a$ by use of Taylor's theorem, we obtain

(2)
$$f(x) = f(a) + f'(a)(x - a) + \frac{f''(a)}{2!}(x - a)^2 + \cdots + \frac{f^{(n)}(a)}{n!}(x - a)^n,$$

where

$$f'(a) = \frac{df}{dx}\bigg|_{x=a} = nc_0a^{n-1} + (n-1)c_1a^{n-2} + \cdots + c_{n-1},$$

$$\vdots$$

$$f^{(n)}(a) = \frac{d^nf}{dx^n}\bigg|_{x=a} = n!c_0.$$

If a is a root of the equation $f(x) = 0$, then it satisfies the equation, and $f(a) = 0$, so that in equation (2) the first term of the right-hand side vanishes. The remaining terms all contain $(x - a)$ as a factor. This is the well-known Factor Theorem. If a is a double root, then $(x - a)^2$ must be a factor of equation (2), which means that the second term of the right-hand side must vanish; in other words, if both $f(a) = 0$ and $f'(a) = 0$, then $(x - a)^2$ is a factor and a is a double root.* Thus we see that a necessary and sufficient condition that $f(x) = 0$ has a double root is that $f(x)$ and $f'(x)$ have the common factor $(x - a)$, which in turn depends upon the coefficients c_i $(i = 0, \cdots, n)$. If we can find the relationship among the c_i which upon vanishing guarantees that $f(x) = 0$ shall have a repeated root, we shall have found the **discriminant** of $f(x)$. From the above discussion it appears that one way to find the relation is to eliminate x between $f(x) = 0$ and $f'(x) = 0$, since the result is a relation among the coefficients of $f(x)$ which states the condition that $f(x) = 0$ and $f'(x) = 0$ can be satisfied simultaneously. Let us illustrate by considering the quadratic equation

$$ax^2 + bx + c = 0.$$

For this equation we have

$$f(x) = ax^2 + bx + c = 0,$$
$$f'(x) = 2ax + b = 0.$$

---

* We may continue to reason in the same manner to obtain the conditions for a triple root, etc.

Eliminating x by solving the second equation for x,

$$x = -\frac{b}{2a},$$

and substituting into the first equation, we have

$$a\left(-\frac{b}{2a}\right)^2 + b\left(-\frac{b}{2a}\right) + c = 0$$

or

$$\frac{b^2}{4a} - \frac{b^2}{2a} + c = 0,$$

which simplifies to the familiar

$$b^2 - 4ac = 0.$$

To be precise, the left-hand side is called the *discriminant*, and the equation with the right-hand side being zero is called the **discriminant relation**.

39. Discriminant Loci. Consider the equation $F(x,y,c) = 0$ as an equation in c with coefficients that are functions of x and y. In the (x,y)-plane it represents a one-parameter family of curves, one curve for each value of c. If it is possible to find values of x and y such that this equation has multiple roots in c, then there are points, (x_i, y_i), through which there pass a smaller number of integral curves than usual. Since these values may be found from the c-discriminant relation, this relation is the locus of such points. In Section 34, we found that the envelope of a family of curves was such a locus. Thus, in Fig. 11 we see that for the points $-a < y < a$, two circles pass through each point, while through each point on $y = \pm a$, only one circle passes.

If an integral curve has a double point such that at this point there will be two branches of the curve with distinct tangents, this point is called a **nodal point** or **node**. If a one-parameter family of curves possesses this property, the nodes form the **nodal locus**. A special case of a double point is one at which the tangents are not distinct, so that the two branches of the curve are tangent to each other. Such a point is called a **cusp,** and the locus of these points for a one-parameter family is known as the **cuspidal locus**. If two distinct members of a family of curves are tangent to each other (have the same tangent) without affecting the number of curves through that point, we may have a locus of such points which is known as the **tac-locus.** Fig. 19 illustrates the loci we have defined.

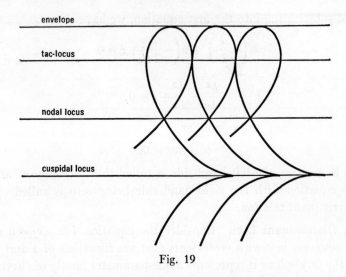

Fig. 19

We shall now discuss the relationship among these loci, the differential of the family of curves, the c-discriminant, and the p-discriminant. Consider the differential equation

(1) $f(x,y,p) = 0$

and the family of curves obtained from the general solution

(2) $F(x,y,c) = 0$.

If we eliminate c between equation (2) and

(3) $\dfrac{\partial F}{\partial c} = 0$,

we obtain the c-discriminant, and if we eliminate p between equation (1) and

(4) $\dfrac{\partial f}{\partial p} = 0$,

we obtain the p-discriminant. Each factor of the c- and p-discriminants set equal to zero will define a locus which usually becomes one of the four defined above and in Section 34. A factor of these discriminants set equal to zero may also become a particular integral obtained from a specific value of c in the general solution. The number of times that a factor appears in each discriminant may also be used to classify the locus, and although exceptions occur, it can be used as a guide. We summarize these associations in the following table showing where the factor occurs and how many times it usually appears for each locus:

c-discriminant		p-discriminant	
envelope	1	envelope	1
nodal locus	2	tac-locus	2
cuspidal locus	3	cuspidal locus	1
particular integral	1	particular integral	3

Illustrations.

1. Obtain the geometrical characteristics of the family of curves which is the solution of the differential equation

(1) $$(3y - a)^2 p^2 - 4y = 0.$$

Solution. The general solution is obtained by solving for p,

(2) $$p = \frac{dy}{dx} = \pm 2y^{\frac{1}{2}}(3y - a)^{-1}$$

or

$$\pm \tfrac{1}{2}(3y^{\frac{1}{2}} - ay^{-\frac{1}{2}})dy = dx,$$

and integrating:

$$\pm y^{\frac{1}{2}}(y - a) = x + c$$

or

(3) $$y(y - a)^2 = (x + c)^2.$$

The partial derivative of (3) with respect to c yields

$$2(x + c) = 0 \quad \text{or} \quad c = -x,$$

and the c-discriminant is

(4) $$y(y - a)^2 = 0, \quad \text{or} \quad y = 0 \quad \text{and} \quad y = a.$$

A substitution of these values into equation (1) reveals that it is satisfied for $y = 0$, and consequently the x-axis is an envelope. Since the factor $(y - a)$ occurs twice, we suspect that $y = a$ is a nodal locus.

The partial derivative of (1) with respect to p is

$$2p(3y - a)^2 = 0, \quad \text{or} \quad p = 0 \quad \text{and} \quad y = \frac{a}{3},$$

and the p-discriminant is

(5) $$y = 0 \quad \text{and} \quad (3y - a)^2 = 0.$$

We have already seen that $y = 0$ is an envelope. The factor $(3y - a)$ occurs twice, and we suspect that $y = \frac{a}{3}$ is a tac-locus.

A few members of the family of curves represented by (3) are shown in Fig. 20.

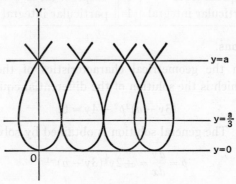

Fig. 20

2. Investigate the family of curves which is the solution of

(1) $$xp^3 + y = 0.$$

Solution. The equation may be solved by eliminating y to obtain the general solution

(2) $$x^{\frac{2}{3}} + y^{\frac{2}{3}} = c^{\frac{2}{3}}.$$

The c-discriminant is

(3) $$x^{\frac{2}{3}} + y^{\frac{2}{3}} = 0.$$

The partial derivative of (1) with respect to p is

(4) $$3xp^2 = 0,$$

with factors $x = 0$ and $p = 0$, so that the p-discriminant is

$$y = 0 \quad \text{and} \quad x = 0.$$

Since these occur once, we suspect that the axes are cuspidal loci. The solution is a family of *hypocycloids of four cusps*. Since the *c*-discriminant, (3), satisfies the original differential equation, it is a singular solution; however, the curve cannot be represented in the real plane.

3. Investigate the family of curves which is the solution of

$$(1) \qquad 2yp^3 - 3xp + 2y = 0.$$

Solution. The equation may be solved by eliminating x to obtain the general solution

$$(2) \qquad 4y^3 = c(3x - 2c)^2.$$

The *c*-discriminant is

$$(3) \qquad 4y^3 = 0 \quad \text{and} \quad 2y^3 - x^3 = 0.$$

The *p*-discriminant is

$$(4) \qquad 2y^3 - x^3 = 0.$$

Since (4) satisfies the differential equation, it is a singular solution. The equation $y = 0$ occurs 3 times in the *c*-discriminant, and we suspect that the *x*-axis is a cuspidal locus. It is left for the student to plot the loci.

40. Orthogonal Trajectories. Let us consider a family of curves,

$$(1) \qquad F(x,y,c) = 0.$$

If a member of another family of curves,

$$(2) \qquad G(x,y,k) = 0,$$

intersects a member of the first family so that the tangents of the two curves at the point of intersection are perpendicular, then the two families are said to be **orthogonal trajectories** of each other. We recall from analytic geometry that if two lines are perpendicular to each other, then the slope of one is the negative reciprocal of the other.* Consequently, if two curves are orthogonal, then the slopes are negative reciprocals of each other. Let the differential equation of the given family be

$$(3) \qquad M\,dx + N\,dy = 0.$$

---

* The coordinate axes form an exception since they are perpendicular to each other and the *y*-axis has no slope in the elementary definition.

Then the slope of the tangent line at any point on a member of the family is

$$\frac{dy}{dx} = -\frac{M}{N}.$$

The slope of the tangent line at any point on a member of the family of curves which form the orthogonal trajectories is given by

$$\frac{dy}{dx} = \frac{N}{M},$$

so that the differential equation of the orthogonal trajectories is

(4) $M \, dy - N \, dx = 0.$

To find the orthogonal trajectories of a given family of curves, we need only to form equation (4) and solve it.

Illustration. Find the orthogonal trajectories of the family of circles

(1) $x^2 + y^2 = c^2.$

Solution. The differential equation of (1) is obtained by differentiating with respect to x; i.e.,

(2) $x \, dx + y \, dy = 0.$

The differential equation of the orthogonal trajectories is

(3) $x \, dy - y \, dx = 0.$

A general solution of (3) is

(4) $y = kx,$

a family of straight lines through the origin. Thus, they are the diameters of the family of circles defined by equation (1).

If two curves which are expressed in terms of polar coordinates cut each other at right angles, then at the point of intersection

$$\rho \, \frac{d\theta}{d\rho}$$

for one curve must be the negative reciprocal of this product for the other curve. [See formula (22) of Section 36.] Thus, if a family of curves has the differential equation

$$P \, d\rho + Q \, d\theta = 0,$$

then

$$\rho \frac{d\theta}{d\rho} = -\frac{P\rho}{Q},$$

and the family of orthogonal trajectories of the given family must satisfy the differential equation

$$\rho \frac{d\theta}{d\rho} = \frac{Q}{P\rho}$$

or

$$Q \, d\rho - \rho^2 P \, d\theta = 0.$$

An interesting example is given in regard to the family of cardioids.

Illustration. Find the orthogonal trajectories of the family of cardioids.

(1) $$\rho = a(1 + \cos \theta).$$

Solution. The value

$$\rho \frac{d\theta}{d\rho} = -\frac{1}{a \sin \theta} (\rho) = -\frac{1}{a \sin \theta} (a)(1 + \cos \theta),$$

so that

(2) $$(1 + \cos \theta) \, d\rho + \rho \sin \theta \, d\theta = 0$$

is the differential equation for (1).

The differential equation for the orthogonal trajectories is

$$\rho \sin \theta \, d\rho - \rho^2 (1 + \cos \theta) d\theta = 0,$$

or after dividing by ρ,

(3) $$\sin \theta \, d\rho - \rho(1 + \cos \theta) d\theta = 0.$$

Separate the variables:

$$\frac{d\rho}{\rho} - \csc \theta \, d\theta - \cot \theta \, d\theta = 0.$$

The solution is

$$\ln \rho - \ln (\csc \theta - \cot \theta) - \ln \sin \theta = \ln k$$

or

(4) $$\rho = k(1 - \cos \theta).$$

Equation (4) is also a family of cardioids, and we have the interesting property that the family of cardioids is self-orthogonal. It is left for the student to draw some members of each family.

41. Exercise XII.

1. Find the equation of each of the following curves or families of curves:

   (a) Having the length of the subnormal equal to 3, and passing through (1,4).

   (b) Having the length of the subtangent equal to $\frac{1}{2}$, and passing through (0,2).

   (c) Having the length of the normal from (x,y) to the x-axis equal to 3.

   (d) Having the length of the perpendicular from the pole to the tangent equal to 2.

   (e) Having the length of the polar subtangent equal to 1.

2. Find the c- and p-discriminants, investigate their loci, and find the general solution and singular solutions (if any) of the following differential equations:

   (a) $27xp^3 = 8$.

   (b) $8p^3 + 12p^2 - 27(x + y) = 0$.

   (c) $p^3 - 4xyp + 8y^2 = 0$.

3. Find the orthogonal trajectories of the following families of curves:

   (a) $y^2 = 4ax$.

   (b) $x^2 - y^2 = 1$.

   (c) $\rho = a \cos \theta$.

   (d) $(1 + 2 \cos \theta)\rho = 2$.

   (e) $xy = k$.

VI

LINEAR EQUATIONS WITH CONSTANT COEFFICIENTS

42. The General Linear Equation. We recall from Chapter II that the degree of a differential equation is the degree of the highest order derivative in the equation. In the study of elementary mathematics, the word *linear* is associated with the words *first degree*. The use of the words *linear* and *nonlinear* in discussing the theory of differential equations needs greater clarification.

Definition. *A differential equation is said to be* **linear** *if each term of the equation is either of the* **first degree** *in all the* **dependent** *variables and their various derivatives, or does not contain any of them.*

A differential equation which is not linear is said to be **nonlinear.**

It is important to realize that although every linear differential equation is of the first degree, not every first degree differential equation is necessarily linear. Furthermore, we focus our attention upon the dependent variables and their derivatives.

Illustrations. Determine the linearity of the following differential equations:

Equation	Type
1. $x^2y' + 2y = 0$	linear
2. $2y'' + 3y' + xy = x^2$	linear
3. $3(y')^2 + y = 0$	nonlinear
4. $yy' + x = 0$	nonlinear

(second degree in y and its derivative)

The general linear differential equation of order n may be written in the form

(1) $a_0(x)y^{(n)} + a_1(x)y^{(n-1)} + \cdots + a_{n-1}(x)y' + a_n(x)y = f(x)$.

The functions a_i $(i = 0, \cdots, n)$ and f are functions of the independent variable x only. If the functions a_i are all constants, the equation is said to be a *linear differential equation with constant coefficients*.

If $f(x) = 0$, equation (1) is said to be a **homogeneous** linear differential equation. It is also called the **reduced** linear differential equation.*

If $f(x) \neq 0$, equation (1) is said to be a **complete** linear differential equation.

43. Solution of a Linear Differential Equation.

Before proceeding to the techniques for obtaining solutions to linear differential equations, let us examine the composition of a general solution. Consider first the homogeneous equation

(1) $a_0 y^{(n)} + a_1 y^{(n-1)} + \cdots + a_{n-1}y' + a_n y = 0$.

If $y_1 = f_1(x)$ and $y_2 = f_2(x)$ are solutions of equation (1) and if c_1 and c_2 are arbitrary constants, then

(2) $y = c_1 y_1 + c_2 y_2$

is a solution of equation (1). To prove this statement we may first substitute each solution into equation (1), since y_1 and y_2 are solutions of (1). We obtain

(3) $a_0 y_1^{(n)} + a_1 y_1^{(n-1)} + \cdots + a_{n-1}y_1' + a_n y_1 = 0$

and

(4) $a_0 y_2^{(n)} + a_1 y_2^{(n-1)} + \cdots + a_{n-1}y_2' + a_n y_2 = 0$.

If equation (2) were to satisfy equation (1), then

(5)

$a_0(c_1 y_1 + c_2 y_2)^{(n)} + a_1(c_1 y_1 + c_2 y_2)^{(n-1)} + \cdots + a_n(c_1 y_1 + c_2 y_2) = 0$.

Since the derivative of a sum is equal to the sum of the derivatives, we have

$$(c_1 y_1 + c_2 y_2)^{(i)} = c_1 y_1^{(i)} + c_2 y_2^{(i)}$$

for $(i = 0, \cdots, n)$. Thus we can rearrange equation (5) to read

---

* Although the newer terminology, *reduced*, is the more practical, we shall retain the more commonly used word, *homogeneous*.

(6) $c_1[a_0y_1^{(n)} + a_1y_1^{(n-1)} + \cdots + a_ny_1]$
$$+ c_2[a_0y_2^{(n)} + a_1y_2^{(n-1)} + \cdots + a_ny_2] = 0.$$

But from equations (3) and (4) we see that each expression in brackets is zero, so that equation (6) is satisfied. Consequently, we conclude that (2) is a solution of (1).

The above is an introduction to the more general theorem:

Theorem. *If* y_1, y_2, $\cdots$, y_n *are* **n** *linearly independent* functions of* x *which satisfy a homogeneous linear differential equation of order* n, *then the function*

$$y = c_1y_1 + c_2y_2 + \cdots + c_ny_n$$

is its general solution.

Let us now consider the equation

(7) $a_0y^{(n)} + a_1y^{(n-1)} + \cdots + a_{n-1}y' + a_ny = f(x).$

Let y_p be any particular solution of equation (7) and let

(8) $y_c = c_1y_1 + c_2y_2 + \cdots + c_ny_n$

be a solution of the corresponding homogeneous equation obtained by letting $f(x) = 0$. Then we shall show that

(9) $y = y_c + y_p$

is a solution of (7). Obtain the derivatives of (9) and substitute into equation (7), remembering that

$$[y_c + y_p]^{(i)} = y_c^{(i)} + y_p^{(i)},$$

so that

$[a_0y_c^{(n)} + a_1y_c^{(n-1)} + \cdots + a_ny_c]$
$$+ [a_0y_p^{(n)} + a_1y_p^{(n-1)} + \cdots + a_ny_p] = f(x).$$

Since y_c is a solution of the homogeneous equation, the first bracket is zero, and since y_p is a solution of equation (7), the second bracket is equal to $f(x)$. Consequently we have

$$0 + f(x) = f(x),$$

and the function y expressed by equation (9) is the general solution of (7). The function y_c is called the **complementary function** for equation (7) and y_p is called a **particular integral.** The result is stated in the important theorem:

---

* See Section 2, VII.

Theorem. *The general solution of a complete linear differential equation is equal to the sum of its complementary function and any particular integral.*

Let $y_i(x)$ be individual general solutions of

(10) $\qquad a_0 y^{(n)} + a_1 y^{(n-1)} + \cdots + a_{n-1} y' + a_n = f_i(x)$

for $i = 1, \cdots, n$. Consider now the equation

(11)
$$a_0 y^{(n)} + a_1 y^{(n-1)} + \cdots + a_{n-1} y' + a_n = f_1(x) + f_2(x) + \cdots + f_n(x).$$

If we substitute

$$y = y_1(x) + y_2(x) + \cdots + y_n(x)$$

into equation (11), we obtain

$$a_0(y_1^{(n)} + \cdots + y_n^{(n)}) + a_1(y_1^{(n-1)} + \cdots + y_n^{(n-1)}) + \cdots$$
$$+ a_{n-1}(y_1' + \cdots + y_n') + a_n(y_1 + \cdots + y_n) = f_1 + f_2 + \cdots + f_n.$$

By rearranging the terms of the left member, we have

$$a_0 y_1^{(n)} + a_1 y_1^{(n-1)} + \cdots + a_{n-1} y_1' + a_n y_1$$
$$+ a_0 y_2^{(n)} + a_1 y_2^{(n-1)} + \cdots + a_n y_2$$
$$+ \cdots$$
$$+ a_0 y_n^{(n)} + a_1 y_n^{(n-1)} + \cdots + a_n y_n$$
$$= f_1(x) + f_2(x) + \cdots + f_n(x).$$

But since y_1 satisfies equation (10) for $i = 1$; y_2, for $i = 2$; etc., we have each line of the left member equal to a corresponding $f_i(x)$; i.e.,

$$f_1(x) + f_2(x) + \cdots + f_n(x) = f_1(x) + f_2(x) + \cdots + f_n(x),$$

so that

$$y = y_1 + y_2 + \cdots + y_n$$

satisfies equation (11). This fact is stated in the **Principle of Superposition:**

If $y_i(x)$ *are solutions of*

$$a_0 y^{(n)} + \cdots + a_{n-1} y' + a_n = f_i(x)$$

for $i = 1, \cdots, n$, *then*

$$y = y_1(x) + y_2(x) + \cdots + y_n(x)$$

is the solution of

$$a_0 y^{(n)} + \cdots + a_{n-1} y' + a_n = f_1(x) + \cdots + f_n(x).$$

We shall now turn our attention to the development of techniques for finding the general solution of a linear differential equation with constant coefficients.

44. Auxiliary Equation with Distinct Roots. Any linear homogeneous differential equation with constant coefficients may be written in the form

$$(1) \qquad a_0 D_x^n y + a_1 D_x^{n-1} y + \cdots + a_{n-1} D_x y + a_n y = \\ (a_0 D_x^n + a_1 D_x^{n-1} + \cdots + a_{n-1} D_x + a_n) y = 0,$$

in which we have employed the notation

$$D_x^n y = \frac{d^n y}{dx^n}.$$

If we make a formal substitution of

$$D_x = m,$$

we obtain a polynomial in m of degree n:

$$g(m) = a_0 m^n + a_1 m^{n-1} + \cdots + a_{n-1} m + a_n,$$

and if we equate this to zero we have an algebraic equation of degree n which must then necessarily have n roots. This equation, $g(m) = 0$, is called the **auxiliary equation** of the differential equation (1).

Theorem. *If* m_1 *is a root of the auxiliary equation,* i.e.,

$$a_0 m_1^n + a_1 m_1^{n-1} + \cdots + a_{n-1} m_1 + a_n = 0,$$

then

$$y = e^{m_1 x}$$

is a solution of the homogeneous linear differential equation

$$(a_0 D^n + a_1 D^{n-1} + \cdots + a_n) y = 0,$$

where the a_i *are constants.*

Proof. By successive differentiation we obtain

$$y = e^{m_1 x}; \qquad y''' = m_1^3 e^{m_1 x} \\ y' = m_1 e^{m_1 x}; \qquad \cdots \cdots \\ y'' = m_1^2 e^{m_1 x}; \qquad y^{(n)} = m_1^n e^{m_1 x}.$$

If we substitute these derivatives into the differential equation, we obtain

$$a_0 m_1^n e^{m_1 x} + a_1 m_1^{n-1} e^{m_1 x} + \cdots + a_{n-1} m_1 e^{m_1 x} + a_n e^{m_1 x} = 0$$

or

$$(a_0 m_1^n + a_1 m_1^{n-1} + \cdots + a_{n-1} m_1 + a_n) e^{m_1 x} = 0,$$

and since m_1 is a root of the auxiliary equation, the expression in the parentheses is equal to zero, and the equation is satisfied.

The solution of the differential equation then reduces to solving the algebraic auxiliary equation for its n roots and forming a linearly independent combination of $c_i e^{m_i x}$ $(i = 1, \cdots, n)$ as the general solution, *if the roots were all distinct*.

Illustration. Find the general solution of

$$y'' - y' - 6y = 0.$$

Solution. The auxiliary equation is

$$m^2 - m - 6 = 0$$

or

$$(m - 3)(m + 2) = 0,$$

which has the roots $m = 3$ and $m = -2$. The solution is

$$y = c_1 e^{3x} + c_2 e^{-2x}.$$

The student should check the answer.

We remind the student that synthetic division is a useful tool in finding the roots of algebraic equations.

Illustration. Find the general solution of

$$2y''' - 5y'' - y' + 6y = 0.$$

Solution. The auxiliary equation is

$$2m^3 - 5m^2 - m + 6 = 0.$$

By a synthetic division

$$
\begin{array}{rrrr|r}
2 & -5 & -1 & 6 & \underline{-1} \\
  & -2 & 7 & -6 & \\
\hline
2 & -7 & 6 & 0 &
\end{array}
$$

we see that $m = -1$, and the resulting quadratic is easily solved to give $m = 2$ and $m = \frac{3}{2}$.

The solution of the differential equation is

$$y = c_1 e^{-x} + c_2 e^{2x} + c_3 e^{\frac{3}{2}x}.$$

45. Auxiliary Equation with Repeated Roots. Let one of the roots of the auxiliary equation be a double root, i.e., $m = m_1$ twice; then in the solution we would have two terms:

$$c_1 e^{m_1 x} + c_2 e^{m_1 x} = (c_1 + c_2)e^{m_1 x}.$$

However, since c_1 and c_2 are arbitrary constants, their sum can be replaced by a new arbitrary constant, $c_1 + c_2 = C_1$, and the solution would no longer contain n arbitrary constants which is required for it to be the general solution.

In order to overcome this difficulty, we have the theorem:

Theorem. *If the auxiliary equation of a homogeneous linear differential equation contains* **r** *as an* **s-fold** *root, then*

$$y = (c_0 + c_1 x + c_2 x^2 + \cdots + c_{s-1} x^{s-1})e^{rx}$$

is a particular solution of the differential equation.

The proof of this theorem will be deferred till Chapter VII, Section 52. We shall, however, now demonstrate the truth of the theorem.

Let us consider the third order equation

$$(1) \qquad a_0 y''' + a_1 y'' + a_2 y' + a_3 y = 0.$$

The auxiliary equation is

$$(2) \qquad a_0 m^3 + a_1 m^2 + a_2 m + a_3 = 0.$$

Let us now assume that r is a double root and that p is the other root; i.e., the auxiliary equation will factor into

$$(3) \qquad (m - r)^2 (m - p) = 0.$$

Since it is no restriction * to let $a_0 = 1$, we know from the theory of equations that

$$
\begin{aligned}
a_0 &= 1, \\
a_1 &= -(r + r + p) = -(2r + p), \\
a_2 &= r^2 + rp + pr = r^2 + 2rp, \\
a_3 &= -pr^2.
\end{aligned}
$$

The theorem states that

$$(4) \qquad y = (c_0 + c_1 x)e^{rx}$$

* We could divide the original equation by a_0 and relabel the resulting coefficients.

is a solution of the differential equation. Let us obtain the derivatives and substitute their values into the differential equation for a check.

$$y' = e^{rx}(c_0 r + c_1 rx + c_1);$$
$$y'' = e^{rx}(c_0 r^2 + c_1 r^2 x + 2c_1 r);$$
$$y''' = e^{rx}(c_0 r^3 + c_1 r^3 x + 3c_1 r^2).$$

After substituting into the differential equation and rearranging terms, we have

(5) $\quad c_0(a_0 r^3 + a_1 r^2 + a_2 r + a_3)e^{rx} + c_1(a_0 r^3 + a_1 r^2 + a_2 r + a_3)xe^{rx}$
$$+ c_1(3a_0 r^2 + 2a_1 r + a_2)e^{rx} = 0.$$

Since r is a root of the auxiliary equation,

$$a_0 r^3 + a_1 r^2 + a_2 r + a_3 = 0,$$

and from the values of a_i in terms of the roots

$$3a_0 r^2 + 2a_1 r + a_2 = 3r^2 - 2(2r + p)r + r^2 + 2rp$$
$$= 3r^2 - 4r^2 - 2rp + r^2 + 2rp$$
$$= 0.$$

Hence, the expressions in each of the parentheses in (5) are zero, and the equation is satisfied.

To solve a homogeneous linear differential equation when the auxiliary equation has multiple roots, multiply the exponential function which has the multiple root as part of its exponent by *a polynomial in* x *of the degree which is one less than the multiplicity of the root.* The remaining parts of the general solution are obtained in the same manner as in Section 44.

Illustration. Find the general solution of

$$y^{(iv)} - 2y''' - 7y'' + 20y' - 12y = 0.$$

Solution. The auxiliary equation is

$$m^4 - 2m^3 - 7m^2 + 20m - 12 = 0.$$

The roots of this equation are

$$m = 1, 2, 2, -3.$$

The general solution of the differential equation is

$$y = c_1 e^x + (c_2 + c_3 x)e^{2x} + c_4 e^{-3x}.$$

46. Auxiliary Equation with Complex Roots. If the auxiliary equation with real coefficients contains a complex root, $a + bi$, then it must also contain its conjugate, $a - bi$. The complementary function for the given differential equation would then contain the terms

$$c_1 e^{(a+bi)x} + c_2 e^{(a-bi)x},$$

which may be written as (see Section 2, V)

$$c_1 e^{ax}(\cos bx + i \sin bx) + c_2 e^{ax}(\cos bx - \sin bx).$$

Let us rearrange the terms to obtain

$$e^{ax}[(c_1 + c_2) \cos bx + i(c_1 - c_2) \sin bx].$$

If we let $c_1 + c_2 = c_3$ and $i(c_1 - c_2) = c_4$, we have

$$(1) \qquad y = e^{ax}(c_3 \cos bx + c_4 \sin bx)$$

as that part of the solution corresponding to the two complex roots $m_1 = a + bi$ and $m_2 = a - bi$. The coefficients c_3 and c_4 are real numbers if we choose c_1 and c_2 as conjugate complex numbers; however, we need not be concerned with this, as the solution with real c_3 and c_4 satisfies the given differential equation.

A second form of this part of the solution can be obtained by choosing

$$c = \sqrt{c_3^2 + c_4^2} \quad \text{and} \quad \tan \alpha = \frac{c_3}{c_4}.$$

Then we have

$$\sin \alpha = \frac{c_3}{c} \quad \text{and} \quad \cos \alpha = \frac{c_4}{c}.$$

Multiplying equation (1) by $\dfrac{c}{c} = 1$, we have

$$y = e^{ax}c \left(\frac{c_3}{c} \cos bx + \frac{c_4}{c} \sin bx \right)$$

or

$$y = ce^{ax}(\sin \alpha \cos bx + \cos \alpha \sin bx)$$
$$= ce^{ax} \sin (bx + \alpha).$$

In this expression, c and α are the two arbitrary constants.

If the complex roots occur as multiple roots, we use the same technique as we did in Section 45. Thus, if $(a \pm bi)$ is an s-fold multiple pair of complex roots, then the corresponding terms of the complementary function are

$$y = e^{ax}[(A_0 + A_1x + \cdots + A_{s-1}x^{s-1}) \cos bx \\ + (B_0 + B_1x + \cdots + B_{s-1}x^{s-1}) \sin bx].$$

Illustrations. Find the general solution of

1. $y''' - 3y'' + 7y' - 5y = 0.$

Solution. The auxiliary equation is

$$m^3 - 3m^2 + 7m - 5 = 0.$$

The root $m = 1$ is removed by synthetic division

$$\begin{array}{rrrr|r} 1 & -3 & +7 & -5 & 1 \\ & 1 & -2 & 5 & \\ \hline 1 & -2 & 5 & 0 & \end{array}$$

and the resulting quadratic equation,

$$m^2 - 2m + 5 = 0,$$

is solved by the quadratic formula to yield

$$m = 1 \pm 2i$$

with $a = 1$ and $b = 2$.

The general solution is given by

$$y = c_1e^x + e^x(c_2 \cos 2x + c_3 \sin 2x).$$

2. $y^{(iv)} + 18y'' + 81 = 0.$

Solution. The auxiliary equation is

$$m^4 + 18m^2 + 81 = 0$$

or

$$(m^2 + 9)^2 = 0.$$

The roots are $m = \pm 3i, \pm 3i$, so that each root, $m_1 = 3i$ and $m_2 = -3i$, occurs twice with $a = 0$ and $b = 3$.

Since $e^{0x} = 1$, the general solution is

$$y = (c_1 + c_2x) \cos 3x + (c_3 + c_4x) \sin 3x.$$

47. Complete Equation; Undetermined Coefficients. We recall from Section 43 that the solution to the *complete* linear differential equation is composed of the sum of the complementary function and a particular integral. Techniques for obtaining the complementary function y_c were developed in Sections 44–46, so there remains only to provide techniques for finding a particular integral in order to obtain the complete solution. In this section we shall discuss the technique called the method of undetermined coefficients. Although this method is not applicable in all cases, it may be used if the right-hand side, $f(x)$, contains only terms which have a finite number of linearly independent derivatives such as x^n, e^{mx}, sin bx, and cos bx, or products of these. The general procedure is to assume a particular integral y_p of a form similar to that of the right member $f(x)$, and containing undetermined coefficients for each term. The necessary derivatives of y_p are then obtained and substituted into the given differential equation. This results in an *identity* in the independent variable, and consequently the coefficients of like terms can be equated, and the values of the undetermined coefficients can be found from the resulting system of linear equations.

Illustration. Find the general solution of

$$y'' - y' - 6y = 6x^3 + 26 \sin 2x.$$

Solution. The auxiliary equation is

$$m^2 - m - 6 = 0,$$

with roots $m = 3, -2$. Consequently, the complementary function is

$$y_c = c_1 e^{3x} + c_2 e^{-2x}.$$

Let the form of a particular integral be

$$y_p = Ax^3 + Bx^2 + Cx + D + E \sin 2x + F \cos 2x,$$

in which we have chosen a third degree polynomial to correspond to the x^3-term in $f(x)$ and a linear combination of sin $2x$ and cos $2x$ to correspond to sin $2x$ in $f(x)$. Obtain the first and second derivatives of y_p:

$$y_p' = 3Ax^2 + 2Bx + C + 2E \cos 2x - 2F \sin 2x;$$
$$y_p'' = 6Ax + 2B - 4E \sin 2x - 4F \cos 2x.$$

Substitute these values into the original differential equation:

$$6Ax + 2B - 4E \sin 2x - 4F \cos 2x$$
$$-[3Ax^2 + 2Bx + C + 2E \cos 2x - 2F \sin 2x]$$
$$-6[Ax^3 + Bx^2 + Cx + D + E \sin 2x + F \cos 2x]$$
$$= 6x^3 + 26 \sin 2x.$$

Collect like terms in the left member:

$$-6Ax^3 - (3A + 6B)x^2 + (6A - 2B - 6C)x + (2B - C - 6D)$$
$$-(4E - 2F + 6E)\sin 2x - (4F + 2E + 6F) \cos 2x$$
$$\equiv 6x^3 + 26 \sin 2x.$$

Since this is an identity in x, we equate coefficients of like terms to obtain

$$-6A = 6; \qquad 2B - C - 6D = 0;$$
$$-3A - 6B = 0; \qquad -10E + 2F = 26;$$
$$6A - 2B - 6C = 0; \qquad -10F - 2E = 0.$$

The solution to this system of equations is

$$A = -1; \qquad\qquad D = \tfrac{13}{36};$$
$$B = \tfrac{1}{2}; \qquad\qquad E = -\tfrac{5}{2};$$
$$C = -\tfrac{7}{6}; \qquad\qquad F = \tfrac{1}{2};$$

and

$$y_p = -x^3 + \tfrac{1}{2}x^2 - \tfrac{7}{6}x + \tfrac{13}{36} - \tfrac{5}{2} \sin 2x + \tfrac{1}{2} \cos 2x.$$

The general solution is

$$y = c_1 e^{3x} + c_2 e^{-2x} - x^3 + \tfrac{1}{2}x^2 - \tfrac{7}{6}x + \tfrac{13}{36} - \tfrac{5}{2} \sin 2x + \tfrac{1}{2} \cos 2x.$$

A minor difficulty arises if the complementary function and the right-hand side, $f(x)$, have like terms.

Illustration. Find the general solution of

(1) $$y'' - 3y' + 2y = 2e^x.$$

Solution. The complementary function is

$$y_c = c_1 e^x + c_2 e^{2x}.$$

We now assume a particular integral of the form

$$y_p = Ae^x,$$

and we obtain the derivatives

$$y_p' = Ae^x \quad \text{and} \quad y_p'' = Ae^x.$$

A substitution into equation (1) yields

$$Ae^x - 3Ae^x + 2Ae^x = 2e^x$$

or

$$0Ae^x = 2e^x,$$

and we cannot find A.

To overcome this difficulty, we employ the same technique as we did for the case of an auxiliary equation with repeated roots (Section 45). We choose a particular integral of the same form as that occurring in $f(x)$ and multiply it by x^r, where r is one greater than the exponent of the corresponding term of the complementary function. Continuing the above illustration, let

$$y_p = Axe^x;$$
$$y'_p = Ae^x + Axe^x;$$
$$y''_p = 2Ae^x + Axe^x.$$

Substitute into equation (1) to obtain

$$(2A + Ax)e^x - 3(A + Ax)e^x + 2Axe^x \equiv 2e^x$$

or

$$[(2A - 3A) + (A - 3A + 2A)x]e^x \equiv 2e^x.$$

Equating coefficients we have

$$-A = 2 \quad \text{or} \quad A = -2.$$

The general solution is

$$y = c_1 e^x + c_2 e^{2x} - 2xe^x$$

or

$$y = (c_1 - 2x)e^x + c_2 e^{2x}.$$

In order to eliminate the unnecessary work encountered by assuming the wrong form for the particular integral, it is recommended that the complementary function be obtained first.

Illustration. Find the general solution of

(1) $$y''' - 3y'' + 3y' - y = 48xe^x.$$

Solution. The auxiliary equation is

$$m^3 - 3m^2 + 3m - 1 = 0,$$

with solution $m = 1, 1, 1$.
The complementary function is

$$y_c = (c_0 + c_1 x + c_2 x^2)e^x.$$

The assumed form of a particular integral to correspond to xe^x would normally be

$$y_p = (A + Bx)e^x.$$

However, since these terms are contained in the complementary function, it is necessary to multiply by x^3 (the exponent being one greater than that occurring in y_c). Thus we choose

$$y_p = (Ax^3 + Bx^4)e^x,$$
$$y_p' = (3Ax^2 + 4Bx^3 + Ax^3 + Bx^4)e^x$$
$$= [3Ax^2 + (4B + A)x^3 + Bx^4]e^x,$$
$$y_p'' = [6Ax + (12B + 6A)x^2 + (8B + A)x^3 + Bx^4]e^x,$$
$$y_p''' = [6A + (24B + 18A)x + (36B + 9A)x^2 + (12B + A)x^3 + Bx^4]e^x.$$

After substituting into equation (1) and collecting terms we have

$$(6A + 24Bx)e^x \equiv (0 + 48x)e^x.$$

Therefore,

$$6A = 0 \quad \text{and} \quad 24B = 48,$$

or

$$A = 0 \quad \text{and} \quad B = 2.$$

The general solution is

$$y = (c_0 + c_1x + c_2x^2 + 2x^4)e^x.$$

The statement of a general rule for the formulation of a particular integral with undetermined coefficients is rather lengthy. We shall summarize it in the following manner:

If $f(x)$ is of the form	choose y_p to be
$a_0 + a_1x + \cdots + a_nx^n$	$A_0 + A_1x + \cdots + A_nx^n$
$(a_0 + a_1x + \cdots + a_nx^n)e^{rx}$	$(A_0 + A_1x + \cdots + A_nx^n)e^{rx}$
$a_0 \sin bx + a_1 \cos bx$	$A_0 \sin bx + A_1 \cos bx$

If the complementary function y_c *contains terms which are like the terms in* $f(x)$, *multiply the corresponding terms of* y_p *by* x^r, *where* r *is one greater than the exponent of* x *in the like term of* y_c.

Be sure to make allowance for missing terms in $f(x)$; for example, the form of y_p for

$$f(x) = x^2e^x + \sin 2x$$

is given by

$$y_p = (A_0 + A_1x + A_2x^2)e^x + B_0 \sin 2x + B_1 \cos 2x.$$

It may turn out that some of the coefficients will be zero, but it is better to determine that from the differential equation than to try to guess it in advance. The algebra involved in simplifying the left side can become tedious, and it is sometimes convenient to collect the coefficients of like terms in tabular form.

Illustration. Find the general solution of

$$(1) \qquad y''' - 2y'' + y' - 2y = 4x + 5e^{2x} + 20 \cos x.$$

Solution. The auxiliary equation is

$$m^3 - 2m^2 + m - 2 = 0,$$

with roots $m = 2, \pm i$. The complementary function is

$$y_c = c_1 e^{2x} + c_2 \sin x + c_3 \cos x.$$

The initial form of y_p is

$$y_p = A + Bx + Ce^{2x} + D \cos x + E \sin x;$$

however, some of these terms are contained in y_c, so it is necessary to multiply by x for the last three terms. Thus

$$y_p = A + Bx + Cxe^{2x} + Dx \cos x + Ex \sin x.$$

The successive derivatives are

$$y_p' = B + (C + 2Cx)e^{2x} + (D + Ex) \cos x + (E - Dx) \sin x;$$
$$y_p'' = (4C + 4Cx)e^{2x} + (2E - Dx) \cos x - (2D + Ex) \sin x;$$
$$y_p''' = (12C + 8Cx)e^{2x} - (3D + Ex) \cos x - (3E - Dx) \sin x.$$

These values are substituted into equation (1) using the following tabular method:

	k	x	e^{2x}	xe^{2x}	$\cos x$	$x \cos x$	$\sin x$	$x \sin x$
y'''	0	0	$12C$	$8C$	$-3D$	$-E$	$-3E$	D
$-2y''$	0	0	$-8C$	$-8C$	$-4E$	$2D$	$4D$	$2E$
y'	B	0	C	$2C$	D	E	E	$-D$
$-2y$	$-2A$	$-2B$	0	$-2C$	0	$-2D$	0	$-2E$
sum $=$	$-2A+B$	$-2B$	$5C$	0	$-2D-4E$	0	$4D-2E$	0
$f(x)$	0	4	5	0	20	0	0	0

$$\therefore \quad \boxed{\begin{array}{c|c|c} B - 2A = 0 & 5C = 5 & -2D - 4E = 20 \\ -2B = 4 & & 4D - 2E = 0 \end{array}}$$

or

$$B = -2; \quad A = -1; \quad C = 1; \quad D = -2; \quad E = -4;$$

and

$$y_p = -1 - 2x + xe^{2x} - 2x \cos x - 4x \sin x.$$

The general solution is

$$y = (c_1 + x)e^{2x} + (c_2 - 4x) \sin x + (c_3 - 2x) \cos x - 1 - 2x.$$

48. Complete Equation; Variation of Parameters. Since the method of undetermined coefficients is limited in its application, we need a method with wider application. The technique we shall discuss is called the **method of variation of parameters.** The procedure consists of replacing the constants in the complementary function by undetermined functions of the independent variable x and then determining these functions so that when the modified complementary function is substituted into the differential equation, $f(x)$ will be obtained on the left side. This places only one restriction on the n arbitrary functions c_i, $(i = 1, \cdots, n)$, and we have $(n - 1)$ conditions at our disposal. We utilize this liberty in the following manner:

(a) As we differentiate y_c to find $D_x y_c$, there will now appear terms which contain $c_i'(x)$. We set this combination of terms equal to zero.

(b) As we differentiate again to find $D_x^2 y_c$, we again set the resulting combination of terms containing $c_i'(x)$ equal to zero.

(c) We continue this process through $D_x^{n-1} y_c$.

(d) We then find $D_x^n y_c$ and substitute all these values into the given differential equation. Since y_c is the complementary function, the results of this substitution will contain only the terms of $D_x^n y_c$ which appear because the c_i are functions of x.

(e) The equations obtained from (d) and the $(n - 1)$ conditions imposed by (a)–(c) will yield a system of n linear equations in the n unknowns $c_i'(x)$, $(i = 1, \cdots, n)$. This may be solved and integrated to yield the n functions $c_i(x)$.

The procedure is not too difficult, providing the order of the linear differential equation is small.

Illustration. Find the general solution of

(1) $$y'' - y = x^2.$$

Solution. The complementary function is

(2) $$y_c = c_1 e^x + c_2 e^{-x}.$$

Let c_i, $(i = 1, 2)$, be functions of x:

(3) $$y_p = c_1(x)e^x + c_2(x)e^{-x}.$$

Differentiate to obtain

(4) $$y_p' = c_1 e^x - c_2 e^{-x} + c_1' e^x + c_2' e^{-x}.$$

Impose the first condition; i.e.,

(5) $$c_1' e^x + c_2' e^{-x} = 0.$$

With this condition imposed on (4), differentiate again to obtain

(6) $$y_p'' = c_1 e^x + c_2 e^{-x} + c_1' e^x - c_2' e^{-x}.$$

Substitute (6) and (3) into (1):

$$c_1 e^x + c_2 e^{-x} + c_1' e^x - c_2' e^{-x} - c_1 e^x - c_2 e^{-x} = x^2,$$

or

(7) $$c_1' e^x - c_2' e^{-x} = x^2.$$

We note again that all terms except those containing the derivatives of c_i, $(i = 1, 2)$, disappear and that much time can be saved by simply setting that part of (6) equal to $f(x)$. Equations (5) and (7) now form a system of linear equations for c_1' and c_2'. Adding these two equations we obtain

$$2c_1' e^x = x^2,$$

or

$$dc_1 = \tfrac{1}{2}x^2 e^{-x} \, dx.$$

An integration yields

$$c_1 = -(1 + x + \tfrac{1}{2}x^2)e^{-x}.$$

From equation (5) we have

$$c_2' = -c_1' e^{2x} = -\tfrac{1}{2}x^2 e^x$$

and

$$c_2 = -(1 - x + \tfrac{1}{2}x^2)e^x.$$

The general solution is

$$y = (c_1 + x - \tfrac{1}{2}x^2)e^x + (c_2 - x - \tfrac{1}{2}x^2)e^{-x}.$$

49. Cauchy's Linear Equation. Although this chapter is devoted to linear equations with constant coefficients, we shall consider an equation in which the coefficients

$$a_i(x) = k_i x^{n-i}, \ (i = 0, \cdots, n).$$

This equation is often referred to as the *Cauchy linear differential equation*,

$$(1) \qquad k_0 x^n y^{(n)} + k_1 x^{n-1} y^{(n-1)} + \cdots + k_{n-1} x y' + k_n y = f(x).$$

It is of special interest because it can be reduced to an equation with constant coefficients by the transformation $x = e^u$. We recall from the calculus that

$$y' = \frac{dy}{dx} = \frac{dy}{du}\frac{du}{dx},$$

and from the transformation $x = e^u$ we have

$$dx = e^u \, du \quad \text{or} \quad \frac{du}{dx} = e^{-u} = \frac{1}{x}.$$

Consequently,

$$y' = \frac{1}{x}\frac{dy}{du} \quad \text{or} \quad xy' = \frac{dy}{du}.$$

The higher derivatives yield

$$y'' = \frac{1}{x^2}\left(\frac{d^2y}{du^2} - \frac{dy}{du}\right);$$

$$y''' = \frac{1}{x^3}\left(\frac{d^3y}{du^3} - 3\frac{d^2y}{du^2} + 2\frac{dy}{du}\right).$$

If we employ the notation $D_u y = \dfrac{dy}{du}$, we can now write

$$xy' = D_u y;$$
$$x^2 y'' = D_u(D_u - 1)y;$$
$$x^3 y''' = D_u(D_u - 1)(D_u - 2)y;$$
$$x^n y^{(n)} = D_u(D_u - 1)(D_u - 2) \cdots (D_u - n + 1)y.$$

Substituting these values into equation (1) we obtain

(2)
$$k_0 D_u(D_u - 1) \cdots (D_u - n + 1)y + \cdots + k_{n-1}D_u y + k_n y = g(u),$$

which is a linear equation with constant coefficients.

The general equation for which this is true is the equation

$$(3) \quad k_0(a+bx)^n y^{(n)} + k_1(a+bx)^{n-1} y^{(n-1)}$$
$$+ \cdots + k_{n-1}(a+bx)y' + k_n y = f(x),$$

which can be reduced to an equation with constant coefficients by the transformation

$$a + bx = e^u.$$

Illustration. Find the solution of

$$x^2 y'' - 2y = \ln x.$$

Solution. The transformation $x = e^u$ yields

$$\frac{d^2y}{du^2} - \frac{dy}{du} - 2y = u.$$

The auxiliary equation is

$$m^2 - m - 2 = 0$$

with roots $m = 2, -1$, so that

$$y_c = c_1 e^{2u} + c_2 e^{-u}.$$

Let

$$y_p = Au + B.$$

Then

$$y_p' = A \quad \text{and} \quad y_p'' = 0.$$

A substitution yields

$$-A - 2Au - 2B \equiv u,$$

so that

$$-2A = 1 \quad \text{and} \quad -A - 2B = 0,$$

or

$$A = -\tfrac{1}{2} \quad \text{and} \quad B = \tfrac{1}{4}.$$

The general solution in terms of u is

$$y = c_1 e^{2u} + c_2 e^{-u} - \tfrac{1}{2}u + \tfrac{1}{4}.$$

Since $x = e^u$, $u = \ln x$, and in terms of x the general solution is

$$y = c_1 x^2 + c_2 x^{-1} - \tfrac{1}{2}\ln x + \tfrac{1}{4}.$$

Illustration. Find the general solution of

$$(1) \quad (2x-3)^2 y'' + (2x-3)y' + y = \sec \ln (2x-3).$$

Solution. The transformation $2x - 3 = e^u$ yields

(2) $$D_u^2 y + y = \sec u.$$

The auxiliary equation is

$$m^2 + 1 = 0$$

with roots $m = \pm i$, so that

$$y_c(u) = c_1 \cos u + c_2 \sin u.$$

Let

$$y_p(u) = c_1(u) \cos u + c_2(u) \sin u.$$

Using the method of variation of parameters we have

(3) $$\begin{cases} c_1' \cos u + c_2' \sin u = 0, \\ -c_1' \sin u + c_2' \cos u = \sec u. \end{cases}$$

Solving for c_1' and c_2', we obtain

$$c_2' = 1;$$
$$c_1' = -\frac{\sin u}{\cos u}.$$

We integrate these equations to obtain

$$c_1 = \ln \cos u;$$
$$c_2 = u.$$

The general solution of (2) is

$$y(u) = c_1 \cos u + c_2 \sin u + u \sin u + (\ln \cos u) \cos u.$$

Since $e^u = 2x - 3$ or $u = \ln(2x - 3)$, the general solution to (1) is

$$y(x) = c_1 \cos \ln(2x - 3) + [c_2 + \ln(2x - 3)] \sin \ln(2x - 3)$$
$$+ [\ln \cos \ln(2x - 3)] \cos \ln(2x - 3).$$

50. Exercise XIII. Solve the following differential equations.

1. $y'' - 12y' + 35y = 0.$
2. $y'' - 2y' = 0.$
3. $9y'' - 30y' + 25y = 0.$
4. $3y'' - 4y' + 2y = 0.$
5. $y^{(iv)} - 6y''' + 7y'' + 6y' - 8y = 0.$
6. $y''' - 2y'' + 3y' - 6y = 0.$
7. $y^{(iv)} - 4y''' + 5y'' - 4y' + 4y = 0.$

8. $y^{(iv)} - 8y''' + 42y'' - 104y' + 169y = 0.$

9. $y''' - 3y'' + 3y' - y = 2x^2 - 3x - 17.$

10. $y'' - 2y' - 3y + 8e^{-x} + 3x = 0.$

11. $y'' + 4y = 2 \tan 2x.$

12. $y'' - y' = 6x^5 e^x.$

VII

OPERATIONAL METHODS

51. Differential Operators. Throughout mathematics there are many formal developments which start with definitions, postulates, and/or axioms, and then properties and theorems are logically demonstrated. A good development then applies these properties and theorems to the solution of problems. Operators and their application form an excellent example of formal mathematics. Consequently, we shall develop the theory of differential operators and their application to the solution of linear differential equations in a formal manner. If this be the student's first introduction to formal mathematics, it is hoped that he will exert additional effort to comprehend the logic as well as the mathematics. For this reason the application of differential operators to the solution of linear differential equations is delayed to the latter part of the chapter.

To *operate* means to *produce an appropriate effect*, and an operator is, of course, that which operates. We have already used the notation

$$D_x^k y = \frac{d^k y}{dx^k}, \quad k = 1, 2, \cdots$$

to indicate the kth derivative of the function y with respect to x. A slight change in this notation in which we simply drop the subscript that indicates the independent variable leads us to use the letter D to denote differentiation with respect to the appropriate independent variable, and more generally D^k denotes the derivative of the order k. We shall call D^k the **differential operator.** Since it must produce an effect, it must operate on a function and must behave according to the rules of differentiation. Thus, the following two properties are valid:

Property 1. If c is a constant,

$$D^k(cy) = cD^k y.$$

Property 2.

$$D^k(y_1 + y_2) = D^k y_1 + D^k y_2.$$

Since the usual use of parentheses in mathematics indicates a grouping and a coefficient indicates a multiplication, the above expressions define a symbolic multiplication, but it is necessary to caution the student about the difference between actual multiplication and this symbolic multiplication. Although many of the properties of multiplication and addition will remain valid, each must be demonstrated; for example, if u and v are both functions of x, then

$$D(uv) \neq u \, Dv.$$

In fact, we know from the calculus that

$$D(uv) = u \, Dv + v \, Du.$$

We shall now develop a logical and consistent set of properties and definitions for the differential operator.

Definition. *The symbol* D^0 *represents the* **identity operator,** *i.e.,* $D^0 y = y$.

Definition. *Polynomials in the operator* D *may be formed:*

$$A = P(D) = a_0 D^n + a_1 D^{n-1} + \cdots + a_{n-1}D + a_n D^0.$$

They are called differential operators of order n *and are defined by the equation*

$$P(D)y = a_0 y^{(n)} + a_1 y^{(n-1)} + \cdots + a_{n-1}y' + a_n y.$$

The coefficients a_i *may be functions of the independent variable or they may be constants.*

Property 3. Two operators A and B are equal if, and only if,

$$Ay = By.$$

Definition. *The product* AB *of the two operators is defined as that operator obtained by using* B *first and then* A; *i.e.,*

$$A By = A(By) = Cy.$$

Property 4. If A, B, and C are any differential operators, they will satisfy the ordinary laws of algebra.

(a) The commutative law of addition:

$$A + B = B + A.$$

(b) The associative law of addition:

$$(A + B) + C = A + (B + C).$$

(c) The associative law of multiplication:

$$(AB)C = A(BC).$$

(d) The distributive law of multiplication:

$$A(B + C) = AB + AC.$$

(e) The commutative law of multiplication if the operators all have constant coefficients:

$$AB = BA.$$

We then have the following useful results in which m, n, and r are positive integers:

$$(D^m + D^n)y = (D^n + D^m)y;$$
$$[(D^m + D^n) + D^r]y = [D^m + (D^n + D^r)]y;$$
$$D^m D^n y = D^{m+n}y;$$
$$D^m(D^n D^r)y = D^{m+n+r}y;$$
$$D^m(D^n + D^r)y = (D^{m+n} + D^{m+r})y.$$

Property 5. The exponential shift. If $P(D)$ is a polynomial in D with constant coefficients, then

(1) $$e^{rx}P(D)y = P(D - r)[e^{rx}y];$$
(2) $$P(D)[e^{rx}y] = e^{rx}P(D + r)y;$$
(3) $$e^{-rx}P(D)[e^{rx}y] = P(D + r)y.$$

Each of these equations essentially states the same property. Let us demonstrate the property by first considering

$$P(D) = aD + b; \text{ then}$$

(i)
$$\begin{aligned}
P(D)(e^{rx}y) &= (aD + b)(e^{rx}y) \\
&= aD(e^{rx}y) + be^{rx}y \\
&= ae^{rx}Dy + are^{rx}y + be^{rx}y \\
&= e^{rx}[a(D + r) + b]y \\
&= e^{rx}P(D + r)y.
\end{aligned}$$

Consider now that $P(D) = P_1(D)P_2(D)$ where $P_1(D)$ and $P_2(D)$ are two linear operators, i.e., of the form $(aD + b)$. Then

$$P(D)(e^{rx}y) = P_1(D)P_2(D)[e^{rx}y]$$
$$= P_1(D)[e^{rx}P_2(D+r)y], \quad \text{by (i)},$$
$$= P_1(D)[e^{rx}V(x)], \quad \text{by letting } V(x) = P_2(D+r)y,$$
$$= e^{rx}P_1(D+r)V(x), \quad \text{by (i)},$$
$$= e^{rx}P_1(D+r)P_2(D+r)y$$
$$= e^{rx}P(D+r)y. \quad \text{See footnote.}$$

By the fundamental theorem of algebra, a polynomial $P(z)$ can be factored into linear factors. Consequently, the above procedure can be continued until all the factors of $P(D)$ have been utilized. Thus, we have demonstrated the form of equation (2). Let us now write equation (2) in the form

$$P(D)[e^{rx}f(x)] = e^{rx}P(D+r)f(x)$$

and let

$$y = e^{rx}f(x) \quad \text{or} \quad f(x) = e^{-rx}y.$$

Then

$$P(D)y = e^{rx}P(D+r)[e^{-rx}y].$$

Multiply by e^{-rx} to obtain

$$e^{-rx}P(D)y = P(D+r)[e^{-rx}y].$$

Let r be replaced by $-r$ to yield

$$e^{rx}P(D)y = P(D-r)[e^{rx}y],$$

which is equation (1). Equation (3) is simply equation (2) multiplied by e^{-rx}.

52. Evaluation of $P(D)[x^m e^{rx}]$. Some very useful and interesting results are obtained from the evaluation of $P(D)[x^m e^{rx}]$ for constant r and integral values of m. We know from calculus that

(1) $$D^k e^{rx} = r^k e^{rx}.$$

Now let

$$P(D) = a_0 D^n + a_1 D^{n-1} + \cdots + a_{n-1}D + a_n.$$

Footnote: In the above evolution of the right-hand side we let

$$V(x) = P_2(D+r)y$$

to emphasize that the operation $P_2(D+r)y$ will result in a function V of the independent variable. We also recall from algebra that if $P(z) = P_1(z)P_2(z)$ and if we let $z = u + r$, then $P_1(u+r)P_2(u+r) = P(u+r)$.

Then
$$P(D)e^{rx} = a_0 r^n e^{rx} + a_1 r^{n-1} e^{rx} + \cdots + a_{n-1} r e^{rx} + a_n e^{rx},$$
or

(2) $$P(D)e^{rx} = e^{rx} P(r).$$

Consider

(3) $$(D - r)[x^m e^{rx}] = m x^{m-1} e^{rx} + r x^m e^{rx} - r x^m e^{rx}$$
$$= m x^{m-1} e^{rx}$$

and
$$(D - r)^2 [x^m e^{rx}] = m(D - r)[x^{m-1} e^{rx}]$$
$$= m(m - 1) x^{m-2} e^{rx}.$$

If we continue the operation, we obtain

(4) $$(D - r)^m [x^m e^{rx}] = m! e^{rx}$$

and

(5) $$(D - r)^n [x^m e^{rx}] = 0, \quad \text{for } n > m.$$

The above properties permit an easy proof of the following theorem:

Theorem. *If the auxiliary equation of a homogeneous linear differential equation contains* r *as an* s-*fold root, then*

$$y = (c_0 + c_1 x + \cdots + c_{s-1} x^{s-1}) e^{rx}$$

is a particular solution.

Proof. The equation can be written in the form
$$P(D)y = 0.$$

If r is an s-fold root of $P(D) = 0$, then
$$P(D) = g(D)(D - r)^s.$$

The differential equation
$$P(D)y = g(D)(D - r)^s y = 0$$
is satisfied if
$$(D - r)^s y = 0.$$

Now by (5)
$$(D - r)^s (x^k e^{rx}) = 0$$

for $k = 0, 1, 2, \cdots, s - 1$; i.e., $s > k$. Consequently,
$$y = x^k e^{rx}, \; k = 0, \cdots, s - 1$$

are all solutions of the differential equation, and therefore a linear combination,

$$y = (c_0 + c_1x + \cdots + c_{s-1}x^{s-1})e^{rx},$$

is a solution.

53. Inverse Differential Operator. To complete our discussion of the differential operator, we now consider the meaning of $D^{-k}y$. In order to be consistent we must have

$$D^{-1}y = \frac{1}{D}\, y = z$$

be an expression such that

$$Dz = y.$$

In other words, the effect called for by a differential operator with a negative index is an integration. This operator is called the **inverse differential operator.**

Definition. The *inverse differential operator,*

$$(D - c)^{-k}, \quad k = 1, 2, \cdots,$$

is defined as the integral

$$(D - c)^{-k}y(x) = \int_{x_0}^{x} \frac{(x - u)^{k-1}}{(k - 1)!}\, e^{c(x-u)}y(u)du,$$

where x_0 is an arbitrary but fixed number.

The following properties can be demonstrated by formal algebra:

Property 1.

(1) $$\frac{1}{P(D)}\, [e^{rx}] = \frac{e^{rx}}{P(r)}, \quad \text{if } P(r) \neq 0.$$

This property follows from equation (2), Section 52, by the formal division by $P(D)P(r)$.

If $P(r) = 0$, then $P(D)$ contains the factor $D - r$, and if r is a multiple root of multiplicity k, then $P(D) = (D - r)^k\varphi(D)$ with $\varphi(D) \neq 0$. Consider now

$$P(D)(x^ke^{rx}) = \varphi(D)(D - r)^k(x^ke^{rx}).$$

Using equation (4), Section 52, we have

$$P(D)(x^ke^{rx}) = \varphi(r)k!e^{rx}.$$

A formal division, since $\varphi(r) \neq 0$, yields

Property 2.

(2)
$$\frac{1}{P(D)} e^{rx} = \frac{x^k e^{rx}}{k!\varphi(r)}.$$

Property 3.

(3)
$$\frac{1}{D^2 + r^2} \sin rx = -\frac{x}{2r} \cos rx.$$

Since

$$\sin rx = \frac{e^{rix} - e^{-rix}}{2i},$$

we have, by use of Property 2,

$$\frac{1}{D^2 + r^2} = \frac{1}{2i}\left[\frac{1}{(D-ri)(D+ri)}\left(e^{rix} - e^{-rix}\right)\right]$$

$$= \frac{1}{2i}\left(\frac{xe^{rix}}{1!2ri} - \frac{xe^{-rix}}{1!(-2ri)}\right)$$

$$= -\frac{x}{2r}\frac{e^{rix} + e^{-rix}}{2}$$

$$= -\frac{x}{2r} \cos rx.$$

Similarly, we have

Property 4.

(4)
$$\frac{1}{D^2 + r^2} \cos rx = \frac{x}{2r} \sin rx.$$

Property 3a.

(3a)
$$\frac{1}{D^2 + r^2} (c \sin bx) = \frac{c}{r^2 - b^2} \sin bx, \quad b \neq r.$$

Property 4a.

(4a)
$$\frac{1}{D^2 + r^2} (c \cos bx) = \frac{c}{r^2 - b^2} \cos bx, \quad b \neq r.$$

Both of these properties (3a and 4a) can easily be obtained by finding the particular integral for each of the two equations

$$(D^2 + r^2)y = c \sin bx$$

and

$$(D^2 + r^2)y = c \cos bx.$$

From the definition of the inverse operator, we have

$$D^{-1}x^n = \frac{x^{n+1}}{n+1},$$

$$D^{-2}x^n = D^{-1}\frac{x^{n+1}}{n+1} = \frac{x^{n+2}}{(n+1)(n+2)},$$

$$D^{-k}x^n = \frac{x^{n+k}}{(n+1)\cdots(n+k)},$$

if we disregard the constants of integration.
The evaluation of

$$\frac{1}{P(D)}\left[x^n\right]$$

can be accomplished by expanding $[P(D)]^{-1}$ in its formal series, in ascending powers of D and then carrying out the indicated operations, using the above formula for $D^{-k}x^n$ if necessary. The general idea can best be illustrated by an example.

Property 5.

(5) $$\frac{1}{D(D^2+1)}\left[x^3\right] = \frac{1}{4}x^4 - 3x^2 + 6.$$

Since

$$\frac{1}{D(D^2+1)} = D^{-1}(1 - D^2 + D^4 - \cdots)$$

$$= D^{-1} - D + D^3 - \cdots,$$

we have

$$\frac{1}{D(D^2+1)}\left[x^3\right] = D^{-1}[x^3] - Dx^3 + D^3x^3 = \cdots$$

$$= \frac{x^4}{4} - 3x^2 + 6.$$

Note that only a finite number of terms in the series expansion appears in the result since $D^k x^r = 0$ if $k > r$.

Property 6.   The Exponential Shift.

(6) $$\frac{1}{P(D)}\left[e^{rx}y\right] = e^{rx}\frac{1}{P(D+r)}[y].$$

From the development of the exponential shift in Section 51, we have

$$P(D)f(x) = e^{rx}P(D+r)[e^{-rx}f(x)].$$

Let

$$f(x) = e^{rx} \frac{1}{P(D+r)} y$$

and substitute into the right member to obtain

$$P(D)f(x) = e^{rx}P(D+r)\left[\frac{1}{P(D+r)} y\right]$$
$$= e^{rx}y.$$

Solve this equation for $f(x)$ to obtain

$$f(x) = \frac{1}{P(D)} e^{rx}y.$$

Equating these two values of $f(x)$ we obtain the property.

Property 7. Special Cases. Because of their frequent occurrence in practice, we shall develop expressions for the inverse operator when $k = 1$ and $k = 2$. By the definition we have

$$(D - c)^{-1}y(x) = \int_{x_0}^{x} e^{c(x-u)}y(u)du$$

and

$$(D - c)^{-2}y(x) = \int_{x_0}^{x} (x - u)e^{c(x-u)}y(u)du.$$

The values of the integrals depend, of course, upon the form of the function $y(x)$. Let us consider the special cases of $y(x) = K$, a constant.

(7a) $(D - c)^{-1}K = \dfrac{K}{c}\left[e^{c(x-x_0)} - 1\right], \quad c \neq 0.$

(7b) $(D - c)^{-2}K = \dfrac{K}{c}\left[\left(x - x_0 - \dfrac{1}{c}\right)e^{c(x-x_0)} + \dfrac{1}{c}\right], \quad c \neq 0.$

54. Practice. In order to develop greater familiarity with the definitions and properties discussed in the previous sections, we shall illustrate with some typical exercises.

Illustrations and *Solutions*. Perform the indicated operations.

  1. $D^2 e^{4x} = D(4e^{4x}) = 16e^{4x};$
                     $= 4^2 e^{4x}$ by (1), Section 52.

  2. $(D - r)e^{rx} = re^{rx} - re^{rx} = 0;$
                     $= 0$ by (5), Section 52.

  3. $(D^2 + 2aD + a^2)(x^2e^{-ax})$
             $= (D + a)^2(x^2e^{-ax})$
             $= 2e^{-ax}$ by (4), Section 52 with $r = -a$.

4. $D^2(D + D^2)(2e^{rx}) = 2(D^3 + D^4)(e^{rx})$
$$= 2(r^3 + r^4)e^{rx}, \text{ by (2), Section 52.}$$

5. $(D + a)^2(x^3e^{-ax}) = 6xe^{-ax}$, by (3), Section 52.

6. $(D - a)x^3e^{-ax} = e^{-ax}(D - 2a)x^3$, by Property 5, Section 51;
$$= e^{-ax}(3x^2 - 2ax^3).$$

7. $(D^2 - 2)^{-1}e^{2x} = (4 - 2)^{-1}e^{2x}$, by Property 1, Section 53;
$$= \tfrac{1}{2}e^{2x}.$$

8. $(D^3 - D^2 - D + 1)^{-1}e^x = [(D - 1)^2(D + 1)]^{-1}e^x$
$$= \tfrac{1}{4}x^2e^x, \text{ by Property 2, Section 53.}$$

9. $(D^2 + 4)^{-1} \sin 2x = -\tfrac{1}{4}x \cos 2x$, by Property 3, Section 53.

10. $[D(D^2 - 1)]^{-1}5x^4 = [-D^{-1} - D - D^3 - D^5 - \cdots](5x^4)$
$$= -x^5 - 20x^3 - 120x, \text{ by Property 5,}$$
Section 53.

55. Exercise XIV.

1. Let $P(D) = D^3 - 3D^2 + 2D - 5$, and perform the indicated operations.
   (a) $P(D)e^{3x}$.
   (b) $P(D) \sin 2x$.
   (c) $P(D)3x^2$.
   (d) $P(D)x^2e^x$.

2. Perform the indicated operations.
   (a) $D^{-1}(3x^2)$.
   (b) $(D - a)e^{ax}$.
   (c) $(D^2 + 2aD + a^2)(x^2e^{-ax})$.
   (d) $(D - 1)^2(x^3e^x)$.
   (e) $(D - a)^{-1}e^{ax}$.
   (f) $(D - 1)^{-1}x^4$.
   (g) $(D^2 + D - 1)(e^{2x} \cos x)$.
   (h) $(D^2 + 2D - 3)(e^{-x} \sin 2x)$.
   (i) $(D^3 + 1)(x^3e^{-x})$.
   (j) $[D^3(D - 1)^2(D + 1)]^{-1}e^x$.

56. Application to the Solution of Linear Differential Equations.
The general linear differential equation of order n,

(1) $\qquad a_0y^{(n)} + a_1y^{(n-1)} + \cdots + a_{n-1}y' + a_n = f(x),$

may be written in the form

(2) $\qquad\qquad\qquad P(D)y = f(x),$

where $P(D)$ is the operator polynomial

(3) $$P(D) = a_0D^n + a_1D^{n-1} + \cdots + a_{n-1}D + a_n.$$

In the case of the homogeneous equation, we have

(4) $$P(D)y = 0.$$

Now if $P(D)$ can be decomposed into two factors, $P_1(D)$ and $P_2(D)$, then

(5) $$P(D)y = P_1(D)P_2(D)y = 0,$$

and if either $P_1(D) = 0$ or $P_2(D) = 0$, equation (5) is satisfied. Thus we can find the solution of two lower order differential equations; and since the sum of any two solutions of a homogeneous linear equation is also a solution, we can add these two to obtain a general solution.

Illustration. Find the general solution of

$$y''' - 4y'' + 4y' = 0.$$

Solution. Write the equation in the form

$$(D^3 - 4D^2 + 4D)y = D(D - 2)^2y = 0.$$

Then

$$Dy = 0 \quad \text{and} \quad (D - 2)^2y = 0,$$

the first of which has the solution

$$y_1(x) = C.$$

We may apply the shifting property, equation (3), Property 5, Section 51, from right to left with $r = -2$, to obtain

$$(D - 2)^2y = e^{2x}D^2(e^{-2x}y) = 0$$

or

$$D^2(e^{-2x}y) = D^2z = 0.$$

Integrating twice we obtain

$$D_z = A.$$
$$z = e^{-2x}y = Ax + B$$

or

$$y_2 = (Ax + B)e^{2x}.$$

The general solution is

$$y_1 + y_2 = (Ax + B)e^{2x} + C.$$

There is little or no advantage in the use of the operator theory to obtain solutions of the homogeneous linear differential equation since the solutions are still dependent upon the factorization of $P(D)$, and once the roots of $P(D) = 0$ have been obtained, the solutions can be written down by the rules of the last chapter. On the other hand, the use of the theory of operators can save some labor in finding particular integrals for the complete linear differential equation,

$$(6) \qquad P(D)y = f(x).$$

If we treat this as a simple algebraic equation, it would be natural to solve for y by a division,

$$(7) \qquad y = \frac{1}{P(D)} f(x).$$

The properties of Section 53 can now be used to good advantage.

Illustrations. Find a particular integral.

1. $\qquad D(D-2)^3(D+1)y = e^{2x}.$

Solution. Solve for y to obtain

$$y_p = [D(D-2)^3(D+1)]^{-1}e^{2x}.$$

By Property 2, Section 53, with $r = 2$, $k = 3$, and

$$\varphi(D) = D(D+1)$$

so that $\varphi(r) = r(r+1) = (2)(3) = 6$, we have

$$y_p = \frac{x^3 e^{2x}}{3!6} = \frac{1}{36} x^3 e^{2x}.$$

Compare this with the method of Chapter VI.

2. $\qquad (D^2+4)y = e^x + 3\sin 2x.$

Solution. Let us use the principle of superposition and solve the two equations

$$(D^2+4)y = e^x \quad \text{and} \quad (D^2+4)y = 3\sin 2x.$$

By Property 1, Section 53:

$$y_1 = (D^2+4)^{-1}e^x = \tfrac{1}{5}e^x.$$

By Property 3, Section 53:

$$y_2 = (D^2+4)^{-1}3\sin 2x = -\tfrac{3}{4}x\cos 2x.$$

The particular integral is

$$y = y_1 + y_2$$
$$= \tfrac{1}{5}e^x - \tfrac{3}{4}x \cos 2x.$$

3. $(D^2 - 6D + 9)y = 2xe^{3x} + 9x^2 - 3.$

Solution. We shall again consider two equations. The first

$$(D - 3)^2 y = 2xe^{3x}$$

is divided by e^{3x} to obtain

$$e^{-3x}(D - 3)^2 y = 2x.$$

By the shifting property, equation (2), Property 5, Section 51,

$$D^2[e^{-3x}y] = 2x.$$

Integrating twice and ignoring the constants of integration, we obtain

$$e^{-3x}y = \tfrac{1}{3}x^3$$

or

$$y_1 = \tfrac{1}{3}x^3 e^{3x}.$$

For the second equation,

$$(D^2 - 6D + 9)y = 9x^2 - 3,$$

let

$$y_2 = Ax^2 + Bx + C,$$
$$y_2' = 2Ax + B,$$
$$y_2'' = 2A.$$

A substitution yields

$$A = 1, \ B = \tfrac{4}{3}, \ C = \tfrac{1}{3}.$$

The complete solution is

$$y = \tfrac{1}{3}(x^3 e^{3x} + 3x^2 + 4x + 1).$$

Although the second equation in the above illustration can be solved by expanding $(D^2 - 6D + 9)^{-1}$ in a series and using Property 5, Section 53, that method appears to involve more labor than the method of undetermined coefficients.

4. $(D^3 + D)y = 2 \cos x.$

Solution. Since $P(D) = D(D^2 + 1)$, we can write

$$(D^2 + 1)Dy = 2 \cos x.$$

Let $Dy = z$; then

$$(D^2 + 1)z = 2 \cos x.$$

By Property 4, Section 53:

$$z = x \sin x$$

or

$$Dy = x \sin x.$$

Integrating we obtain

$$y_p = \sin x - x \cos x.$$

57. Exercise XV.

Find the complete solution of the following linear differential equations:

1. $(D^2 - 4D + 4)y = xe^{2x}$.
2. $(D^2 + 4)y = 4 \cos 2x$.
3. $(D^3 - 6D^2 + 9D)y = x^3 + e^x$.   (Hint: let $Dy = z$.)
4. $(D^2 + 2aD + a^2)y = x^2e^{-ax}$.
5. $D(D - 1)^3y = xe^x$.
6. $(D^2 + 6D + 9)y = 2e^{-2x} \sin x$.
7. $D(D^2 + 2D + 1)y = e^{-x} \sin x$.

VIII

APPLICATIONS

58. Introduction. Before continuing with the development of additional techniques for solving differential equations, we shall pause again to consider some applications of what we have already learned. In Chapter V we discussed some geometric applications; we shall now turn to some problems which are based upon physical laws. The solution of the problems can be made easier by employing a systematic approach. It is therefore recommended that all symbols be well defined, that a rough sketch be drawn to give a geometric visualization, and that directions, which define the algebraic signs, be clearly indicated. For the statements of the laws we shall use, the student is referred to Chapter I.

59. Acceleration, Velocity, Distance. In our study of the calculus we encountered the definitions for rectilinear motion:

(1) $$\text{Distance} \equiv s = f(t).$$

(2) $$\text{Velocity} \equiv v = \frac{ds}{dt} = \dot{s}.$$

(3) $$\text{Acceleration} \equiv a = \frac{dv}{dt} = \frac{d^2s}{dt^2} = \ddot{s}.$$

We also recall that

(4) $$\frac{dv}{dt} = \frac{ds}{dt}\frac{dv}{ds} = v\frac{dv}{ds}.$$

By Newton's law we have

$$F = ma = m\ddot{s},$$

which is a second order differential equation. However, if the force F is a function of s, we can change to a first order equation by (4), and if F is a known function of v and t, we can change to a first order equation by (3).

Let us consider a body of mass m falling with a velocity v under the action of gravity and being retarded by a force proportional to v^n. The motion is then expressed by

$$ma = mg - kv^n,$$

where k is the constant of proportionality. This equation may be written in the form

$$m \frac{dv}{dt} = mg - kv^n,$$

which is a first order equation with variables separable,

$$\frac{dv}{g - \alpha v^n} = dt, \quad \text{where } \alpha = \frac{k}{m}$$

The integral of the left member can be expressed in terms of elementary functions for various values of n. Let us consider the case with $n = 1$. Then

$$-\frac{1}{\alpha} \ln (g - \alpha v) = t + c$$

or

$$g - \alpha v = A e^{-\alpha t},$$

which can be solved for v to yield

$$v = \frac{1}{\alpha} g - B e^{-\alpha t}.$$

If the body starts at rest, then $v = 0$ at $t = 0$, and

$$B = \frac{g}{\alpha}$$

so that

$$v = \frac{g}{\alpha} (1 - e^{-\alpha t}).$$

As $t \to \infty$, the second term approaches 0 and v approaches the *terminal velocity*,

$$\frac{g}{\alpha} = \frac{mg}{k}.$$

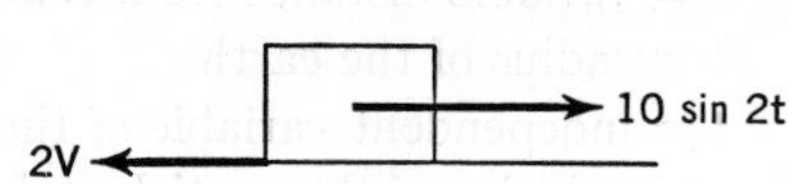

Fig. 21

Illustration. A mass of 2 slugs, constrained to move horizontally, is subjected to the periodic force 10 sin 2t and is retarded in its motion by a frictional drag equal to twice the velocity. If the body starts from rest, what is its velocity as a function of the time?

Solution. We have

$$v \equiv \text{velocity},$$
$$m = 2,$$
$$a = \dot{v}.$$

By Newton's law

$$2\dot{v} = 10 \sin 2t - 2v$$

or

$$\dot{v} + v = 5 \sin 2t.$$

This is a first order linear differential equation with an integrating factor, e^t, so that

$$ve^t = 5 \int e^t \sin 2t$$
$$= e^t(\sin 2t - 2 \cos 2t) + c.$$

Solve for v to obtain

$$v = \sin 2t - 2 \cos 2t + ce^{-t}.$$

At $t = 0$ we have (since the body starts from rest) $v = 0$, so that

$$0 = -2 + c \quad \text{or} \quad c = 2.$$

The solution is

$$v = \sin 2t - 2 \cos 2t + 2e^{-t}.$$

60. Velocity of Escape from the Earth. Let us consider the simple problem of finding the velocity of a particle projected in a radial direction outward from the earth and acted upon only by the gravitational attraction of the earth. Newton's law of gravitation states that the acceleration of the particle will be inversely proportional to the square of the distance from the particle to the center of the earth. We define the following notation:

$r \equiv$ variable distance from center 0 to particle at any time t.
$R \equiv$ radius of the earth.
$t \equiv$ independent variable of time.
$v \equiv$ velocity of the particle, taken to be positive outward.
$a \equiv$ acceleration of the particle.
$k \equiv$ constant of proportionality.
$g \equiv$ acceleration at the surface of the earth.

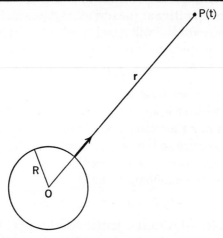

Fig. 22

By Newton's law we have

(1) $$a = \frac{dv}{dt} = \frac{k}{r^2},$$

which is negative since the velocity is decreasing as t and r are increasing. Furthermore, at $r = R$ we have $a = -g$ so that

$$-g = \frac{k}{R^2} \quad \text{or} \quad k = -gR^2.$$

We then have, since $D_t r = v$,

(2) $$a = -\frac{gR^2}{r^2} = \frac{dv}{dt} = v\frac{dv}{dr}$$

as the differential equation for the velocity. Separating the variables, we obtain

(3) $$v\,dv = -gR^2 r^{-2}\,dr,$$

which has the solution

(4) $$v^2 = \frac{2gR^2}{r} + c \cdot$$

Let the initial velocity be v_0; that is, $v = v_0$ when $r = R$. Then

(5) $$c = v_0^2 - 2gR.$$

The velocity equation of the particle then is

(6) $$v^2 = 2gR^2 r^{-1} + v_0^2 - 2gR.$$

The velocity v is positive at the surface of the earth if the particle is projected outward and will remain positive as long as the right-hand side of equation (6) is positive. This is true if and only if

$$(7) \qquad v_0^2 - 2gR \geq 0,$$

for if this expression were negative, then there would exist a value of r for which $v = 0$, thus causing the particle to stop. For a larger value of r the velocity would become negative, causing the particle to return to the earth. Consequently, if it is desired that the velocity always remain positive, then the inequality (7) must hold, and the minimum value is

$$(8) \qquad v_0^2 - 2gR = 0 \quad \text{or} \quad v_0 = \sqrt{2gR}.$$

A particle projected with this initial velocity would escape from the earth. This velocity is often called the *velocity of escape*, v_e. With appropriate values of R and g, equation (8) yields the velocity of escape of a particle from any member of the solar system. In the case of the earth, let us use the approximate values

$$R = 3960 \text{ miles};$$
$$g = 32.17 \text{ feet/sec.}^2 = .006093 \text{ miles/sec.}^2$$

Then

$$v_e = \sqrt{2(.006093)(3960)} = 6.947 \text{ miles/sec.}$$
$$= 25,000 \text{ miles/hr., approximately.}^*$$

61. Other Rate Problems. Let us consider two more rate problems, each of which will illustrate a point.

Illustration 1. A sled and its occupants weigh 1,000 pounds. It is coasting down a 5°45′ incline, the force of friction is 40.2 lbs., and the air resistance (drag) is 2 times the velocity in feet per second. Find an expression for the velocity after t seconds from rest, the velocity after 10 seconds, and the terminal velocity.

Solution. The units of measure are foot-second-slug-pound, so that

$$W(\text{weight}) = m(\text{mass}) \times g.$$

---

* This is an idealized problem; if we were considering a rocket, then other factors such as the effects of air resistance and other earth-atmosphere conditions would also have to be accounted for.

The force exerted by the pull of gravity is vertically downward, and we must resolve this along the line of motion. Referring to Fig. 23 we have

$$F_1 = mg \sin \alpha$$
$$= 1000 \sin 5°45'$$
$$= 100.2.$$

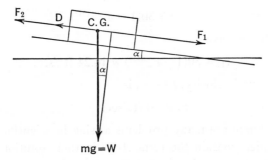

mg = W

Fig. 23

We shall use four significant figures for this problem, which means that $g = 32.17$ and not 32 which we frequently use for convenience. The total force is therefore

$$F = 100.2 - 40.2 - 2v = 60 - 2v.$$

The equation of motion, $ma = F$, is

$$\frac{1000}{32.17} \frac{dv}{dt} = 60 - 2v$$

or

$$\frac{dv}{30 - v} = \frac{32.17}{500} dt = .06434 dt.$$

The solution of this equation is obtained by an integration, and since we are also determining the constant of integration let us use the definite integral. The conditions state:

t	0	t	10	∞
v	0	v	v_{10}	v_∞

Therefore

$$\int_0^v \frac{-dv}{30 - v} = -\int_0^t .06434 \, dt,$$

or

$$\ln (30 - v) - \ln 30 = -.06434t.$$

Then

$$\frac{30 - v}{30} = e^{-.06434t},$$

or

$$v = 30(1 - e^{-.06434t}).$$

At $t = 10$ we have

$$v_{10} = 30(1 - e^{-.6434}) = 14.24 \text{ ft./sec.}$$

The terminal velocity, $t \to \infty$, is

$$v_{\infty} = 30 \text{ ft./sec.}$$

Note. There are many problems arising in scientific investigations which contain the term $Ae^{-\alpha t}$ in their solution. Since this term will approach zero as t approaches infinity, such terms are called **transient terms,** the connotation being that they usually are not present for long.

Illustration 2. A projectile fired from the point O with an angle of departure φ and an initial velocity v_0 is acted upon by the force of gravity in the vertical direction and retarded by air resistance R in the direction of the tangent to the trajectory opposite to the direction of motion. Find the equations of motion.

Solution. The geometric sketch of the problem is shown in Fig. 24.

$\theta \equiv$ angle between direction of motion and horizontal axis at any time t.

$mg \equiv$ force of gravity.

$R \equiv$ resistance (drag).

$v \equiv$ instantaneous velocity along tangent line.

$\dot{x} \equiv$ instantaneous velocity in x direction.

$\dot{y} \equiv$ instantaneous velocity in y direction.

From the velocity triangle,

$$\sin \theta = \frac{\dot{y}}{v}, \quad \text{and} \quad \cos \theta = \frac{\dot{x}}{v}.$$

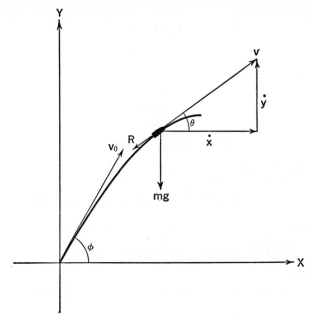

Fig. 24

In the x direction:

$$F = m\ddot{x} = -R\cos\theta = -R\frac{\dot{x}}{v}.$$

In the y direction:

$$F = m\ddot{y} = -mg - R\sin\theta$$

$$= -mg - R\frac{\dot{y}}{v}.$$

These equations can be solved for x, y, $\dot{x}$, and $\dot{y}$ by our techniques if R is proportional to v. The initial values of $\dot{x}$ and $\dot{y}$ are obtained from v_0 and φ:

$$\dot{x}_0 = v_0\cos\varphi \quad \text{and} \quad \dot{y}_0 = v_0\sin\varphi.$$

Illustration 3. Solve for $\dot{x}$, $\dot{y}$, x, and y in illustration 2 if $R = .1mv$, $v_0 = 5000$ ft./sec., and $\varphi = 45°$.

Solution. From illustration 2, we have

$$\begin{cases} m\ddot{x} = -.1m\dot{x}, \\ m\ddot{y} = -mg - .1m\dot{y} \end{cases}$$

which reduce to

$$\begin{cases} \ddot{x} + .1\dot{x} = 0, \\ \ddot{y} + .1\dot{y} = -g. \end{cases}$$

The solutions are

$$\begin{cases} x = c_1 + c_2 e^{-.1t}; \\ y = c_3 + c_4 e^{-.1t} - 10gt; \\ \dot{x} = -.1c_2 e^{-.1t}; \\ \dot{y} = -.1c_4 e^{-.1t} - 10g. \end{cases}$$

At $t = 0$, $v = 5000$, $\varphi = 45°$:

$$\dot{x}_0 = 5000\,\frac{\sqrt{2}}{2} = 2500\sqrt{2}; \quad \dot{y}_0 = 2500\sqrt{2};$$

so that

$$2500\sqrt{2} = -.1c_2 e^0 \text{ or } c_2 = -25000\sqrt{2}$$

and

$$2500\sqrt{2} = -.1c_4 - 10g \text{ or } c_4 = -25000\sqrt{2} - 100g.$$

At $t = 0$, $x = 0$, $y = 0$:

$$0 = c_1 - 25000\sqrt{2}, \quad \text{or} \quad c_1 = 25000\sqrt{2};$$
$$0 = c_3 - (25000\sqrt{2} + 100g), \quad \text{or} \quad c_3 = 25000\sqrt{2} + 100g.$$

$$\therefore \begin{cases} x = 25000\sqrt{2}(1 - e^{-.1t}); \\ y = (25000\sqrt{2} + 100g)(1 - e^{-.1t}) - 10gt; \\ \dot{x} = +2500\sqrt{2}e^{-.1t}; \\ \dot{y} = (2500\sqrt{2} + 10g)e^{-.1t} - 10g. \end{cases}$$

Illustration 4. A 100 gal. tank is full of pure water. Let pure water run into the tank at the rate of 2 gals./min., and a brine solution containing $\frac{1}{2}$ pound of salt per gallon run in at the rate of 2 gals./min. The mixture flows out at the rate of 4 gals./min. Assuming perfect mixing, what is the amount of salt in the tank after t minutes?

Solution. Let s be the amount of salt in the tank in pounds at time t.

$$\frac{s}{100} = \text{concentration of salt};$$

$$\frac{ds}{dt} = \text{rate of gain in lbs./min.} - \text{rate of loss in lbs./min.}$$

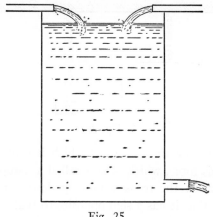

Fig. 25

Then

$$\frac{ds}{dt} = 1 - 4\,\frac{s}{100} = 1 - \frac{s}{25},$$

or

$$\frac{ds}{25 - s} = \frac{dt}{25}.$$

The solution is

$$\int_0^s \frac{-ds}{25 - s} = -\int_0^t \frac{dt}{25}$$

or

$$\ln(25 - s) - \ln 25 = -\tfrac{1}{25}t,$$

which simplifies to

$$s = 25(1 - e^{-t/25}).$$

62. Oscillatory Systems. Vibration. Let a particle of mass m be attached to a weightless spring which is hanging in a vertical position. Let the unstretched spring position of the mass be at $x = 0$, with the positive distance x being downward. Let the system be subjected to a force $f(t)$ in the x direction. There is a natural spring force given by Hooke's law which is proportional to the displacement x from the zero position. The constant of proportionality is called the spring constant, and the force tends to return the spring to the unstretched position, thus acting in the negative x direction. Let there also be a retarding force

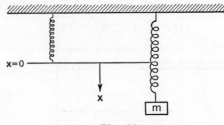

Fig. 26

(such as friction or air resistance) which is proportional to the velocity. This force, which is also called a damping force, will act upward when the mass is moving downward ($v > 0$) and vice versa, so that it has a sign opposite to that of v. The total force is given by

$$F = -kx - b\dot{x} + f(t).$$

Newton's law of motion asserts that

$$m\ddot{x} = -kx - b\dot{x} + f(t),$$

or

(1) $$m\ddot{x} + b\dot{x} + kx = f(t).$$

This is a familiar second order linear differential equation with constant coefficients. Let us divide through by m, assume $k > 0$, and let

$$2\alpha = \frac{b}{m} \quad \text{and} \quad \gamma^2 = \frac{k}{m},$$

so that the equation becomes

(2) $$\ddot{x} + 2\alpha\dot{x} + \gamma^2 x = f(t).$$

The solution of this equation depends upon the roots of the auxiliary equation

$$r_1 = -\alpha + \sqrt{\alpha^2 - \gamma^2} \quad \text{and} \quad r_2 = -\alpha - \sqrt{\alpha^2 - \gamma^2}.$$

The nature of the solution is characterized by the discriminant, $\alpha^2 - \gamma^2$.

Let us first consider the situation in which $f(t) = 0$, which is called the case of **free vibration**.

Case 1. $\alpha > \gamma$. Then $\alpha^2 - \gamma^2 = \beta^2 > 0$, and the roots r_1 and r_2 are real and unequal. The solution is

$$x = e^{-\alpha t}(c_1 e^{\beta t} + c_2 e^{-\beta t}).$$

If $\alpha > 0$ the motion is *aperiodic* and *overcritically damped;* in other words, α is larger than it need be to remove the oscillations.

Case 2. $\boldsymbol{\alpha = \gamma}$.   Then $\alpha^2 - \gamma^2 = 0$, and the roots are real and equal to $-\alpha$.   The solution is

$$x = e^{-\alpha t}(c_1 + c_2 t).$$

The motion is *aperiodic* and *critically damped.*

Case 3. $\boldsymbol{\alpha < \gamma}$.   Then $\alpha^2 - \gamma^2 = -\beta^2 < 0$, and the roots are conjugate complex.   The solution is

$$x = e^{-\alpha t}(c_1 \sin \beta t + c_2 \cos \beta t)$$
$$= Ce^{-\alpha t} \sin (\beta t + \delta).$$

The motion is *oscillatory* and is *undercritically damped.*   The trigonometric portion of the solution is periodic with

$$period \equiv \frac{2\pi}{\beta} \ and \ frequency \equiv \frac{\beta}{2\pi}.$$

Since $f(t) = 0$, the frequency is called the *natural* frequency of the system.   Fig. 27 shows the solution for critically and under-critically damped.

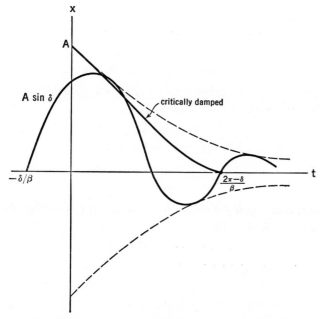

Fig. 27

During the time interval $t = \dfrac{2\pi}{\beta}$ = period, the amplitude decreases in the ratio $e^{-\alpha 2\pi/\beta}$. The natural logarithm of the amplitude decreases by $\dfrac{-\alpha 2\pi}{\beta}$, which is called the *logarithmic decrement*.

Case 4. $\boldsymbol{\alpha = 0.}$ Then we have *no damping* and the solution is
$$x = A \sin (\beta t + \delta),$$
which is a simple sine wave, and the motion is called *simple harmonic motion*.

Let us now consider the situation in which $f(t) \neq 0$, which is called the case of **forced vibration**. It now becomes necessary to find a particular integral as well as the complementary function. In practical application the form of $f(t)$ is usually
$$f(t) = A \sin (\omega t + \sigma),$$
in which A, ω, and σ are constants. Let us consider the case with $\sigma = \dfrac{\pi}{2}$, i.e.,
$$f(t) = A \cos \omega t.$$
A particular integral is
$$\begin{cases} x_p = A_1 \cos \omega t + B_1 \sin \omega t, \\ \dot{x}_p = -\omega A_1 \sin \omega t + \omega B_1 \cos \omega t, \\ \ddot{x}_p = -\omega^2 A_1 \cos \omega t - \omega^2 B_1 \sin \omega t. \end{cases}$$
Substitution into the differential equation (2) yields the required identity, and we solve for A_1 and B_1.
$$A_1 = \frac{\gamma^2 - \omega^2}{(\gamma^2 - \omega^2)^2 + 4\alpha^2\omega^2} A;$$
$$B_1 = \frac{2\alpha\omega}{(\gamma^2 - \omega^2)^2 + 4\alpha^2\omega^2} A.$$
We shall now employ a substitution which is frequently used in practical problems. Let
(3) $$r^2 = (\gamma^2 - \omega^2)^2 + 4\alpha^2\omega^2,$$
and consider the right triangle of Fig. 28 with
$$a = 2\alpha\omega;$$
$$b = \gamma^2 - \omega^2;$$
$$c = r.$$

Then

(4)
$$\begin{cases} \sin \lambda = \dfrac{a}{c} = \dfrac{2\alpha\omega}{r}, \\[2ex] \cos \lambda = \dfrac{b}{c} = \dfrac{\gamma^2 - \omega^2}{r}. \end{cases}$$

Consequently, we have

$$A_1 = \frac{\gamma^2 - \omega^2}{r^2} A = \frac{A}{r} \cos \lambda;$$

$$B_1 = \frac{2\alpha\omega}{r^2} A = \frac{A}{r} \sin \lambda.$$

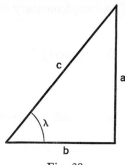

Fig. 28

The particular integral then becomes

$$x_p = \frac{A}{r} \cos \lambda \cos \omega t + \frac{A}{r} \sin \lambda \sin \omega t$$

$$= \frac{A}{r} \cos (\omega t - \lambda).$$

If we take Case 3 for the complementary function, we have the complete solution

$$x = Ce^{-\alpha t} \sin (\beta t + \delta) + \frac{A}{r} \cos (\omega t - \lambda),$$

where A, C, δ, and ω are constants, with r and λ given by equations (3) and (4). Since the vibration is damped, the first term will die out after a long period of time, and the only motion will be that of the forced vibration as indicated by the particular integral. The first term is therefore called the **transient term** and the second one is called the **steady-state term**. The steady-state condition is a vibration with

$$\text{period} \equiv \frac{2\pi}{\omega}; \qquad\qquad \text{amplitude} \equiv \frac{A}{r};$$

$$\text{frequency} \equiv \frac{\omega}{2\pi}; \qquad\qquad \text{phase angle} \equiv \lambda.$$

From a mathematical point of view we have one more case to worry about, namely, what happens if $r = 0$. This can occur if $\alpha = 0$ and $\gamma = \omega$. The differential equation would then be

$$\ddot{x} + \gamma^2 x = A \cos \gamma t.$$

The complementary function is

$$x = c_1 \cos \gamma t + c_2 \sin \gamma t.$$

Using Property 4, Section 53, we find the particular integral to be

$$x_p = \frac{A}{2\gamma} t \sin \gamma t.$$

The complete solution is

$$x = c_1 \cos \gamma t + c_2 \sin \gamma t + \frac{A}{2\gamma} t \sin \gamma t.$$

In this equation the first two terms are bounded since

$$|\sin \gamma t| \le 1 \quad \text{and} \quad |\cos \gamma t| \le 1,$$

but the last term is not bounded since it contains the variable factor t as a multiplier. Thus the vibration can build up larger and larger amplitudes as t increases. This phenomenon is called **resonance.**[*]

Illustration. An 8-pound weight which stretches a spring 6 inches is pulled down 3 inches farther and released. Find the equation of motion, its period, and its frequency.

Solution. It is first necessary to change to the appropriate units:

$$6 \text{ in.} = \tfrac{1}{2} \text{ ft.} \quad \text{and} \quad 3 \text{ in.} = \tfrac{1}{4} \text{ ft.}$$

If 8 pounds stretches the spring $\tfrac{1}{2}$ ft., then 16 pounds would stretch the spring 1 ft.; i.e., $k = 16$. The equation of motion is

$$m\ddot{x} + 16x = mg,$$

or since $W = mg = 8$,

$$\ddot{x} + 64x = 32,$$

with solution

$$x = c_1 \sin 8t + c_2 \cos 8t + \tfrac{1}{2}.$$

At $t = 0$, $x = 9$ inches $= \tfrac{3}{4}$ ft., and

$$\tfrac{3}{4} = 0 + c_2 + \tfrac{1}{2}, \quad \text{or} \quad c_2 = \tfrac{1}{4}.$$

[*] Section 62 is a discussion of the application of differential equations in analyzing vibrations and is not a complete discussion of vibration. For further information on this subject, the student should consult a book on mechanics.

Furthermore, $\dot{x} = 0$ at $t = 0$, so that

$$0 = 8c_1 \cos 8(0) - 8c_2 \sin 8(0), \quad \text{or} \quad c_1 = 0.$$

$$\therefore \quad x = \tfrac{1}{4} \cos 8t + \tfrac{1}{2},$$

with period $= \dfrac{\pi}{4}$, frequency $= \dfrac{4}{\pi}$.

63. Electric Circuits. The application of differential equations to electric circuits and networks is based on Kirchhoff's laws (see Chapter I). We shall use the following notation:

$q \equiv$ quantity of electricity; charge on a capacitor;
$i \equiv$ current; time rate of flow of electricity $= D_t q$;
$e \equiv$ voltage; electromotive force;
$R \equiv$ resistance;
$L \equiv$ inductance;
$C \equiv$ capacitance.

Let us consider the circuit of Fig. 29.

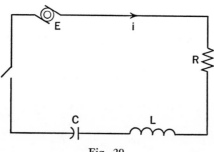

Fig. 29

The impressed electromotive force $e = E$ causes the flow of electricity and thus contributes a voltage rise; the effect of resistance is to dissipate electric energy and contributes a voltage drop of Ri; the effect of inductance is to oppose change of current and contributes a voltage drop of $LD_t i$; the capacity is associated with the storage of electricity, and its contribution is $C^{-1}q$. By Kirchhoff's law we then have

(1) $$L\frac{di}{dt} + Ri + \frac{1}{C}q - E = 0.$$

Since

$$i = \frac{dq}{dt}, \frac{di}{dt} = \frac{d^2q}{dt^2},$$

so that q must satisfy

(2)
$$L \frac{d^2q}{dt^2} + R \frac{dq}{dt} + \frac{1}{C} q = E.$$

The auxiliary equation is

$$LCm^2 + RCm + 1 = 0,$$

with roots

$$m = \frac{-RC \pm \sqrt{R^2C^2 - 4LC}}{2LC},$$

and the form of the complementary function depends upon the discriminant $R^2C^2 - 4LC$. The particular integral depends upon the form of E. If E is a constant, then $q_p = CE$ is a particular solution. The solution for q,

$$q = q_c + q_p$$

yields the current by a differentiation:

$$i = \frac{dq}{dt} = D_t q_c + D_t q_p.$$

Consider the special case of no condenser. Equation (1) becomes

(3)
$$L \frac{di}{dt} + Ri = E,$$

which is a first order linear differential equation. The integrating factor is

$$e^{\int \alpha \, dt} = e^{\alpha t}, \ \alpha = \frac{R}{L},$$

and the solution is

$$ie^{\alpha t} = \int e^{\alpha t} E \, dt + k.$$

If we let $E = E_0 \sin \omega t$, then

$$i = E_0 \frac{RL \sin \omega t - \omega L^2 \cos \omega t}{R^2 + \omega^2 L^2} + ke^{-\alpha t},$$

and we have the familiar transient term and steady-state term which we encountered in the mechanical system. In fact, the analogy between electrical and mechanical systems extends to more complicated systems, and the mathematical treatments are identical. A direct comparison of equation (1) of this section and equation (1) of Section 62 draws the analogy:

inductance — mass;

resistance — coefficient of friction;

capacitance — reciprocal of spring constant;

charge on

condenser — displacement.

64. Exercise XVI.

1. A ship weighing 64,000 tons starts from rest under the impetus of a constant propeller thrust of 200,000 pounds. If the resistance of the water is $10,000v$ pounds, find the velocity v in feet per second as a function of the time, and the terminal velocity in miles per hour. (Let $g = 32$.)

2. Find the x- and y-coordinates of the points on the trajectory of a rocket shot at an angle of 80° with an initial velocity of 100,000 ft./sec. if the air resistance is $.01mv$. What is the value of x and y in miles after 10 seconds?

3. A 5-pound weight hangs on a spring whose spring constant is 10. The weight is pulled 6 inches farther down and released. Find the equation of motion, its period, and its frequency. (Let $g = 32$.)

4. A circuit consists of an inductance L and a resistance R connected in series with a condenser having capacity C which has an impressed voltage E. Initially the current and the charge are zero. Find i and q at any time t if $R^2C < 4L$.

5. A tank contains 200 gallons of brine with 100 pounds of dissolved salt in solution. Salt water containing 1 pound of salt per gallon enters the tank at the rate of 5 gallons per minute, and brine flows out at the same rate. Find the amount of salt in the tank at the end of one hour.

6. Consider the electrical circuit of Fig. 30, p. 140.
Verify the equations

$$L\frac{di_1}{dt} = E_0 \sin \omega t, \quad Ri_3 = E_0 \sin \omega t,$$

$$\frac{dq}{dt} = i_4, \quad \frac{q}{C} = E_0 \sin \omega t,$$

$$i = i_1 + i_2 = i_1 + i_3 + i_4.$$

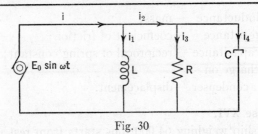

Fig. 30

Solve the equations for q, i, i_1, i_3, i_4 in terms of t for $i_1 = 0$ at $t = 0$.

7. Let the initial acceleration of an automobile starting from rest be 10 ft./sec.[2] Assume that the acceleration then decreases linearly with the distance traveled until it is zero after the automobile has traveled 160 ft. If the automobile has traveled 80 ft. after 2π seconds, what is the distance it has traveled after 4π seconds?

8. The "linearized" equation of a simple pendulum for small oscillations is given by

$$\frac{d^2\theta}{dt^2} + \frac{g}{l}\theta = 0.$$

Find the period and frequency.

9. The fundamental equation of simple beam theory is given by

$$\frac{d^2}{dx^2}\left[EI\frac{d^2y}{dx^2}\right] = q(x),$$

where q is the load per unit length and EI is the flexural rigidity. Solve this equation if EI is constant, $q(x) = 24x$, and $y = 0$, $y'' = 0$ at both $x = 0$ and $x = L$.

10. A gas is absorbed by a liquid through a process of diffusion at a rate which is proportional to the gradient of the gas concentration c. Let us assume that the gas diffuses into the liquid in the direction x. We can then evaluate the concentration c as a function of x by the equation

$$\frac{d^2c}{dx^2} - \frac{k}{r}c = 0,$$

where r is a constant of proportionality. Solve this equation if $c = c_0$ at $x = 0$, and $c = 0$ at $x = L$.

IX

SYSTEMS OF EQUATIONS

65. Introduction. The student has already encountered systems of algebraic equations in his study of algebra. Systems of simultaneous differential equations also occur in many applied problems. Such systems are composed of unknown functions of the same independent variable and their derivatives; $x(t)$, $y(t)$, $z(t)$, $\cdots$, $\dot{x}(t)$, $\dot{y}(t)$, $\dot{z}(t)$, $\cdots$, $\ddot{x}(t)$, etc., in which t is the independent variable and $x, y, z, \cdots$ are dependent variables. By the *solution* of such a system we mean a set of functions which when substituted into the system will yield a set of identities in the independent variable. We shall limit our discussion to systems of linear differential equations.

66. Solution by Elimination. If we write the system of linear differential equations in the notation of operators, the method of solution can be very similar to the method of elimination for systems of linear algebraic equations. Let us write

(1)
$$\begin{cases} P_1(D)x + Q_1(D)y + R_1(D)z = f_1(t), \\ P_2(D)x + Q_2(D)y + R_2(D)z = f_2(t), \\ P_3(D)x + Q_3(D)y + R_3(D)z = f_3(t) \end{cases}$$

as a system of three equations in the three unknowns x, y, z which are functions of the independent variable t. By a strictly formal procedure, we can eliminate z from the first two equations by "multiplying" the first by $R_2(D)$, the second by $R_1(D)$, and subtracting. We can then eliminate z from the second and third equations by a similar procedure and obtain two equations in x and y. A continuation of the process will result in one equation in one unknown which we can solve by our known techniques. We must, however, exercise caution in the application of the procedure. The "multiplication" by operator polynomials actually involves differentiations of the equations. This will

141

introduce extraneous constants in the general solutions. Consequently, it is necessary to substitute the solutions of the derived equations in *all* the equations of the original system.

Illustration 1. Find a general solution of the system

(1) $$(D - 1)x + y = t^2,$$
(2) $$(D + 1)x - Dy = t.$$

Solution. Multiply the first equation by D:

$$\begin{cases} D(D - 1)x + Dy = D(t^2) = 2t, \\ (D + 1)x - Dy = t. \end{cases}$$

Add: $$(D^2 + 1)x = 3t.$$

Solve: $$x = c_1 \sin t + c_2 \cos t + 3t.$$

Then from equation (1)

$$y = t^2 - (D - 1)x$$
$$= t^2 - (c_1 \cos t - c_2 \sin t + 3) + c_1 \sin t + c_2 \cos t + 3t$$
$$= t^2 + 3t - 3 + (c_1 + c_2) \sin t + (c_2 - c_1) \cos t.$$

Substitute into (2) (we need not substitute into (1) since it was used to find y):

$$c_1 \cos t - c_2 \sin t + 3 + c_1 \sin t + c_2 \cos t$$
$$+ 3t - 2t - 3 - (c_1 + c_2) \cos t + (c_2 - c_1) \sin t = t$$

or

$$(c_1 + c_2 - c_1 - c_2) \cos t + (c_2 - c_1 - c_2 + c_1) \sin t + t = t.$$

$$\therefore \qquad t = t.$$

The solution of systems of equations by the method of elimination requires that the student choose the dependent variable to be eliminated. Unfortunately, there is no rule for this choice and frequently the work will be made easier by a judicious choice.

Illustration 2. Solve the system

(1) $$(D + 3)x + Dy = \cos t,$$
(2) $$(D - 1)x + y = \sin t.$$

Solution. Eliminate y to obtain

$$(D^2 - 2D - 3)x = 0$$

with solution

$$x = c_1 e^{3t} + c_2 e^{-t}.$$

Solve for y from equation (2):

$$y = -3c_1e^{3t} + c_2e^{-t} + c_1e^{3t} + c_2e^{-t} + \sin t$$
$$= -2c_1e^{3t} + 2c_2e^{-t} + \sin t.$$

Check in equation (1):

$$3c_1e^{3t} - c_2e^{-t} + 3c_1e^{3t} + 3c_2e^{-t} - 6c_1e^{3t} - 2c_2e^{-t} + \cos t = \cos t$$

and

$$\cos t = \cos t.$$

It is left as an exercise for the student to discover that there would have been considerably more work involved if we had eliminated x first.

67. Solution by Determinants. Let us consider the system

(1)
$$\begin{cases} P_1(D)x + Q_1(D)y + R_1(D)z = f_1(t), \\ P_2(D)x + Q_2(D)y + R_2(D)z = f_2(t), \\ P_3(D)x + Q_3(D)y + R_3(D)z = f_3(t). \end{cases}$$

If we view these as three simultaneous algebraic equations in the three unknowns, x, y, and z, we may solve the equations by Cramer's rule to obtain

(2)
$$x = \frac{\begin{vmatrix} f_1 & Q_1 & R_1 \\ f_2 & Q_2 & R_2 \\ f_3 & Q_3 & R_3 \end{vmatrix}}{\Delta(D)}, \quad y = \frac{\begin{vmatrix} P_1 & f_1 & R_1 \\ P_2 & f_2 & R_2 \\ P_3 & f_3 & R_3 \end{vmatrix}}{\Delta(D)}, \quad z = \frac{\begin{vmatrix} P_1 & Q_1 & f_1 \\ P_2 & Q_2 & f_2 \\ P_3 & Q_3 & f_3 \end{vmatrix}}{\Delta(D)}$$

where

(3)
$$\Delta(D) = \begin{vmatrix} P_1(D) & Q_1(D) & R_1(D) \\ P_2(D) & Q_2(D) & R_2(D) \\ P_3(D) & Q_3(D) & R_3(D) \end{vmatrix},$$

if $\Delta(D) \neq 0$.

If system (1) represents three simultaneous linear differential equations with constant coefficients, we may use the same procedure providing we make the proper interpretation of formulas (2) and (3). Consider first one of the numerators,

$$
(4) \quad
\begin{vmatrix}
f_1 & Q_1 & R_1 \\
f_2 & Q_2 & R_2 \\
f_3 & Q_3 & R_3
\end{vmatrix}
= f_1
\begin{vmatrix}
Q_2 & R_2 \\
Q_3 & R_3
\end{vmatrix}
- f_2
\begin{vmatrix}
Q_1 & R_1 \\
Q_3 & R_3
\end{vmatrix}
+ f_3
\begin{vmatrix}
Q_1 & R_1 \\
Q_2 & R_2
\end{vmatrix},
$$

and let us define the cofactors

$$
(5) \quad P_1^A(D) =
\begin{vmatrix}
Q_2(D) & R_2(D) \\
Q_3(D) & R_3(D)
\end{vmatrix}
= Q_2(D)R_3(D) - R_2(D)Q_3(D),
$$

$$
(6) \quad P_2^A(D) = -
\begin{vmatrix}
Q_1(D) & R_1(D) \\
Q_3(D) & R_3(D)
\end{vmatrix}
= Q_3(D)R_1(D) - Q_1(D)R_3(D),
$$

$$
(7) \quad P_3^A(D) =
\begin{vmatrix}
Q_1(D) & R_1(D) \\
Q_2(D) & R_2(D)
\end{vmatrix}
= Q_1(D)R_2(D) - R_1(D)Q_2(D).
$$

Then the determinant (4) may be written

$$P_1^A(D)f_1(t) + P_2^A(D)f_2(t) + P_3^A(D)f_3(t).$$

If we define $Q_i^A(D)$ and $R_i^A(D)$, $(i = 1, 2, 3)$, as the cofactors of the elements $Q_i(D)$ and $R_i(D)$ in $\Delta(D)$, then we may write equations (2) in the form

$$
(8) \qquad \Delta(D)x = P_1^A(D)f_1(t) + P_2^A(D)f_2(t) + P_3^A(D)f_3(t),
$$
$$
(9) \qquad \Delta(D)y = Q_1^A(D)f_1(t) + Q_2^A(D)f_2(t) + Q_3^A(D)f_3(t),
$$
$$
(10) \qquad \Delta(D)z = R_1^A(D)f_1(t) + R_2^A(D)f_2(t) + R_3^A(D)f_3(t),
$$

each of which is a linear differential equation in but one unknown. The auxiliary equation,

$$\Delta(m) = 0,$$

is the same for each of the three equations. Unfortunately, not every solution of equations (8), (9), and (10) is necessarily a solution of the system (1) and it is necessary to substitute the solutions into the original system and determine the relationships of the constants.

Illustration. Solve the system

$$
\begin{aligned}
(D+1)x - (D^2 - 1)y + (D+1)z &= e^{2t}, \\
(D-1)x - (D+1)^2 y - (D+1)z &= 0, \\
x + (D-1)y + \qquad\quad z &= 0.
\end{aligned}
$$

Solution. The characteristic determinant is

$$\Delta(D) = \begin{vmatrix} D+1 & -D^2+1 & D+1 \\ D-1 & -(D+1)^2 & -D-1 \\ 1 & D-1 & 1 \end{vmatrix} = 4D(D+1)(D-1).$$

Since $f_2 = f_3 = 0$ it is necessary to find only

$$P_1^A(D) = -2(D+1), \quad Q_1^A(D) = -2D, \quad R_1^A(D) = 2(D^2+1).$$

Equations (8), (9), and (10) for this example are

$$\Delta(D)x = -2(D+1)e^{2t} = -6e^{2t},$$
$$\Delta(D)y = -2De^{2t} = -4e^{2t},$$
$$\Delta(D)z = 2(D^2+1)e^{2t} = 10e^{2t}.$$

The auxiliary equation

$$\Delta(m) = 4m(m+1)(m-1) = 0$$

has the roots

$$m = 0, \; m = -1, \; m = 1$$

so that the complementary functions are

$$x_c = c_0 + c_1 e^t + c_2 e^{-t},$$
$$y_c = b_0 + b_1 e^t + b_2 e^{-t},$$
$$z_c = a_0 + a_1 e^t + a_2 e^{-t}.$$

The particular integrals are

$$x_p = -\tfrac{1}{4}e^{2t},$$
$$y_p = -\tfrac{1}{6}e^{2t},$$
$$z_p = \tfrac{5}{12}e^{2t},$$

so that we have

$$\begin{cases} x = c_0 + c_1 e^t + c_2 e^{-t} - \tfrac{1}{4}e^{2t}, \\ y = b_0 + b_1 e^t + b_2 e^{-t} - \tfrac{1}{6}e^{2t}, \\ z = a_0 + a_1 e^t + a_2 e^{-t} + \tfrac{5}{12}e^{2t}. \end{cases}$$

These values are substituted into the original system of equations to obtain

$$\begin{cases} a_0 + b_0 + c_0 + 2(a_1+c_1)e^t + 0e^{-t} + e^{2t} \equiv e^{2t}, \\ a_0 + b_0 + c_0 + 2(a_1+2b_1)e^t + 2c_2 e^{-t} + 0e^{2t} \equiv 0, \\ a_0 - b_0 + c_0 + (a_1+c_1)e^t + (a_2+c_2-2b_2)e^{-t} \equiv 0. \end{cases}$$

Since each of these must form an identity in t, we have

e^0	e^t	e^{-t}
$a_0 + b_0 + c_0 = 0$	$a_1 + c_1 = 0$	$0 = 0$
$a_0 + b_0 + c_0 = 0$	$a_1 + 2b_1 = 0$	$c_2 = 0$
$a_0 - b_0 + c_0 = 0$	$a_1 + c_1 = 0$	$a_2 + c_2 - 2b_2 = 0$

In order for the first three to be true, we must have

$$b_0 = 0 \quad \text{and} \quad a_0 = -c_0.$$

In order for the second three to be true, we must have

$$a_1 = -c_1 \quad \text{and} \quad b_1 = -\tfrac{1}{2}a_1 = \tfrac{1}{2}c_1.$$

In order for the last three to be true, we must have

$$c_2 = 0 \quad \text{and} \quad a_2 = 2b_2.$$

The arbitrary choices therefore are

$$c_0, c_1, \text{ and } b_2,$$

and the solutions are

$$x = c_0 + c_1 e^t - \tfrac{1}{4} e^{2t},$$
$$y = \tfrac{1}{2} c_1 e^t + b_2 e^{-t} - \tfrac{1}{6} e^{2t},$$
$$z = -c_0 - c_1 e^t + 2b_2 e^{-t} + \tfrac{5}{12} e^{2t}.$$

68. Initial Value Problems. We shall now discuss two special initial value problems. Consider the system

$$(1) \quad \begin{cases} P_1(D)x + Q_1(D)y + R_1(D)z = f_1(t), \\ P_2(D)x + Q_2(D)y + R_2(D)z = f_2(t), \\ P_3(D)x + Q_3(D)y + R_3(D)z = f_3(t), \end{cases}$$

and, by applying Cramer's rule, let us write the solutions in the form

$$(2) \quad \begin{cases} x(t) = \dfrac{P_1^A(D)}{\Delta(D)} f_1(t) + \dfrac{P_2^A(D)}{\Delta(D)} f_2(t) + \dfrac{P_3^A(D)}{\Delta(D)} f_3(t), \\[2ex] y(t) = \dfrac{Q_1^A(D)}{\Delta(D)} f_1(t) + \dfrac{Q_2^A(D)}{\Delta(D)} f_2(t) + \dfrac{Q_3^A(D)}{\Delta(D)} f_3(t), \\[2ex] z(t) = \dfrac{R_1^A(D)}{\Delta(D)} f_1(t) + \dfrac{R_2^A(D)}{\Delta(D)} f_2(t) + \dfrac{R_3^A(D)}{\Delta(D)} f_3(t). \end{cases}$$

For this system there exist two initial value theorems which we shall state without proof.*

Theorem 1. *If the operator polynomials,* $P_i(D)$, $Q_i(D)$, *and* $R_i(D)$, *are all of degree* ≤ 1 *and if the determinant,* $\Delta(D)$, *formed from them is of degree* 3, *then the system* (1) *has one and only one solution satisfying the initial conditions*

$$x(t) = y(t) = z(t) = 0$$

at t = t_0 *and the solution is given by* (2).

Theorem 2. *If the operator polynomials in* (1) *are of degree* ≤ 2 *and if* $\Delta(D)$ *is of degree* 6, *then the system* (1) *has one and only one solution satisfying the initial conditions*

$$x(t) = Dx = y(t) = Dy = z(t) = Dz = 0$$

at t = t_0 *and the solution is given by* (2).

Let us illustrate the application of these two theorems.

Illustration 1. Find the solution of

$$\begin{cases} Dx \quad + (D-1)y = 0, \\ (D+2)y + (D+2)z = 2, \\ x \quad\ \ + (D-1)z = 0, \end{cases}$$

for which $x = y = z = 0$ at $t = 0$.

Solution. The characteristic determinant is

$$\Delta(D) = \begin{vmatrix} D & D-1 & 0 \\ 0 & D+2 & D+2 \\ 1 & 0 & D-1 \end{vmatrix} = (D-1)(D+1)(D+2)$$

and is of degree 3, thus satisfying the hypothesis of Theorem 1. Since $f_1(t) = f_3(t) = 0$ we need to find only

$$P_2^\Delta = -(D-1)^2, \ Q_2^\Delta = D(D-1), \ R_2^\Delta = D-1,$$

and the quotients

$$\frac{P_2^\Delta}{\Delta} = -\frac{D-1}{(D+1)(D+2)} = \frac{2}{D+1} - \frac{3}{D+2},$$

$$\frac{Q_2^\Delta}{\Delta} = \frac{D}{(D+1)(D+2)} = -\frac{1}{D+1} + \frac{2}{D+2},$$

---

* See M. Golomb and M. Shanks, *Elements of Ordinary Differential Equations* (New York: McGraw-Hill, 1950), p. 208.

$$\frac{R_2^\Delta}{\Delta} = \frac{1}{(D+1)(D+2)} = \frac{1}{D+1} - \frac{1}{D+2}.$$

By Theorem 1 the solutions are

$$\begin{cases} x = \dfrac{2}{D+1}\,(2) - \dfrac{3}{D+2}\,(2), \\[2mm] y = -\dfrac{1}{D+1}\,(2) + \dfrac{2}{D+2}\,(2), \\[2mm] z = \dfrac{1}{D+1}\,(2) - \dfrac{1}{D+2}\,(2). \end{cases}$$

We evaluate the right-hand side by Property 7a, Section 53, with $K = 2$.

$$\begin{cases} x = 2(-2e^{-t} + 2) - 3(-e^{-2t} + 1) = -4e^{-t} + 3e^{-2t} + 1, \\ y = -(-2e^{-t} + 2) + 2(-e^{-2t} + 1) = 2e^{-t} - 2e^{-2t}, \\ z = (-2e^{-t} + 2) - (-e^{-2t} + 1) = -2e^{-t} + e^{-2t} + 1. \end{cases}$$

The above method eliminates the work of solving for the arbitrary constants in the general solution but is limited in practicality by the ability to factor $\Delta(D)$ into simple factors. If these factors become cumbersome, the above method is not recommended. Let us now consider an example of Theorem 2.

Illustration. Find the solution of

$$\begin{cases} D^2x = 1, \\ (D+1)x + (D^2-9)y + (D+1)z = 0, \\ 5x + (D^2-4)z = 2, \end{cases}$$

for which $x = y = z = Dx = Dy = Dz = 0$ at $t = 0$.

Solution. The characteristic determinant is

$$\Delta(D) = \begin{vmatrix} D^2 & 0 & 0 \\ D+1 & D^2-9 & D+1 \\ 5 & 0 & D^2-4 \end{vmatrix} = D^2(D^2-9)(D^2-4)$$

which is of degree 6, and Theorem 2 applies. We need the following quotients:

$$X_1 = \frac{P_1^\Delta}{\Delta} = \frac{(D^2-9)(D^2-4)}{\Delta} = \frac{1}{D^2},$$

$$X_3 = \frac{P_3^\Delta}{\Delta} = 0,$$

$$Y_1 = \frac{Q_1^\Delta}{\Delta} = -\frac{(D+1)(D^2-9)}{\Delta} = \frac{\frac14}{D} + \frac{\frac14}{D^2} - \frac{\frac{3}{16}}{D-2} - \frac{\frac{1}{16}}{D+2},$$

$$Y_3 = \frac{Q_3^\Delta}{\Delta} = -\frac{(D+1)(D^2)}{\Delta} = \frac{\frac{3}{20}}{D-2} + \frac{\frac{1}{20}}{D+2} - \frac{\frac{2}{15}}{D-3} - \frac{\frac{1}{15}}{D+3},$$

$$Z_1 = \frac{R_1^\Delta}{\Delta} = -\frac{5(D^2-9)}{\Delta} = \frac{\frac54}{D^2} - \frac{\frac{5}{16}}{D-2} + \frac{\frac{5}{16}}{D+2},$$

$$Z_3 = \frac{R_3^\Delta}{\Delta} = \frac{D^2(D^2-9)}{\Delta} = \frac{\frac14}{D-2} - \frac{\frac14}{D+2}.$$

Since $f_1(t) = 1$ and $f_3(t) = 2$, we use Property 7, Section 53. The necessary integrals with $t_0 = 0$ are

$$\begin{aligned}
D^{-1}K &= Kt, & (D+2)^{-1}K &= -\tfrac12 K(e^{-2t}-1),\\
D^{-2}K &= \tfrac12 Kt^2, & (D-3)^{-1}K &= \tfrac13 K(e^{3t}-1),\\
(D-2)^{-1}K &= \tfrac12 K(e^{2t}-1), & (D+3)^{-1}K &= -\tfrac13 K(e^{-3t}-1).
\end{aligned}$$

The solutions are now obtained by substituting into equations (2):

$$\begin{aligned}
x(t) &= X_1(1) = \tfrac12 t^2,\\
y(t) &= Y_1(1) + Y_3(2)\\
&= \tfrac14\left[t + \tfrac12 t^2 - \tfrac34(\tfrac12)(e^{2t}-1) - \tfrac14(-\tfrac12)(e^{-2t}-1)\right]\\
&\quad + \tfrac14\left[\tfrac35(e^{2t}-1) + \tfrac15(-1)(e^{-2t}-1)\right]\\
&\quad - \tfrac{1}{15}\left[2(\tfrac23)(e^{3t}-1)\right.\\
&\quad\left. + (-\tfrac23)(e^{-3t}-1)\right]\\
&= \tfrac14 t + \tfrac18 t^2 + \tfrac{9}{160}e^{2t} - \tfrac{3}{160}e^{-2t} - \tfrac{4}{45}e^{3t} + \tfrac{2}{45}e^{-3t} + \tfrac{1}{144},\\
z(t) &= Z_1(1) + Z_3(2)\\
&= \tfrac54(\tfrac12 t^2) - \tfrac{5}{16}(\tfrac12)(e^{2t}-1) + \tfrac{5}{16}(-\tfrac12)(e^{-2t}-1)\\
&\quad + \tfrac14(e^{2t}-1) - \tfrac14(-1)(e^{-2t}-1)\\
&= \tfrac{3}{32}e^{2t} + \tfrac{3}{32}e^{-2t} + \tfrac58 t^2 - \tfrac{3}{16}.
\end{aligned}$$

69. Symmetric Form. If there is given the general problem of n differential equations in $n+1$ unknowns (i.e., the "independent" variable is also considered unknown), the solution is the most general set of n independent relations among the variables which satisfies the given differential equations. Let us consider the simple case of two first order equations in three unknowns.

$$(1) \qquad \begin{cases} P_1\,dx + Q_1\,dy + R_1\,dz = 0,\\ P_2\,dx + Q_2\,dy + R_2\,dz = 0, \end{cases}$$

where P_i, Q_i, and R_i are functions of x, y, and z.

Let us divide through by dz to obtain

(2)
$$
\begin{cases}
P_1 \dfrac{dx}{dz} + Q_1 \dfrac{dy}{dz} + R_1 = 0, \\[2mm]
P_2 \dfrac{dx}{dz} + Q_2 \dfrac{dy}{dz} + R_2 = 0,
\end{cases}
$$

and solve for each derivative; thus, provided $R \neq 0$,

(3)
$$
\begin{cases}
\dfrac{dx}{dz} = \dfrac{\begin{vmatrix} Q_1 & R_1 \\ Q_2 & R_2 \end{vmatrix}}{\begin{vmatrix} P_1 & Q_1 \\ P_2 & Q_2 \end{vmatrix}} = \dfrac{P}{R}, \\[6mm]
\dfrac{dy}{dz} = \dfrac{\begin{vmatrix} R_1 & P_1 \\ R_2 & P_2 \end{vmatrix}}{\begin{vmatrix} P_1 & Q_1 \\ P_2 & Q_2 \end{vmatrix}} = \dfrac{Q}{R},
\end{cases}
$$

where

$$
P = \begin{vmatrix} Q_1 & R_1 \\ Q_2 & R_2 \end{vmatrix}, \quad Q = \begin{vmatrix} R_1 & P_1 \\ R_2 & P_2 \end{vmatrix}, \quad R = \begin{vmatrix} P_1 & Q_1 \\ P_2 & Q_2 \end{vmatrix}.
$$

If equations (3) are viewed as ratios of algebraic expressions, we can rearrange the quantities into

$$
\frac{dx}{P} = \frac{dz}{R} \quad \text{and} \quad \frac{dy}{Q} = \frac{dz}{R}
$$

and finally

(4)
$$
\boldsymbol{\frac{dx}{P} = \frac{dy}{Q} = \frac{dz}{R},}
$$

which is usually called the **symmetric form** of the system of differential equations given by (1). The symmetric form may permit a solution by simple integration, or it may be possible to change the symmetric form to an expression which is a total differential and thus is integrable. The latter is accomplished by finding functions of x, y, and z which can be used as multipliers. We recall from the properties of ratios that

$$
\frac{dx}{P} = \frac{dy}{Q} = \frac{dz}{R} = \frac{l\,dx + m\,dy + n\,dz}{lP + mQ + nR}.
$$

If a proper choice of l, m, n makes

$$lP + mQ + nR = 0,$$

it is desired that

$$l\,dx + m\,dy + n\,dz = 0$$

for the same values. If, furthermore, the left side is a total differential

$$du = l\,dx + m\,dy + n\,dz = 0$$

we have a solution by a simple integration.

Illustration. Solve

$$\frac{dx}{y} = \frac{dy}{x} = \frac{dz}{x}.$$

Solution. Consider first

$$\frac{dx}{y} = \frac{dy}{x} \quad \text{or} \quad x\,dx = y\,dy.$$

Integrate to obtain

$$x^2 - y^2 = c_1.$$

The last two ratios yield

$$\frac{dy}{x} = \frac{dz}{x} \quad \text{or} \quad dy = dz.$$

Integrate to obtain

$$y = z + c_2.$$

The two equations

$$x^2 - y^2 = c_1 \quad \text{and} \quad y = z + c_2$$

form the general solution of the given system of equations.

Frequently it is possible to use the first part of the solution to obtain the second equation.

Illustration. Solve

$$\frac{2dx}{y+z} = \frac{dy}{yx} = \frac{dz}{xz}.$$

Solution. The last two ratios yield

$$\frac{dy}{y} = \frac{dz}{z} \quad \text{or} \quad y = c_1 z.$$

Substituting this value into the first ratio we have

$$\frac{2dx}{c_1 z + z} = \frac{dz}{xz}$$

or

$$2x \, dx = (1 + c_1)dz.$$

The solution is

$$x^2 = z + c_1 z + c_2$$
$$= z + \quad y + c_2.$$

The choice of l, m, and n becomes a matter of technique and improves with practice.

Illustration. Solve

$$\frac{dx}{ay - bz} = \frac{dy}{cz - ax} = \frac{dz}{bx - cy}.$$

Solution. First we desire that

(1) $$l(ay - bz) + m(cz - ax) + n(bx - cy) = 0.$$

This equation will hold if $l = c$, $m = b$, $n = a$, for then

$$acy - bcz + bcz - abx + abx - acy = 0.$$

At the same time we must have

$$l \, dx + m \, dy + n \, dz = 0$$

or

$$c \, dx + b \, dy + a \, dz = 0,$$

which we can integrate to obtain

$$cx + by + az = k_1.$$

Now equation (1) will also be satisfied if $l = x$, $m = y$, and $n = z$, so that we have

$$x \, dx + y \, dy + z \, dz = 0$$

or

$$x^2 + y^2 + z^2 = k_2.$$

70. Reduction of a Higher Order Equation to a System of First Order Equations. Consider the differential equation

(1) $$(D^n + a_1 D^{n-1} + \cdots + a_{n-1}D + a_n)y = f(x).$$

We can solve this equation for the highest ordered derivative,

(2) $$D^n y = f(x) - (a_1 D^{n-1} + \cdots + a_n)y.$$

Now introduce the new variables

(3) $$y_i = \frac{d^i y}{dx^i}, \ (i = 1, \cdots, n-1).$$

In other words, write the system of differential equations

$$\frac{dy}{dx} = y_1,$$

$$D_x^2 y = \frac{dy_1}{dx} = y_2,$$

$$D_x^3 y = \frac{dy_2}{dx} = y_3,$$

$$\cdots \cdots \cdots$$

$$D_x^n y = \frac{dy_{n-1}}{dx} = f(x) - (a_1 y_{n-1} + \cdots + a_{n-1} y_1 + a_n y).$$

This is a system of first order differential equations, and the solution of this system yields the solution of the original nth order differential equation.

Illustration. Solve

$$(D^2 - 1)y = 0.$$

Solution. Form the system

$$\frac{dy}{dx} = y_1,$$

$$D^2 y = \frac{dy_1}{dx} = y,$$

which we can write in the symmetric form

$$\frac{dx}{1} = \frac{dy}{y_1} = \frac{dy_1}{y}.$$

The last two ratios yield

$$y \, dy = y_1 \, dy_1 \quad \text{or} \quad y^2 = y_1^2 + c_1^2.$$

Then

$$dx = \frac{dy}{\sqrt{y^2 - c_1^2}}$$

or

$$x = \ln\left(y + \sqrt{y^2 - c_1^2}\right) - \ln c_2.$$

A simplification yields

$$c_2 e^x = y + \sqrt{y^2 - c_1^2}.$$

If we removed the radical and solved for y, we would obtain

$$y = k_1 e^x + k_2 e^{-x},$$

a result which is more easily obtained by our previous techniques.

Although this technique is seldom used for equations in which our previously studied methods readily apply, it plays an important role in numerical methods for the solution of differential equations. These methods will be studied in Chapter XI.

71. Exercise XVII. Solve the following system of differential equations:

A. By elimination:

    1. $(D + 1)x + (D + 1)y = 0,$
        $Dx - (D - 1)y = t.$

    2. $Dy - 3z = 5,$
       $y - Dz - x = 3 - 2t,$
       $z + Dx = -1.$

    3. $(D^2 - 1)x + y = e^t,$
       $(D + 1)x - (D + 1)y = 3e^t.$

B. By determinants:

    4. Problem 1.

    5. $(D - 2)x + (D - 2)y = 1,$
       $Dy + (D + 1)z = 2,$
       $3x + (D + 1)z = 3,$ with initial conditions $x = y = z = 0$ at $t = 0.$

C. By any method:

    6. $\dfrac{dx}{y} = \dfrac{dy}{x} = \dfrac{dz}{z}.$

    7. $\dfrac{dx}{y^2 - z^2} = \dfrac{dy}{-xy - 3x^2 z} = \dfrac{dz}{3x^2 y + xz}.$

    8. $\dfrac{dx}{2xy} = \dfrac{dy}{x^2 + y^2 + z^2} = \dfrac{dz}{2yz}.$

9. $\dot{x} + 3x - y = \dot{y} + y - 3x = 0.$

10. $(D - 1)x - 2y = (D - 2)y - 3x = 0.$

11. $\dfrac{dx}{4t - 2y} = \dfrac{dy}{4 - 2x} = dt.$

12. $(D + 1)y - (D^2 - 1)x = e^t,$
$\quad Dy - (D - 1)x = e^{-t}.$

X

SOLUTION IN POWER SERIES

72. Introduction. The best technique for finding the solution of a general linear differential equation with variable coefficients is based upon the use of power series. In order to develop the technique we need a little knowledge of functions and power series. From the calculus we recall that a function may be represented by a Taylor Series,

$$f(x) = f(x_0) + f'(x_0)(x - x_0) + \frac{f''(x_0)}{2!}(x - x_0)^2 + \cdots,$$

provided all the derivatives exist at $x = x_0$. We shall further say that a function is **analytic** at $x = x_0$ if $f(x)$ can be expanded in a power series valid about some point.

Consider the linear differential equation

(1) $[a_0(x)D^n + a_1(x)D^{n-1} + \cdots + a_n(x)]y = f(x)$

in which $a_i(x)$, $(i = 0, \cdots, n)$, are polynomials.

Definition.* *The point* $x = x_0$ *is called an* **ordinary point** *of the equation if* $a_0(x_0) \neq 0$. *Any point* $x = x_1$ *for which* $a_0(x_1) = 0$ *is called a* **singular point** *of the differential equation. The point* $x = x_1$ *is called a* **regular singular** *point if equation* (1) *with* $f(x) = 0$ *can be written in the form*

(2) $[(x - x_1)^n D^n + (x - x_1)^{n-1} b_1(x) D^{n-1}$
$\qquad + (x - x_1)^{n-2} b_2(x) D^{n-2}$
$\qquad + \cdots + (x - x_1)b_{n-1}(x)D + b_n(x)]y = 0$

where $b_i(x)$, $(i = 1, \cdots, n)$, *are analytic at* $x = x_1$.

Illustrations. List the singular points for:
1. $(x - 3)y'' + (x + 1)y = 0$. *Solution.* $x = 3$.
2. $(x^2 + 1)y''' + y'' - x^2 y = 0$. *Solution.* $x = \pm i$.

---

* In our discussion we shall not consider the "point at infinity," or in other words we shall omit the phrase "in the finite plane" from our statements.

3. $8y''' - 3x^3y'' + 4 = 0$. *Solution.* None.

4. $(x-1)^2y'' - x(x-1)y' + xy = 0$. *Solution.* $x = 1$ (regular).

The use of power series to express a function which is a solution of a given differential equation is based upon the fact (which we shall accept) that there exists a series which contains the necessary arbitrary constants and *which converges inside a circle with center at* $x = x_0$ *and extends out to the singular point nearest to* $x = x_0$. We shall concern ourselves with the techniques for finding the coefficients of the series expansion.

The expression, "find a solution about the point $x = x_0$," is used in discussing power series solutions of differential equations. It means to obtain a series in powers of $(x - x_0)$ which is valid in a region (neighborhood) about the point x_0 and which is an expansion of a function $y(x)$ which will satisfy the given differential equation.

73. Method of Successive Differentiation. If the given differential equation can be solved for the highest derivative, $y(n)$, and the initial conditions state the values of $y, y', y'', \cdots, y^{(n-1)}$ at an ordinary point, then the series expansion of the integral of the differential equation can be continued by successive differentiation.

Illustration. Find the series solution for

$$xy'' + x^3y' - 3y = 0$$

that satisfies $y = 0$ and $y' = 2$ at $x = 1$.

Solution. Solve for y'' and differentiate to obtain

$$y'' = -x^2y' + 3x^{-1}y,$$
$$y''' = -x^2y'' - (2x - 3x^{-1})y' - 3x^{-2}y,$$
$$y^{iv} = -x^2y''' - (4x - 3x^{-1})y'' - (2 + 6x^{-2})y' + 6x^{-3}y.$$

Evaluate these derivatives at $x = 1$:

$$y''(1) = -2,$$
$$y'''(1) = 4,$$
$$y^{iv}(1) = -18.$$

The solution is

$$y(x) = 0 + 2(x-1) - \tfrac{2}{2}(x-1)^2 + \tfrac{4}{6}(x-1)^3 - \tfrac{18}{24}(x-1)^4 + \cdots$$
$$= 2(x-1) - (x-1)^2 + \tfrac{2}{3}(x-1)^3 - \tfrac{3}{4}(x-1)^4 + \cdots.$$

The series solution may reveal a known function; i.e., it may be the series expansion of an elementary function. See V, Section 2, Chapter I.

Illustration. Find the solution of

$$(x - 1)y''' + y'' + (x - 1)y' + y = 0$$

if $y = y'' = 0$, $y' = 1$ at $x = 0$.

Solution. Solve for y''' and differentiate

$$y''' = -(x - 1)^{-1}y'' - y' - (x - 1)^{-1}y,$$
$$y^{iv} = -(x - 1)^{-1}y''' + [(x - 1)^{-2} - 1]y''$$
$$- (x - 1)^{-1}y' + (x - 1)^{-2}y,$$
$$y^v = -(x - 1)^{-1}y^{iv} + [2(x - 1)^{-2} - 1]y'''$$
$$- [2(x - 1)^{-3} + (x - 1)^{-1}]y'' + 2(x - 1)^{-2}y' - 2(x - 1)^{-3}y.$$

At $x = 0$ we have

$$y'''(0) = -1,$$
$$y^{iv}(0) = 0,$$
$$y^v(0) = 1.$$

The series is

$$y(x) = 0 + x + 0 - \frac{1}{3!}x^3 + 0 + \frac{1}{5!}x^5 + \cdots$$

$$= x - \frac{1}{3!}x^3 + \frac{1}{5!}x^5 - \cdots$$

$$= \sin x.$$

74. Method of Undetermined Coefficients. If x_0 is an ordinary point of the given differential equation, the solution can be expanded in the form

$$(1) \quad y(x) = c_0 + c_1(x - x_0) + c_2(x - x_0)^2 + \cdots + c_k(x - x_0)^k + \cdots$$

$$= \sum_{i=0}^{\infty} c_i(x - x_0)^i.$$

It remains to determine the coefficients c_i, $(i = 0, \cdots)$. Differentiate the series (1), term by term, to obtain

$$y'(x) = c_1 + 2c_2(x - x_0) + 3c_3(x - x_0)^2 + \cdots$$

$$= \sum_{i=0}^{\infty} ic_i(x - x_0)^{i-1};$$

$$y''(x) = 2c_2 + 3 \cdot 2c_3(x - x_0) + 4 \cdot 3c_4(x - x_0)^2 + \cdots$$

$$= \sum_{i=0}^{\infty} i(i - 1)c_i(x - x_0)^{i-2};$$

etc.

These values are now substituted into the given differential equation and regrouped into terms of $(x - x_0)^i$; i.e.,

$$\sum_{i=0}^{\infty} C_i(x - x_0)^i = 0,$$

where C_i are functions of c_i, and the equation is an identity in $(x - x_0)$ so that $C_i = 0$ for $i = 0, \cdots$. This will determine the values of c_i.

Illustration. Find a series solution of

(1) $(x^2 - 1)y'' - 2xy' - 4y = 0.$

Solution. Since we desire a series solution for an ordinary point, we choose the simplest such point, which is $x = 0$ for this example. We then write

$$y(x) = c_0 + c_1x + c_2x^2 + c_3x^3 + \cdots,$$
$$y'(x) = c_1 + 2c_2x + 3c_3x^2 + 4c_4x^3 + \cdots,$$
$$y''(x) = 2c_2 + 6c_3x + 12c_4x^2 + 20c_5x^3 + \cdots.$$

Substitute these values into equation (1) and collect like terms in x; it is recommended that this be done in tabular form as follows:

	x^0	x	x^2	x^3	x^4	x^5
x^2y''			$2c_2$	$6c_3$	$12c_4$	$\cdots$
$-y''$	$-2c_2$	$-6c_3$	$-12c_4$	$-20c_5$	$-30c_6$	$\cdots$
$-2xy'$		$-2c_1$	$-4c_2$	$-6c_3$	$-8c_4$	$\cdots$
$-4y$	$-4c_0$	$-4c_1$	$-4c_2$	$-4c_3$	$-4c_4$	$\cdots$
Sum	0	0	0	0	0	$\cdots$

Add to obtain

$$2c_2 + 4c_0 = 0; \qquad c_2 = -2c_0;$$
$$6c_3 + 6c_1 = 0; \qquad c_3 = -c_1;$$
$$12c_4 + 6c_2 = 0; \qquad c_4 = -\tfrac{1}{2}c_2 = c_0;$$
$$20c_5 + 4c_3 = 0; \qquad c_5 = -\tfrac{1}{5}c_3 = \tfrac{1}{5}c_1;$$
$$30c_6 + 0c_4 = 0; \qquad c_6 = 0.$$

The first few terms of the series can now be written in the form

$$y(x) = c_0 + c_1 x - 2c_0 x^2 - c_1 x^3 + c_0 x^4 + \tfrac{1}{5} c_1 x^5 + 0 x^6 + \cdots$$
$$= c_0(1 - 2x^2 + x^4 + \cdots) + c_1(x - x^3 + \tfrac{1}{5} x^5 + \cdots).$$

The above procedure will also determine the form of the general term. Let us consider the series expansion about the point $x_0 = 0$ and use the summation notation. The expressions are given by

$$(2) \qquad \begin{cases} y(x) = \displaystyle\sum_{i=0}^{\infty} c_i x^i, \\[2mm] y'(x) = \displaystyle\sum_{i=0}^{\infty} i c_i x^{i-1}, \\[2mm] y''(x) = \displaystyle\sum_{i=0}^{\infty} i(i-1) c_i x^{i-2}, \end{cases}$$

etc.

For convenience of notation, let us limit our discussion to a second order differential equation.

$$(3) \qquad a_0(x) y'' + a_1(x) y' + a_2(x) y = 0.$$

A substitution of equations (2) into equation (3) yields

$$(4) \quad a_0(x) \sum i(i-1) c_i x^{i-2} + a_1(x) \sum i c_i x^{i-1} + a_2(x) \sum c_i x^i = 0$$

with all summations going from $i = 0$ to $i = \infty$.*

The next step in the procedure is to multiply out the terms of equation (4) and collect like terms of x. This, of course, depends upon the form of $a_i(x)$, $(i = 0, 1, 2)$. In order to be more specific let us, therefore, assume some form of these functions,

$$(5) \qquad a_0(x) = 2x^2 + 1, \; a_1(x) = 3x, \; a_2(x) = -3.$$

Equation (4) would then take the form

$$(6) \quad (2x^2 + 1) \sum i(i-1) c_i x^{i-2} + 3x \sum i c_i x^{i-1} - 3 \sum c_i x^i = 0.$$

After performing the indicated multiplication we obtain

$$(7) \quad \sum 2i(i-1) c_i x^i + \sum i(i-1) c_i x^{i-2} + \sum 3i c_i x^i - \sum 3 c_i x^i = 0.$$

It is desired to find the coefficient of x^k by taking particular

---

* The only summations for i that we shall consider in this chapter will be from 0 to ∞, and thus we shall drop these values from our notation when i is the index of summation.

values of i. Thus let $i = k$ in the first, third, and fourth term and let $i = k + 2$ in the second term; then the coefficient of x^k becomes

$$2k(k-1)c_k + (k+2)(k+1)c_{k+2} + 3kc_k - 3c_k$$
$$= (k+2)(k+1)c_{k+2} + (2k^2 + k - 3)c_k.$$

We set this coefficient equal to zero and solve for c_{k+2} to obtain

$$(8) \qquad c_{k+2} = -\frac{(2k+3)(k-1)}{(k+2)(k+1)} c_k.$$

We have thus solved for c_j in terms of a c with a lower subscript; such a formula is called a **recursion formula.** By choosing values of $k = 0, 1, 2, \cdots$ we can find all c_j in terms of c_0 and c_1. For our particular choice of $a_i(x)$ we have

$$k = 0: \ c_2 = -\frac{(-3)}{2} c_0 = \frac{3}{2} c_0,$$

$$k = 1: \ c_3 = -\frac{(5)(0)}{(3)(2)} c_1 = 0,$$

$$k = 2: \ c_4 = -\frac{(7)(1)}{(4)(3)} c_2 = -\frac{7}{12} \left(\frac{3}{2}\right) c_0 = -\frac{7}{8} c_0.$$

Since the subscripts in the recursion formula differ by 2, we have quantities with even subscripts in terms of lower even subscripts and similarly for the odd subscripts. Now since $c_3 = 0$ all terms with the larger odd subscripts will also be zero. In this example we need only consider the remaining even subscripts.

$$k = 4: \qquad c_6 = -\frac{(11)(3)}{(6)(5)} c_4 = -\frac{11}{10}\left(-\frac{7}{8}\right) c_0 = \frac{77}{80} c_0,$$

$$k = 2n - 2:^* \ c_{2n} = (-1)^{n+1} \frac{3 \cdot 7 \cdot 11 \cdots (4n-1)}{2^n(2n-1)n!} c_0.$$

The solution to our case with an arbitrary c_0 and c_1 can now be written in the form

$$y(x) = c_1 x + c_0 \left[1 + \sum_{n=1}^{\infty} \frac{(-1)^{n+1} 3 \cdot 7 \cdot 11 \cdots (4n-1)}{2^n(2n-1)n!} x^{2n} \right].$$

---

* The development of the case $k = 2n - 2$ may require some algebraic gymnastics, and if the student did not obtain sufficient practice along these lines during his study of series in the calculus he should write the first half-dozen terms, the $k = 2n - 4$, and the $k = 2n - 2$ terms, and then obtain the product.

The solution of a differential equation about a point x_0 other than $x_0 = 0$ can be obtained by a translation of the origin to that point and then finding the power series about the new origin. Thus actually we need to consider only expansions about the point $x_0 = 0$. The translation is given by $x - x_0 = v$ and $D_x^i y = D_v^i y$, $(i = 0, 1, \cdots)$ since $D_x v = 1$.

Illustration. Find a series solution of

$$(x^2 - 2x + 2)y'' + 2(x - 1)y' = 0$$

about the point $x = 1$.

Solution. Translate the origin to $x = 1$ by

$$v = x - 1, \quad y'' = D_v^2 y, \quad \text{and} \quad y' = D_v y.$$

The differential equation becomes

$$(v^2 + 1)D_v^2 y + 2v D_v y = 0.$$

The power series solution is

$$y(v) = \sum c_i v^i$$

so that

$$(v^2 + 1)\sum i(i - 1)c_i v^{i-2} + 2v \sum i c_i v^{i-1} = 0$$

or

$$\sum i(i - 1)c_i v^i + \sum i(i - 1)c_i v^{i-2} + \sum 2i c_i v^i = 0.$$

The coefficient of v^k is

$$k(k - 1)c_k + (k + 2)(k + 1)c_{k+2} + 2k c_k.$$

Set this expression equal to zero and solve for c_{k+2} to obtain

$$c_{k+2} = -\frac{k(k + 1)}{(k + 2)(k + 1)} c_k = -\frac{k}{k + 2} c_k.$$

In terms of c_0 and c_1 we have

$k = 0$: $c_2 = 0 c_0 = 0$; $\therefore c_{2n} = 0$ for $n > 0$.

$k = 1$: $c_3 = -\frac{1}{3}c_1$.

$k = 3$: $c_5 = -\frac{3}{5}c_3 = -\frac{3}{5}(-\frac{1}{3})c_0 = \frac{1}{5}c_0$.

$k = 2n - 1$: $c_{2n+1} = \pm \dfrac{(2n - 1)(2n - 3) \cdots 1}{(2n + 1)(2n - 1) \cdots 1} c_0 = \pm \dfrac{1}{2n + 1} c_0$.

Thus

$$y(v) = c_0 + c_1 \left[v - \frac{v^3}{3} + \frac{v^5}{5} - \frac{v^7}{7} + \cdots + (-1)^n \frac{v^{2n+1}}{2n + 1} + \cdots \right]$$

$$= c_0 + c_1 \arctan v.$$

In terms of x we have, $v = x - 1$,

$$y(x) = c_0 + c_1 \text{ arc tan } (x - 1).$$

75. Solutions Near a Regular Singular Point.

The discussion of solutions about a regular singular point will be limited to $x_0 = 0$ and for a second order differential equation. The first of these restrictions is not a severe one since we can always translate the origin to the regular singular point x_0. The second restriction is merely an expression of laziness, since higher order equations do not impose theoretical hardships but only involve considerably more labor. Consider the differential equation

$$(1) \qquad b_0(x)y'' + b_1(x)y' + b_2(x)y = 0$$

with a regular singular point at $x_0 = 0$. The definition of a regular singular point at $x_0 = 0$ states that equation (1) can be written in the form

$$(2) \qquad y'' + p(x)y' + q(x)y = 0$$

in which $p(x)$ can have at the most x to the first power in the denominator and $q(x)$ can have at the most x^2 in the denominator; in other words, we may write

$$p(x) = \frac{P(x)}{x} \quad \text{and} \quad q(x) = \frac{Q(x)}{x^2}$$

where P and Q are rational functions of x which exist at $x = 0$ and thus can be expanded in a power series about $x = 0$. Consequently, we have

$$(3) \qquad \begin{cases} p(x) = \dfrac{p_0}{x} + p_1 + p_2 x + p_3 x^2 + \cdots, \\[2mm] q(x) = \dfrac{q_0}{x^2} + \dfrac{q_1}{x} + q_2 + q_3 x + \cdots, \end{cases}$$

both valid in the neighborhood of $x = 0$.

Let us assume that the solution of equation (1) can be written in the form

$$(4) \qquad y(x) = \sum_{i=0}^{\infty} c_i x^{i+r} = c_0 x^r + c_1 x^{r+1} + \cdots.$$

Our problem then reduces to finding values for c_i and r. If we substitute the values from equations (3) and (4) into equation (2), we obtain

$$r(r-1)c_0x^{r-2} + (r+1)rc_1x^{r-1} + (r+2)(r+1)c_2x^r + \cdots$$

$$+ \left[\frac{p_0}{x} + p_1 + \cdots\right]\left[rc_0x^{r-1} + (r+1)c_1x^r + \cdots\right]$$

$$+ \left[\frac{q_0}{x^2} + \frac{q_1}{x} + \cdots\right]\left[c_0x^r + c_1x^{r+1} + c_2x^{r+2} + \cdots\right] = 0.$$

After performing the indicated multiplication and collecting the like terms in x, we obtain

$$[r(r-1)c_0 + p_0rc_0 + q_0c_0]x^{r-2}$$
$$+ [(r+1)rc_1 + p_0(r+1)c_1 + p_1rc_0 + q_0c_1 + q_1c_0]x^{r-1}$$
$$+ \cdots = 0.$$

Since this is an identity in x, we have

$$[r(r-1) + p_0r + q_0]c_0 = 0,$$
$$[(r+1)r + p_0(r+1) + q_0]c_1 + [p_1r + q_1]c_0 = 0,$$
$$\text{etc.}$$

The first of these equations involves only c_0 of the c_i and we shall always take $c_0 \neq 0$; in other words, let c_0 be the coefficient of the first term which exists in the power series. Consequently, we must have

(5) $$r(r-1) + p_0r + q_0 = 0,$$

and we shall call this equation the **indicial equation**. It will be used to determine the values of r, and for a second order it will always be a quadratic in r with two solutions, r_1 and r_2. This fact creates trouble and we are forced to consider individual cases.

Case I. **Difference between r_1 and r_2 nonintegral.** If the difference between r_1 and r_2 is not an integer, we can develop the two series of the form of equation (4) in a straightforward manner.

   Illustration. Find a solution of

$$3x^2y'' + x(x-5)y' + 5y = 0$$

about the point $x = 0$.

   Solution. Assume the power series

$$y(x) = \sum c_ix^{r+i}$$

and substitute into the differential equation to obtain

$$\sum 3(i+r)(i+r-1)c_i x^{r+i} + \sum (i+r)c_i x^{r+i+1}$$
$$- \sum 5(i+r)c_i x^{r+i} + \sum 5c_i x^{r+i} = 0.$$

Let $i = 0$ and consider the term which has x to the smallest exponent, in this case x^r,

$$[3r(r-1) - 5r + 5]c_0.$$

The indicial equation is

$$3r^2 - 8r + 5 = (3r - 5)(r - 1) = 0.$$

Thus $r_1 = 1$ and $r_2 = \frac{5}{3}$.
With $r_1 = 1$, the series is

$$\sum 3(i+1)ic_i x^{i+1} + \sum (i+1)c_i x^{i+2}$$
$$- 5 \sum (i+1)c_i x^{i+1} + 5 \sum c_i x^{i+1} = 0.$$

The coefficient of x^k is

$$3k(k-1)c_{k-1} + (k-1)c_{k-2} - 5kc_{k-1} + 5c_{k-1} = 0$$

or

$$(3k - 5)(k - 1)c_{k-1} = -(k - 1)c_{k-2}$$

so that

$$c_{k-1} = - \frac{1}{3k - 5} c_{k-2}.$$

The first few terms are

$$k = 2: \quad c_1 = - \frac{1}{6 - 5} c_0 = -c_0,$$

$$k = 3: \quad c_2 = - \frac{1}{9 - 5} c_1 = \frac{1}{4} c_0,$$

$$k = 4: \quad c_3 = - \frac{1}{12 - 5} c_2 = - \frac{1}{7}\left(\frac{1}{4}\right)c_0,$$

and

$$y_1(x) = c_0 x[1 - x + \tfrac{1}{4}x^2 - \tfrac{1}{28}x^3 + \cdots]$$
$$= c_0 x + c_0 \sum_{k=2}^{\infty} \frac{(-1)^{k-1}}{1 \cdot 4 \cdot 7 \cdot 10 \cdots (3k-5)} x^k.$$

With $r_2 = \frac{5}{3}$, the series is

$$x^{\frac{5}{3}}\left[\sum 3(i+\tfrac{5}{3})(i+\tfrac{5}{3}-1)c_i x^i + \sum (i+\tfrac{5}{3})c_i x^{i+1}\right.$$
$$\left. - 5 \sum (i+\tfrac{5}{3})c_i x^i + 5 \sum c_i x^i\right] = 0.$$

Consider the coefficient of x^k in the bracket

$$3(k + \tfrac{5}{3})(k + \tfrac{5}{3} - 1)c_k + (k - 1 + \tfrac{5}{3})c_{k-1} - 5(k + \tfrac{5}{3})c_k + 5c_k = 0.$$

or

$$c_k = -\frac{1}{3k}\, c_{k-1}.$$

The first few terms are

$$k = 1: \quad c_1 = -\tfrac{1}{3}c_0,$$

$$k = 2: \quad c_2 = -\frac{1}{6}\, c_1 = \frac{1}{6} \cdot \frac{1}{3}\, c_0 = \frac{1}{2} \cdot \frac{1}{3^2}\, c_0,$$

$$k = 3: \quad c_3 = -\frac{1}{9}\, c_2 = -\frac{1}{3} \cdot \frac{1}{2} \cdot \frac{1}{3^3}\, c_0 = -\frac{1}{3!3^3}\, c_0,$$

$$\cdots \qquad \cdots \qquad \bullet\bullet\bullet \qquad \cdots$$

$$k = n: \quad c_n = \frac{(-1)^n}{3^n n!}\, c_0.$$

Since this c_0 is not the same as the c_0 for $r_1 = 1$, we change the notation to b_0 and the second series is

$$y_2(x) = b_0 x^{\frac{5}{3}}\left[1 + \sum_{n=1}^{\infty} \frac{(-1)^n}{3^n n!}\, x^n \right].$$

The complete solution is given by

$$y(x) = y_1(x) + y_2(x).$$

Case II. $r_1 = r_2$. When the indicial equation has equal roots the above procedure would obtain only $y_1(x)$. To obtain $y_2(x)$, however, something new must be added. In the previous technique we were anxious to obtain the values of r from the indicial equation so that we could treat them separately. In the following technique we shall retain r as long as possible.

Consider the differential equation

(6) $$L(y) = x^2 y'' + x(x + 3)y' + y = 0$$

which has a regular singular point at $x = 0$. A division by x^2 reveals that

$$p(x) = \frac{x + 3}{x} = \frac{3}{x} + 1,$$

$$q(x) = \frac{1}{x^2}.$$

Thus $p_0 = 3$ and $q_0 = 1$ so that the indicial equation is

$$r(r - 1) + 3r + 1 = r^2 + 2r + 1 = 0$$

with roots $r_1 = r_2 = -1$. Let the solution be expressed by

$$(7) \qquad y(x) = \sum c_i x^{r+i}$$

and substitute into equation (6) to obtain

$$L(y) = \sum (r + i)(r + i - 1)c_i x^{r+i} + \sum (r + i)c_i x^{r+i+1}$$
$$+ \sum 3(r + i)c_i x^{r+i} + \sum c_i x^{r+i}$$
$$= \sum [(r + i)^2 + 2(r + i) + 1]c_i x^{r+i} + \sum (r + i)c_i x^{r+i+1}.$$

The coefficient of the term containing x^{r+k} is

$$[(r + k)^2 + 2(r + k) + 1]c_k + (r + k - 1)c_{k-1}$$

and would yield the indicial equation for $k = 0$. Let us avoid this value of k and set this coefficient equal to zero for $k \geq 1$; we have

$$(r + k + 1)^2 c_k = -(r + k - 1)c_{k-1}.$$

We can thus obtain the values of c_k in terms of c_0 and r. The individual values are

$$c_1 = -\frac{r}{(r + 2)^2} c_0,$$

$$c_2 = -\frac{r + 1}{(r + 3)^2} c_1,$$

· · · · · ·

$$c_k = (-1)^k \frac{r(r + 1) \cdots (r + k - 1)}{[(r + 2)(r + 3) \cdots (r + k + 1)]^2} c_0.$$

The function (7) can thus be written as a function of x and r, namely,

$$(8) \qquad y(x,r) = c_0 x^r + \sum_{k=1}^{\infty} c_k(r) x^{r+k}$$

with

$$(9) \qquad c_k(r) = (-1)^k \frac{r(r + 1) \cdots (r + k - 1)}{[(r + 2)(r + 3) \cdots (r + k + 1)]^2} c_0.$$

We have thus obtained a function which when substituted into the differential equation $L(y) = 0$ will make all the terms on the left-hand side zero except the term for $k = 0$. Thus a substitution of the function (8) into equation (6) yields

(10) $L[y(x,r)] = -(r + 1)^2 c_0 x^r$.

It is desired to find a function y which will make $L(y) = 0$. A choice of $r = -1$ will make the right member of equation (10) zero and is the one solution which we could obtain from the indicial equation. Let $c_0 = 1$ and $y_1(x,-1)$ becomes a particular integral. To obtain the second solution let us differentiate both members of (10) with respect to r, thus * (with $c_0 = 1$)

(11) $\dfrac{\partial}{\partial r} L[y(x,r)] = L\left[\dfrac{\partial y(x,r)}{\partial r}\right]$

$= -[2(r + 1)x^r + (r + 1)^2 x^r \ln x]$.

The right member of this equation is also zero for $r = -1$; consequently, we have found a second function which will satisfy the original differential equation, namely,

$$y_2 = \left[\dfrac{\partial y(x,r)}{\partial r}\right]_{r=-1}.$$

From the definition of $y(x,r)$ given by equation (8), with $c_0 = 1$, we have

$$\dfrac{\partial y(x,r)}{\partial r} = x^r \ln x + \sum_{k=1}^{\infty} c_k(r)x^{r+k} \ln x + \sum_{k=1}^{\infty} c_k'(r)x^{k+r}$$

$$= y(x,r) \ln x + \sum_{k=1}^{\infty} c_k'(r)x^{k+r}$$

where $c_k'(r) = D_r c_k(r)$. Using the technique for the derivative of a product of functions (see Section 2, VIII, Chapter I) we have from (9), with $c_0 = 1$,

(12) $c_k'(r) = c_k(r)\left[\dfrac{1}{r} + \dfrac{1}{r+1} - \dfrac{1}{r+2} - \cdots - \dfrac{2}{r+k} - \dfrac{2}{r+k+1}\right]$.

The next step is to evaluate $c_k(r)$ and $c_k'(r)$ for $r = -1$. From (9) we have, with $c_0 = 1$,

$$c_1(-1) = -\frac{-1}{(-1+2)^2} = 1,$$

$$c_k(-1) = 0 \text{ for } k \geq 2.$$

---

* Since both x and r may be taken as independent variables in $y(x,r)$, the order of differentiation is interchangeable.

The evaluation of $c_k'(-1)$ is obtained by letting $r = -1$ in equation (12); however, we must exercise some care since $r + 1$ occurs in one of the denominators. Let us rewrite (12) and at the same time exhibit the first two values for k.

$$k = 1: \quad c_1'(r) = -\frac{r}{(r+2)^2}\left[\frac{1}{r} - \frac{2}{r+2}\right]$$

$$= -\frac{1}{(r+2)^2} + \frac{2r}{(r+2)^3},$$

$$k = 2: \quad c_2'(r) = \frac{r}{[(r+2)(r+3)]^2} + \frac{r(r+1)}{[(r+2)(r+3)]^2}\left[\frac{1}{r} - \frac{2}{r+2} - \frac{2}{r+3}\right],$$

$$k > 2: \quad c_k'(r) = (-1)^k \frac{r(r+2)\cdots(r+k-1)}{K(r)}$$

$$+ c_k(r)\left[\frac{1}{r} - \frac{1}{r+2} - \cdots - \frac{2}{r+k+1}\right],$$

where

$$K(r) = [(r+2)(r+3)\cdots(r+k+1)]^2.$$

Now letting $r = -1$ we obtain

$$c_1'(-1) = -3,$$

$$c_2'(-1) = \frac{-1}{(1 \cdot 2)^2} + 0 = -\tfrac{1}{4},$$

and for $k > 2$

$$c_k'(-1) = (-1)^k \frac{(-1)[1 \cdot 2 \cdot 3 \cdots (k-2)]}{(1 \cdot 2 \cdot 3 \cdots k)^2} + 0$$

$$= (-1)^{k+1} \frac{(k-2)!}{(k!)^2}.$$

The two solutions then become

$$y_1 = x^{-1} + 1,$$

$$y_2 = (x^{-1} + 1)\ln x - 3 - \frac{1}{4}x + \sum_{k=3}^{\infty} \frac{(-1)^{k+1}(k-2)!}{(k!)^2} x^{k-1}.$$

The general solution is a linear combination of y_1 and y_2,

$$y = Ay_1 + By_2,$$

where A and B are the necessary arbitrary constants.

The above procedure for finding a power series solution about a regular singular point for a second order differential equation when the roots of the indicial equation are equal will always yield two linearly independent solutions of the form

$$y_1 = x^{r_1} + \sum_{k=1}^{\infty} c_k x^{k+r_1},$$

$$y_2 = y_1 \ln x + \sum_{k=1}^{\infty} b_k x^{k+r_1}.$$

Case III. **Difference between r_1 and r_2 a positive integer.** If the difference of the roots of the indicial equation, r_1 and r_2, is a positive integer, $r_1 - r_2 = n$, then the solution

$$y = \sum c_k x^{r+i}$$
$$= x^{r_1} \sum c_i x^i + x^{r_2} \sum b_i x^i$$

would possess like terms in the two series, and the initial c_0 and b_0 may not be arbitrary. In other words, it may be possible to find only one series by our usual technique. The possibility does exist that if we start with the smaller value r_1, the coefficients c_i may be such that c_{r_2} is arbitrary and then we can obtain the two solutions by our usual procedures.

Illustration. Find a solution of

(1) $$(x^2 + x)y'' - (2x + 5)y' - 4y = 0$$

about the point $x = 0$.

Solution. Since $x = 0$ is a regular singular point, let the solution have the form

(2) $$y(x) = \sum c_i x^{i+r}.$$

Substitute (2) into (1) to obtain

$$\sum (i+r)(i+r-1)c_i x^{i+r} + \sum (i+r)(i+r-1)c_i x^{i+r-1}$$
$$- \sum 2(i+r)c_i x^{i+r} - \sum 5(i+r)c_i x^{i+r-1} - \sum 4c_i x^{i+r} = 0.$$

The coefficient of x^{r-1} for $i = 0$ yields the indicial equation

$$r(r-1) - 5r = 0$$

with roots $r_1 = 0$ and $r_2 = 6$. Let $r = r_1 = 0$ and set the coefficient of x^k equal to zero.

$$k(k-1)c_k + (k+1)kc_{k+1} - 2kc_k - 5(k+1)c_{k+1} - 4c_k = 0.$$

Solve for c_{k+1}:

$$(k+1)(k-5)c_{k+1} = -(k+1)(k-4)c_k$$

or

$$c_{k+1} = -\frac{k-4}{k-5}c_k.$$

But the division by $k - 5$ should not be made until $k > 5$. We therefore write out the first five terms from the relation

$$(k-5)c_{k+1} = -(k-4)c_k,$$

$k = 0:$ $c_1 = -\frac{4}{5}c_0,$

$k = 1:$ $c_2 = -\frac{3}{4}c_1 = \frac{3}{5}c_0,$

$k = 2:$ $c_3 = -\frac{2}{3}c_2 = -\frac{2}{5}c_0,$

$k = 3:$ $c_4 = -\frac{1}{2}c_3 = \frac{1}{5}c_0,$

$k = 4:$ $c_5 = 0c_4 = 0,$

$k = 5:$ $0 \cdot c_6 = -c_5 = 0,$

which is satisfied for any value of c_6, so that c_6 is arbitrary and we have

$$k = 6:\qquad c_7 = -\frac{2}{1}c_6 = -2c_6,$$

$$k \geq 6:\ c_{k+1} = -\frac{k-4}{k-5}c_k = -(k-4)c_6.$$

The solutions are

$$y_1 = c_0(1 - \tfrac{4}{5}x + \tfrac{3}{5}x^2 - \tfrac{2}{5}x^3 + \tfrac{1}{5}x^4)$$
$$= A(5 - 4x + 3x^2 - 2x^3 + x^4),$$

$$y_2 = c_6\Big[x^6 - \sum_{k=7}^{\infty}(k-5)x^k\Big].$$

The above procedure will fail if c_{r_2} cannot be chosen arbitrarily. Consider the equation

$$2x^2y'' + x(x-6)y' + 6y = 0.$$

The solution about the regular singular point $x = 0$ yields the indicial equation

$$2r^2 - 8r + 6 = 0$$

with roots $r_1 = 3$ and $r_2 = 1$ and the difference $r_1 - r_2 = 2$. The usual procedure leads to the formula, for $r = 1$,

$$2(k-2)c_k = -c_{k-1}$$

and we have

$$k = 1: \ -2c_1 = -c_0,$$
$$k = 2: \ 0 \cdot c_2 = -c_1 = -\tfrac{1}{2}c_0,$$

which is possible only if $c_0 = 0$. However, we have stated that c_0 is the coefficient of the first term of the power series which exists, and thus $c_0 \neq 0$.

The solution of this type of equation is obtained in a manner very similar to that employed in Case II. In other words, we shall retain r in the evaluation of c_k, and obtain a function $y(x,r)$ which will satisfy the given differential equation except for the term $i = 0$. Let us continue with the example

$$L(y) = 2x^2y'' + x(x - 6)y' + 6y = 0,$$
$$y(x,r) = \sum c_i x^{i+r}, \quad 2(k + r - 3)c_k = -c_{k-1},$$
$$L[y(x,r)] = -2(r - 1)(r - 3)c_0 x^r.$$

It is clear that $L[y(x,r)] = 0$ for $r = 1$ or $r = 3$, but as we saw above only one series will be generated. A second series for which $L[y(x,r)] = 0$ could be obtained by evaluating the partial derivative of L with respect to r at r_1 provided the right member of $L[y(x,r)]$ contains the factor $(r - r_1)$ to the second degree so that it becomes zero at $r = r_1$. To obtain a particular solution before, we let $c_0 = 1$. In this case *let* $c_0 = (r - r_1)$ *where* r_1 *is the smaller of the roots* r_1, r_2. Thus in the example

$$L[y(x,r)] = -2(r - 1)^2(r - 3)x^r$$

and

$$y(x,r) = (r - 1)x^r + \sum_{k=1}^{\infty} c_k x^{k+r}$$

where now

$$c_k = \frac{(-1)^k(r - 1)}{2^k(r - 2)(r - 1)r(r + 1) \cdots (r + k - 3)}$$

so that the $r - 1$ in the numerator will remove the $r - 1$ in the denominator and the value for c_k will exist at $r = 1$. Since $(r - 1)$ does not occur in the denominator until $k = 2$, let us write $y(x,r)$ in the following manner:

$$y(x,r) = (r - 1)x^r - \frac{r - 1}{2(r - 2)} x^{r+1} + \frac{1}{4(r - 2)} x^{r+2}$$
$$+ \sum_{k=3}^{\infty} \frac{(-1)^k}{2^k(r - 2)r(r + 1) \cdots (r + k - 3)} x^{k+r}.$$

Differentiation with respect to r yields

$$\frac{\partial y(x,r)}{\partial r} = y(x,r) \ln x + x^r$$

$$- \frac{(r-1)}{2(r-2)} \left[\frac{1}{r-1} - \frac{1}{r-2} \right] x^{r+1} - \frac{1}{4(r-2)^2} x^{r+2}$$

$$+ \sum_{k=2}^{\infty} \frac{(-1)^k \left[-\frac{1}{r-2} - \frac{1}{r} - \frac{1}{r+1} - \cdots - \frac{1}{r+k-3} \right]}{2^k(r-2)r(r+1)\cdots(r+k-3)} x^{r+k}.$$

We can now find the two solutions y_1 and y_2 by letting $r = 1$ in $y(x,r)$ and its partial derivative with respect to r. Thus

$$y_1 = 0x + 0x^2 - \frac{1}{4}x^3 + \sum_{k=3}^{\infty} \frac{(-1)^{k+1} x^{k+1}}{2^k(k-2)!},$$

$$y_2 = y_1 \ln x + x + \frac{1}{2}x^2 - \frac{1}{4}x^3 + \sum_{k=3}^{\infty} \frac{(-1)^k \left[\frac{1}{2} + \frac{1}{3} + \cdots + \frac{1}{k-2} \right] x^{k+1}}{2^k(k-2)!}$$

$$= y_1 \ln x + x + \frac{1}{2}x^2 - \frac{1}{4}x^3 + \sum_{k=3}^{\infty} \frac{(-1)^k(H_k - 1)x^{k+1}}{2^k(k-2)!},$$

where

$$H_k = 1 + \frac{1}{2} + \frac{1}{3} + \cdots + \frac{1}{k} = \sum_{i=1}^{k} \frac{1}{i}.$$

The complete solution is

$$y(x) = A y_1(x) + B y_2(x)$$

where A and B are arbitrary constants.

Remarks. In the preceding sections we presented a brief introduction to the use of power series as a method for finding solutions of linear differential equations with variable coefficients. In particular we discussed expansions about an ordinary point and about a regular singular point. This is by no means a complete discussion since there are many more aspects of this problem. We could discuss special equations such as Bessel's equation or Legendre's equation or others. We could discuss the behavior of the solutions for large values of x. However, it is the opinion of this author that a more detailed discussion concerning the use of power series to represent solutions to differential equations should be reserved for an advanced course where the topics can be given the rigor which they deserve.*

76. Exercise XVIII.

1. Find the series solution for

$$2y''' + xy'' + 2y' + xy = 0$$

   if $y = 1$, $y' = 0$, $y'' = -1$ at $x = 0$.

2. Find a series solution about $x = 0$ for
   (a) $(2x - 1)y'' - 3y' = 0$.
   (b) $(2x^2 + 1)y'' + 3xy' - 6y = 0$.
   (c) $(x^2 - 2x)y'' + (3x + 1)y' + y = 0$.
   (d) $x^2 y'' + (x^2 - 3x)y' + (x + 4)y = 0$.
   (e) $x^2 y'' + x^2 y' - (x + 2)y = 0$.
   (f) $y' + y^2 - x = 0$.
   (g) $x^2 y'' + 3xy' - 3y = 0$.

3. The equation

$$x^2 y'' + xy' + (x^2 - n^2)y = 0$$

   is called the Bessel equation. Find the series solution about $x = 0$.

---

* For more information see E. L. Ince, *Ordinary Differential Equations* (London: Longmans, Green and Co., 1927).

XI

NUMERICAL METHODS

77. Introduction. Unfortunately there are many differential equations for which we cannot develop an explicit formula for the solution. However, if initial conditions are given, we can generate a function which will approximate the solution to a given degree of accuracy. The procedure used to generate the function is usually called a *numerical method* for obtaining solutions to differential equations. There are many techniques which can be employed; in fact, they are so numerous that a thorough discussion would require considerable space.* The techniques also require extensive arithmetic and consequently are designed for use in conjunction with modern computing machines. We shall limit our discussion to three specific techniques and consider only relatively simple examples.

78. Euler's Method. A fairly simple technique for the numerical solution of a differential equation is known as *Euler's method*. Unfortunately, this technique can be very inaccurate. Let us consider a first order differential equation

$$(1) \qquad \frac{dy}{dx} = f(x,y), \ y(x_1) = y_1,$$

the solution of which should be a function

$$(2) \qquad y = F(x).$$

If this function has a smooth curve, we know from their definitions that the differentials and increments have the geometric relations shown in Fig. 31, p. 176.

---

* See K. L. Nielsen, *Methods in Numerical Analysis* (New York: The Macmillan Company, 1956), Chapter VII; or W. E. Milne, *Numerical Solutions of Differential Equations* (New York: John Wiley & Sons, Inc., 1953).

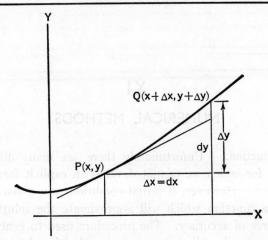

Fig. 31

If Δx is sufficiently small, a good approximation to Δy is given by

(3) $$\Delta y \doteq \left(\frac{dy}{dx}\right)\Delta x$$

and if this is evaluated at a particular point (x_i, y_i), the next value of y could be obtained by

(4) $$y_{i+1} = y_i + \Delta y_i = y_i + \left(\frac{dy}{dx}\right)_i \Delta x.$$

Since the derivative is given by equation (1), we have

$$\left(\frac{dy}{dx}\right)_i = f(x_i, y_i).$$

With given initial values we can thus generate the function $y = F(x)$ in a step-by-step procedure. The size of the increment, Δx, is a matter of choice. We desire to choose it large enough to reduce the amount of the labor and yet not so large that the solution becomes too inaccurate. Let us consider a simple example.

Illustration. Solve the differential equation

$$y' = x + y$$

with $y_0 = 1$ at $x_0 = 0$.

Solution. Let us choose $\Delta x = 0.1$ and arrange the work in a table. First the x column and y_0 are written down and then the values of y_i and y_i' are calculated by formulas (3) and (4) at each value of x; i.e., $y_0'=0+1=1$; $y_1=y_0+\Delta y_0=1+1(.1)=1.1$, $y_1' = x_1 + y_1 = .1 + 1.1 = 1.2$, etc.

x	y	y'
0.0	1.000	1.000
.1	1.100	1.200
.2	1.2200	1.4200
.3	1.3620	1.6620
.4	1.5282	1.9282
.5	1.7210	2.2210
.6	1.9431	2.5431
.7	2.1974	2.8974
.8	2.4871	3.2871
.9	2.8158	3.7158
1.0	3.1874	4.1874

In the above illustration the equation was chosen to make the arithmetic simple. We can, of course, solve this simple linear first order equation and obtain

$$y = 2e^x - x - 1.$$

The values for $x = 0.5$ and 1.0 are

$$y(0.5) = 1.7974 \quad \text{and} \quad y(1) = 3.4366$$

to five significant figures. A comparison:

x	0	0.5	1.0
y (with $\Delta x = .1$)	1.0000	1.7210	3.1874
y (exact)	1.0000	1.7974	3.4366

shows that the values obtained by Euler's method differ from the exact values by 4.3% at $x = 0.5$ and 7.3% at $x = 1$. Some improvement can be obtained by taking a smaller value for Δx; thus for $\Delta x = .05$ we obtain

$$y(0.5) = 1.7577 \quad \text{and} \quad y(1) = 3.3117;$$

however, this doubles the amount of work. Euler's method is recommended only when it is desired to have a "quick and dirty" look at the function.

79. The Runge-Kutta Method. A method which usually gives good results and which requires no special formulas to start the problem is one known as the *Runge-Kutta method*. Consider again a first order equation

(1) $$y' = f(x,y)$$

with initial values x_0 and y_0. Again we choose an increment Δx, and the values of x will grow according to

(2) $$x_{i+1} = x_i + \Delta x.$$

However, it will be necessary to compute some temporary values at $\frac{1}{2}\Delta x$, and we make room for that in our organization of the table. The values of y are obtained by the formula

$$\Delta y_1 = \frac{\Delta x}{6}\left[y'_{11} + 2y'_{12} + 2y'_{13} + y'_{14}\right],$$

where the first subscript in the double subscript indicates the value $y_1, y_2, \cdots$, and the second subscript indicates the step for the calculation of the value for $y_1, y_2, \cdots$. We shall exhibit the individual formulas in a table which will also show the schematic for the calculations. Read this table carefully.

x	y	y'
$x_{11} = x_0$	$y_{11} = y_0$	$y'_{11} = f(x_{11}, y_{11})$
$x_{12} = x_{11} + \dfrac{\Delta x}{2}$	$y_{12} = y_{11} + y'_{11}\dfrac{\Delta x}{2}$	$y'_{12} = f(x_{12}, y_{12})$
$x_{13} = x_{11} + \dfrac{\Delta x}{2}$	$y_{13} = y_{11} + y'_{12}\dfrac{\Delta x}{2}$	$y'_{13} = f(x_{13}, y_{13})$
$x_{14} = x_{11} + \Delta x$	$y_{14} = y_{11} + y'_{13}\Delta x$	$y'_{14} = f(x_{14}, y_{14})$
		$\Delta y_1 = \left(\dfrac{\Delta x}{6}\right)(y'_{11} + 2y'_{12} + 2y'_{13} + y'_{14})$
$x_{21} = x_{11} + \Delta x$	$y_{21} = y_{11} + \Delta y_1$	$y'_{21} = f(x_{21}, y_{21})$
$x_{22} = x_{21} + \dfrac{\Delta x}{2}$	$y_{22} = y_{21} + y'_{21}\dfrac{\Delta x}{2}$	$y'_{22} = f(x_{22}, y_{22})$
$x_{23} = x_{21} + \dfrac{\Delta x}{2}$	$y_{23} = y_{21} + y'_{22}\dfrac{\Delta x}{2}$	$y'_{23} = f(x_{23}, y_{23})$
$x_{24} = x_{21} + \Delta x$	$y_{24} = y_{21} + y'_{23}\Delta x$	$y'_{24} = f(x_{24}, y_{24})$
		$\Delta y_2 = \left(\dfrac{\Delta x}{6}\right)(y'_{21} + 2y'_{22} + 2y'_{23} + y'_{24})$
$x_{31} = x_{21} + \Delta x$	$y_{31} = y_{21} + \Delta y_2$	$y'_{31} = f(x_{31}, y_{31})$

We call attention to the fact that at each stage of computation of y within a block, after the first step, the value of y at the beginning of the block is always used; for example,

$$y_{24} = y_{21} + y'_{23}\,\Delta x.$$

Let us consider the same example as we did in Section 78.

Illustration. Find a solution of

$$y' = x + y,$$
$$y_0 = 1,\ x_0 = 0 \text{ by the Runge-Kutta method.}$$

Solution. Choose $\Delta x = 0.2$.

x	y	y'
0.0	1.0000	1.0000
.1	1.1000	1.2000
.1	1.1200	1.2200
.2	1.2440	1.4440
		.2428
.2	1.2428	1.4428
.3	1.3871	1.6871
.3	1.4115	1.7115
.4	1.5851	1.9851
		.3408
.4	1.5836	1.9836
.5	1.7820	2.2820
.5	1.8118	2.3118
.6	2.0460	2.6460
		.4606
.6	2.0442	2.6442
.7	2.3086	3.0086
.7	2.3451	3.0451
.8	2.6532	3.4532
		.6068
.8	2.6510	3.4510
.9	2.9961	3.8961
.9	3.0406	3.9406
1.0	3.4391	4.4391
		.7854
1.0	3.4364	

The values for y are given as the first entry of each block, and the other values should not be considered in the representation of y. We notice that although we took twice the interval length, Δx, the values for y are better approximations than those obtained by Euler's method.

Another advantage of the Runge-Kutta method is the ability to change the length of the increment on the independent variable from block to block. Thus we could start with $\Delta x = .2$ in going from $x = 0$ to $x = .2$, then change to $\Delta x = .1$ and go from $x = .2$ to $x = .3$, etc.

The extension to higher order equations is straightforward, using formulas for each derivative similar to those used for building the values of the function. Thus for a second order differential equation we calculate the values of the first derivative terms by

$$y'_{i1} = y'_{i-1,1} + \Delta y'_{i-1},$$
$$y'_{i2} = y'_{i1} + y''_{i1}\frac{\Delta x}{2},$$
$$y'_{i3} = y'_{i1} + y''_{i2}\frac{\Delta x}{2},$$
$$y'_{i4} = y'_{i1} + y''_{i3}\Delta x$$

and

$$y'_i = \frac{\Delta x}{6}(y''_{i1} + 2y''_{i2} + 2y''_{i3} + y''_{i4}),$$

where $i = 1, 2, \cdots$ is the subscript denoting the block.

Let us exhibit the formulas and schematic for a second order equation $y'' = f(y,y', x)$ with the initial values y_0, y'_0, and x_0.

x	y	y'	y''
$x_{11} = x_0$	$y_{11} = y_0$	$y'_{11} = y'_0$	$y''_{11} = f(y_0, y'_0, x_0)$
$x_{12} = x_{11} + \dfrac{\Delta x}{2}$	$y_{12} = y_{11} + y'_{11}\dfrac{\Delta x}{2}$	$y'_{12} = y'_{11} + y''_{11}\dfrac{\Delta x}{2}$	$y''_{12} = f(y_{12}, y'_{12}, x_{12})$
$x_{13} = x_{11} + \dfrac{\Delta x}{2}$	$y_{13} = y_{11} + y'_{12}\dfrac{\Delta x}{2}$	$y'_{13} = y'_{11} + y''_{12}\dfrac{\Delta x}{2}$	$y''_{13} = f(y_{13}, y'_{13}, x_{13})$
$x_{14} = x_{11} + \Delta x$	$y_{14} = y_{11} + y'_{13}\,\Delta x$	$y'_{14} = y'_{11} + y''_{13}\,\Delta x$	$y''_{14} = f(y_{14}, y'_{14}, x_{14})$
		$\Delta y_1 = \dfrac{\Delta x}{6}\,(y'_{11} + 2y'_{12} + 2y'_{13} + y'_{14})$	$\Delta y'_1 = \dfrac{\Delta x}{6}\,(y''_{11} + 2y''_{12} + 2y''_{13} + y''_{14})$
$x_{21} = x_{11} + \Delta x$	$y_{21} = y_{11} + \Delta y_1$	$y'_{21} = y'_{11} + \Delta y'_1$	$y''_{21} = f(y_{21}, y'_{21}, x_{21})$
$x_{22} = x_{21} + \dfrac{\Delta x}{2}$	$y_{22} = y_{21} + y'_{21}\dfrac{\Delta x}{2}$	$y'_{22} = y'_{21} + y''_{21}\dfrac{\Delta x}{2}$	$y''_{22} = f(y_{22}, y'_{22}, x_{22})$
$x_{23} = x_{21} + \dfrac{\Delta x}{2}$	$y_{23} = y_{21} + y'_{22}\dfrac{\Delta x}{2}$	$y'_{23} = y'_{21} + y''_{22}\dfrac{\Delta x}{2}$	$y''_{23} = f(y_{23}, y'_{23}, x_{23})$
$x_{24} = x_{21} + \Delta x$	$y_{24} = y_{21} + y'_{23}\,\Delta x$	$y'_{24} = y'_{21} + y''_{23}\,\Delta x$	$y''_{24} = f(y_{24}, y'_{24}, x_{24})$
		$\Delta y_2 = \dfrac{\Delta x}{6}\,(y'_{21} + 2y'_{22} + 2y'_{23} + y'_{24})$	$\Delta y'_2 = \dfrac{\Delta x}{6}\,(y''_{21} + 2y''_{22} + 2y''_{23} + y''_{24})$
$x_{31} = x_{21} + \Delta x$	$y_{31} = y_{21} + \Delta y_2$	$y'_{31} = y'_{21} + \Delta y'_2$	$y''_{31} = f(y_{31}, y'_{31}, x_{31})$

Illustration.   Find the function $y(x)$, $0 \leq x \leq 1$, which satisfies
$$2y'' = 12xy + 5$$
if $y = y' = 1$ at $x = 0$.

Solution.

x	y	y'	y''
0.0	1.	1.	2.5
.1	1.1	1.25	3.16
.1	1.125	1.316	3.175
.2	1.2632	1.6350	4.0158
		.2589	.6395
.2	1.2589	1.6395	4.0107
.3	1.4228	2.0406	5.0610
.3	1.4630	2.1456	5.1334
.4	1.6880	2.6662	6.5512
		.4226	1.0317
.4	1.6815	2.6712	6.5356
.5	1.9486	3.3248	8.3458
.5	2.0140	3.5058	8.5420
.6	2.3827	4.3796	11.0777
		.6904	1.7130
.6	2.3719	4.3842	11.0388
.7	2.8103	5.4881	14.3033
.7	2.9207	5.8145	14.7669
.8	3.5348	7.3376	19.4670
		1.1442	2.9549
.8	3.5161	7.3391	19.3773
.9	4.2500	9.2768	25.4500
.9	4.4438	9.8841	26.4965
1.0	5.4929	12.6384	35.4574
		1.9433	5.2909
1.0	5.4594	12.6300	

80. Power Series Method.   The function $y(x)$ which is a solution of a given differential equation with initial conditions may be approximated for a range of values of the independent variable, $a \leq x \leq b$, by a power series provided the series converges for the specified values of x. The method used is identical to that discussed in Section 73. Let us consider again the example of the last section.

Illustration. Find the function $y(x), 0 \leq x \leq 1$, which satisfies

$$2y'' = 12xy + 5$$

if $y = y' = 1$ at $x = 0$.

Solution. By successive differentiation we obtain

$$
\begin{aligned}
y'' &= 6xy + 2.5, & y''(0) &= 2.5, \\
y''' &= 6y + 6xy', & y'''(0) &= 6, \\
y^{\mathrm{iv}} &= 12y' + 6xy'', & y^{\mathrm{iv}}(0) &= 12, \\
y^{\mathrm{v}} &= 18y'' + 6xy''', & y^{\mathrm{v}}(0) &= 45, \\
y^{\mathrm{vi}} &= 24y''' + 6xy^{\mathrm{iv}}, & y^{\mathrm{vi}}(0) &= 144, \\
y^{\mathrm{vii}} &= 30y^{\mathrm{iv}} + 6xy^{\mathrm{v}}, & y^{\mathrm{vii}}(0) &= 360, \\
\cdots & \\
y^{(k)} &= 6(k-2)y^{(k-3)} + 6xy^{(k-2)}.
\end{aligned}
$$

The function is approximated by

$$y(x) = y(0) + y'(0)x + \frac{y''(0)}{2!}x^2 + \cdots + \frac{y^{(k)}(0)}{k!}x^k + \cdots$$

$$= 1 + x + \tfrac{5}{4}x^2 + x^3 + \tfrac{1}{2}x^4 + \tfrac{3}{8}x^5 + \tfrac{1}{5}x^6 + \tfrac{1}{14}x^7 + \tfrac{9}{224}x^8 + \cdots.$$

The values at $x = .2, .4, .6, .8,$ and 1 can now be evaluated by substitution into the series. To obtain the accuracy desired all terms of the series up to the term of "no effect" must be evaluated.

$$
\begin{aligned}
y(.2) &= 1 + .2 + \tfrac{5}{4}(.04) + (.008) + \tfrac{1}{2}(.0016) + \tfrac{3}{8}(.00032) + \tfrac{1}{5}(.000064) \\
&= 1 + .2 + .05 + .008 + .0008 + .00012 + .0000128 \\
&= 1.2589 \text{ to five significant digits,} \\
y(.4) &= 1.6817, \\
y(.6) &= 2.3722, \\
y(.8) &= 3.5168, \\
y(1.0) &= 5.4613.
\end{aligned}
$$

The use of series is greatly influenced by the rate of convergence. In the above example 14 terms had to be used to obtain $y(1.0)$ to five significant digits. Slower convergence necessitates a greater amount of arithmetic. On the other hand some series converge very rapidly and the arithmetic is rather easy.

Illustration. Obtain values of the function $y(x)$ which satisfies the differential equation

$$y'' = .5x^2y + .2x + .1$$

with $y(0) = .5$, $y'(0) = 0$ at $x = 0$.

Solution. By successive differentiation we obtain the representation

$$y(x) = \tfrac{1}{2} + \tfrac{1}{20}x^2 + \tfrac{1}{30}x^3 + \tfrac{1}{48}x^4 + \tfrac{1}{1200}x^6 + \tfrac{1}{2520}x^7 + \tfrac{1}{5376}x^8 \cdots$$
$$= .5 + .05x^2 + .0333x^3 + .0208x^4 + .0008x^6 + .0004x^7$$
$$+ .0002x^8 + \cdots.$$

For values of $x < .5$ we need use only the first four terms to obtain a value for y to 4 decimal place accuracy.

81. Exercise XIX.

1. Generate the function $y(x)$, $0 \leq x \leq 1$, which satisfies the differential equations:
   (a) $y' = x^3y + 1$; $y = 1$ at $x = 0$,
   (b) $y' = xy - 2$; $y = 0$ at $x = 0$,
      by the three methods discussed in this chapter.

2. Use the Runge-Kutta method to solve

   $$y'' = x - y$$

   if $y = 1$, $y' = 0$ at $x = 0$.

3. Find the first three non-zero terms of the power series representation of the solution of

   $$y' = \sin y + \sin x$$

   if $y = 0$ at $x = 0$. Evaluate the series for $x = 0.1$.

XII

PARTIAL DIFFERENTIAL EQUATIONS
OF THE FIRST ORDER

82. Introduction. A partial differential equation is an equation which contains one or more partial derivatives (see Chapter II). These equations are important in both pure and applied mathematics. A thorough study of this subject must be deferred until the student has reached a greater maturity in both mathematics and applied science than that presupposed for an elementary differential equations book. However, it is possible to consider the subject in an elementary manner and discuss the basic concepts. As has been mentioned so often before, a solution to any equation is a relation among the variables which satisfies the equation. This, of course, is also true for a partial differential equation. Thus to prove that a given relation is a solution of a particular partial differential equation, we substitute the relation and its required partial derivatives into the differential equation and see if it satisfies that equation.

Illustration. Show that

$$z = ax^2 + ay + c$$

is a solution of

$$\frac{\partial z}{\partial x} = 2x \frac{\partial z}{\partial y}.$$

Solution. Find the partial derivatives of z with respect to x and y:

$$\frac{\partial z}{\partial x} = 2ax, \quad \frac{\partial z}{\partial y} = a.$$

Substitute into the differential equation to obtain the identity

$$2ax = 2x(a).$$

185

The classical literature on differential equations makes frequent use of a notation which is convenient to write but not very descriptive. Let us consider x and y to be two independent variables and z to be the dependent variable; then we define

$$p = \frac{\partial z}{\partial x}, \; q = \frac{\partial z}{\partial y}, \; r = \frac{\partial^2 z}{\partial x^2}, \; s = \frac{\partial^2 z}{\partial x \, \partial y}, \; t = \frac{\partial^2 z}{\partial y^2}.$$

A much more descriptive notation is one which employs subscripts to denote partial differentiation. Let $\varphi(x,y)$ be a function of two independent variables x and y. Then we may define:

First Order Partials.

$$\varphi_x = \frac{\partial \varphi}{\partial x} \quad \text{and} \quad \varphi_y = \frac{\partial \varphi}{\partial y}.$$

Second Order Partials.

$$\varphi_{xx} = \frac{\partial^2 \varphi}{\partial x^2}, \; \varphi_{xy} = \frac{\partial^2 \varphi}{\partial x \, \partial y}, \; \varphi_{yy} = \frac{\partial^2 \varphi}{\partial y^2}.$$

Unfortunately, a similar notation is used in the theory of difference equations, and the student should be familiar with the subject under discussion before completely adopting any notation.

83. Partial Differential Equations from Known Integrals.

If we are given a function of two variables, it is possible to find a partial differential equation which is satisfied by this function. The procedure is similar to that for ordinary differential equations.

Illustration. Find a partial differential equation whose solution is

$$z = (a+2)x + (a^2+1)y + b.$$

Solution. Differentiate the function partially with respect to x and y to obtain

$$\frac{\partial z}{\partial x} = p = a + 2,$$

$$\frac{\partial z}{\partial y} = q = a^2 + 1.$$

Eliminate a from these equations to obtain

$$q = (p - 2)^2 + 1$$

or

$$\frac{\partial z}{\partial y} = \left(\frac{\partial z}{\partial x} - 2\right)^2 + 1,$$

which is the desired partial differential equation.

In the above illustration the given function contained two arbitrary constants which were easily eliminated by obtaining the first order partial derivatives. In some cases this elimination may lead to more than one differential equation.

Illustration. Find a partial differential equation whose solution is

$$z = ax^2 + by^2 + c.$$

Solution. The first partial derivatives yield

$$p = 2ax \quad \text{and} \quad q = 2by$$

and it is not possible to eliminate the arbitrary constants a, b, and c. Consequently, it is necessary to take the second partial derivatives:

$$r = 2a, \quad s = 0, \quad \text{and} \quad t = 2b,$$

and we now have six equations from which to eliminate the three constants. The result is three equations:

$$s = 0, \quad p = rx, \quad \text{and} \quad q = ty,$$

each of which is satisfied by the given function.

84. Solutions. Solutions of partial differential equations may be categorized in a manner similar to that for ordinary differential equations. A function which satisfies a given partial differential equation is often referred to as an *integral* of that equation. This integral may contain arbitrary functions, in which case it is called the **general solution.** If it contains independent arbitrary constants but not arbitrary functions, it is called the **complete solution.**

We recall from the calculus that if z is defined as a function of x and y by the equation

(1) $$F(x,y,z) = 0$$

and we let $u = F(x,y,z)$, then

(2)
$$\begin{cases} \dfrac{\partial u}{\partial x} = F_x + F_z \dfrac{\partial z}{\partial x} = 0, \\[2mm] \dfrac{\partial u}{\partial y} = F_y + F_z \dfrac{\partial z}{\partial y} = 0; \end{cases}$$

and

(3)
$$dz = \frac{\partial z}{\partial x}\,dx + \frac{\partial z}{\partial y}\,dy.$$

Consider the first order partial differential equation

(4)
$$f(x,y,z,z_x,z_y) = 0$$

and let its complete solution be

(5)
$$\varphi(x,y,z,a,b) = 0$$

where a and b are arbitrary constants and equations (2) are

(6)
$$\begin{cases} \varphi_x + \varphi_z \dfrac{\partial z}{\partial x} = 0, \\[2mm] \varphi_y + \varphi_z \dfrac{\partial z}{\partial y} = 0. \end{cases}$$

If we now treat a and b as functions of x and y, then equations (6) become

(7)
$$\begin{cases} \varphi_x + \varphi_z \dfrac{\partial z}{\partial x} + \varphi_a \dfrac{\partial a}{\partial x} + \varphi_b \dfrac{\partial b}{\partial x} = 0, \\[2mm] \varphi_y + \varphi_z \dfrac{\partial z}{\partial y} + \varphi_a \dfrac{\partial a}{\partial y} + \varphi_b \dfrac{\partial b}{\partial y} = 0. \end{cases}$$

If equations (6) and (7) are to be satisfied simultaneously then we must have

(8)
$$\begin{cases} \varphi_a \dfrac{\partial a}{\partial x} + \varphi_b \dfrac{\partial b}{\partial x} = 0, \\[2mm] \varphi_a \dfrac{\partial a}{\partial y} + \varphi_b \dfrac{\partial b}{\partial y} = 0, \end{cases}$$

which is satisfied if

(9)
$$\varphi_a = 0 \quad \text{and} \quad \varphi_b = 0.$$

The elimination of a and b between equations (9) and (5) gives the equation of the envelope of the surfaces represented by $\varphi(x,y,z,a,b) = 0$, which is called the **singular solution**.

85. Equations Containing Only Partials of One Variable. The class of partial differential equations which contain only the partial derivations with respect to a single variable may be solved by ordinary differential equation techniques.

Illustration. Find the solution of

$$\frac{\partial z}{\partial x} = ax + y.$$

Solution. Since the differentiation is with respect to x only, we may treat y as a constant and separate the variables into

$$dz = (ax + y)dx.$$

An integration yields

$$z = \tfrac{1}{2}ax^2 + xy + \psi(y)$$

where the "constant" of integration, $\psi(y)$, is an arbitrary function of y.

This technique also applies to higher order equations.

Illustration. Find the solution of

$$\frac{\partial^2 z}{\partial y^2} + a\,\frac{\partial z}{\partial y} = x^2 + 3y^2.$$

Solution. Let us integrate with respect to y while treating x as a constant and recalling that the integral of a second derivative should yield the first derivative except for a constant. Thus

$$\int^y \frac{\partial^2 z}{\partial y^2} + \int a\,dz = \int (x^2 + 3y^2)dy$$

yields

$$\frac{\partial z}{\partial y} + az = x^2 y + y^3 + \psi_1(x).$$

This equation is again treated as an ordinary differential equation with y as the independent variable. It is a first order linear differential equation whose integrating factor is e^{ay}; thus

$$ze^{ay} = \int x^2 y e^{ay}\,dy + \int y^3 e^{ay}\,dy + \int \psi_1(x)e^{ay}\,dy$$
$$= e^{ay}\big[x^2(a^{-1}y - a^{-2}) + a^{-1}y^3 - 3a^{-2}y^2 + 6a^{-3}y - 6a^{-4} + a^{-1}\psi_1(x)\big]$$
$$\quad + \psi_2(x).$$

86. Linear Equation of the First Order. The general linear partial differential equation of the first order in x, y, and z is written in the form

$$(1) \qquad P(x,y,z)z_x + Q(x,y,z)z_y = R(x,y,z).$$

The technique for finding the general solution of this equation is to find two integrals of the system of ordinary differential equations,

$$(2) \qquad \frac{dx}{P(x,y,z)} = \frac{dy}{Q(x,y,z)} = \frac{dz}{R(x,y,z)},$$

say, $u(x,y,z) = a$ and $v(x,y,z) = b$. Then either

$$(3) \qquad \varphi(u,v) = 0 \quad \text{or} \quad u = \psi(v)$$

is a general solution of (1).

Illustration. Find the general solution of

$$x^2 z_x - xy z_y = y^2.$$

Solution. Form the system of ordinary differential equations

$$\frac{dx}{P} = \frac{dy}{Q} = \frac{dz}{R} \quad \text{or} \quad \frac{dx}{x^2} = \frac{dy}{-xy} = \frac{dz}{y^2}.$$

We desire to find two independent solutions of this sytem. The first is obtained from

$$\frac{dx}{x^2} = \frac{dy}{-xy} \quad \text{or} \quad \frac{dx}{x} + \frac{dy}{y} = 0$$

which yields

$$xy = c_1.$$

The second integral is obtained by using the first solution in the equation of the last two fractions, thus

$$\frac{dy}{-c_1} = \frac{dz}{y^2} \quad \text{or} \quad y^2\, dy = -c_1\, dz,$$

which has the solution

$$\tfrac{1}{3}y^3 + c_1 z = c_2$$

or since $c_1 = xy$

$$y^2 + 3xz = 3c_2 y^{-1} = c_3 x.$$

Since c_3 is an arbitrary constant we can let it be an arbitrary function of c_1, $\varphi(c_1)$, and then replace c_1 by its equivalence, $c_1 = xy$, to obtain the general solution

$$y^2 + 3xz = x\varphi(xy).$$

This technique was developed by the French mathematician Lagrange and is known as the *method of Lagrange*. It is based upon the fact that any solution, $u(x,y,z) = c$, of the system

(4)
$$\frac{dx}{P} = \frac{dy}{Q} = \frac{dz}{R}$$

is also a solution of

(5)
$$P\frac{\partial u}{\partial x} + Q\frac{\partial u}{\partial y} + R\frac{\partial u}{\partial z} = 0,$$

and furthermore any solution of (5) is also a solution of

(6)
$$Pz_x + Qz_y = R.$$

The truth of this statement becomes evident by considering a function $u(x,y,z) = c$ to be a solution of (4). The total differential of u must equal zero, since $u = c$, so that

$$du = \frac{\partial u}{\partial x}\,dx + \frac{\partial u}{\partial y}\,dy + \frac{\partial u}{\partial z}\,dz = 0.$$

The properties of proportions yield

$$\frac{\dfrac{\partial u}{\partial x}\,dx + \dfrac{\partial u}{\partial y}\,dy + \dfrac{\partial u}{\partial z}\,dz}{\dfrac{\partial u}{\partial x}\,P + \dfrac{\partial u}{\partial y}\,Q + \dfrac{\partial u}{\partial z}\,R} = \frac{dx}{P} = \frac{dy}{Q} = \frac{dz}{R}.$$

Now if the numerator of the first term is zero, then the denominator must also be zero so that

$$\frac{\partial u}{\partial x}\,P + \frac{\partial u}{\partial y}\,Q + \frac{\partial u}{\partial z}\,R = 0;$$

consequently, $u = c$ satisfies equation (5). If we differentiate $u = c$ with respect to x and y, we have by equations (2), Section 84,

$$\frac{\partial u}{\partial x} = -\frac{\partial u}{\partial z}\,z_x \quad \text{and} \quad \frac{\partial u}{\partial y} = -\frac{\partial u}{\partial z}\,z_y.$$

Substituting these into equation (5) yields

$$-\frac{\partial u}{\partial z} z_x P - \frac{\partial u}{\partial z} z_y Q + \frac{\partial u}{\partial z} R = 0$$

or solving for R

$$P z_x + Q z_y = R$$

so that if $u = c$ satisfies (5) then it also satisfies (6).

Since the method depends upon the ability to find two integrals of the system

$$\frac{dx}{P} = \frac{dy}{Q} = \frac{dz}{R},$$

let us consider this system in some detail.

I. It may be possible to reduce two of the equations to two others, each of which contains only two variables.

Illustration. Find two integrals of

$$\frac{dx}{z^2} = \frac{dy}{x(z - y)} = \frac{dz}{x}.$$

Solution. Consider the equation

$$\frac{dx}{z^2} = \frac{dz}{x} \quad \text{or} \quad x\,dx = z^2\,dz,$$

which contains only the two variables x and z, with the variables separated. The solution is obtained by an integration,

$$\tfrac{1}{2}x^2 = \tfrac{1}{3}z^3 + c_1.$$

Consider the equation

$$\frac{dy}{x(z - y)} = \frac{dz}{x}.$$

A multiplication by x yields an equation containing only y and z:

$$dy = (z - y)dz$$

or

$$\frac{dy}{dz} + y = z,$$

which is a first order linear equation with solution

$$y = z - 1 + c_2 e^{-z}.$$

Thus we have the two integrals

$$3x^2 - 2z^3 = c_3 \quad \text{and} \quad e^z(y + 1 - z) = c_2.$$

II. If one integral has been found, this solution may be used to obtain an equation in only two variables and the arbitrary constant of the first solution.

Illustration. Find two integrals of

$$\frac{dx}{x} = \frac{dy}{y} = \frac{dz}{xy}.$$

Solution. The first equation

$$\frac{dx}{x} = \frac{dy}{y}$$

has for its solution the function $y = c_1 x$.

Substitute this solution into the denominator of dz to obtain

$$\frac{dx}{x} = \frac{dz}{c_1 x^2} \quad \text{or} \quad c_1 x \, dx = dz.$$

An integration yields

$$\tfrac{1}{2} c_1 x^2 = z + c_2$$

or

$$2z = yx + c_2$$

and we have the two integrals

$$y = c_1 x \quad \text{and} \quad 2z = xy + c_2.$$

III. It may be possible to find multipliers $\lambda(x,y,z)$, $\mu(x,y,z)$, and $\nu(x,y,z)$ which permit us to use the property of proportions which yields

(7) $$\frac{dx}{P} = \frac{dy}{Q} = \frac{dz}{R} = \frac{\lambda \, dx + \mu \, dy + \nu \, dz}{\lambda P + \mu Q + \nu R}.$$

Then we may:

(a) Use the last member of (7) with one of the others to find an integral;

(b) Find another set of multipliers such that

$$\frac{\lambda_1 \, dx + \mu_1 \, dy + \nu_1 \, dz}{\lambda_1 P + \mu_1 Q + \nu_1 R} = \frac{\lambda_2 \, dx + \mu_2 \, dy + \nu_2 \, dz}{\lambda_2 P + \mu_2 Q + \nu_2 R}$$

may be solved;

(c) If $\lambda P + \mu Q + \nu R = 0$, solve $\lambda \, dx + \mu \, dy + \nu \, dz = 0$.

Illustration. Find two integrals of

$$\frac{dx}{cy - bz} = \frac{dy}{az - cx} = \frac{dz}{bx - ay}.$$

Solution. Let $\lambda = a$, $\mu = b$, $\nu = c$, then

$$\lambda P + \mu Q + \nu R = a(cy - bz) + b(az - cx) + c(bx - ay) = 0.$$

Consequently, we have

$$a \, dx + b \, dy + c \, dz = 0$$

and an integration yields

$$ax + by + cz = k_1.$$

Let $\lambda = x$, $\mu = y$, $\nu = z$, then

$$\lambda P + \mu Q + \nu R = x(cy - bz) + y(az - cx) + z(bx - ay) = 0.$$

Thus

$$x \, dx + y \, dy + z \, dz = 0 \quad \text{and} \quad x^2 + y^2 + z^2 = k_2.$$

87. Integrating Factors for Ordinary Differential Equations.
The solution of first order ordinary differential equations of the
first degree was discussed in Chapter III, and in Section 27 it
was pointed out that a general integrating factor $\mu(x,y)$ could
be found for the equation

$$(1) \qquad M(x,y)dx + N(x,y)dy = 0.$$

We recall that an integrating factor makes the equation exact,
so that

$$(2) \qquad \mu M \, dx + \mu N \, dy = 0$$

must possess the property that

$$(3) \qquad \frac{\partial(\mu M)}{\partial y} = \frac{\partial(\mu N)}{\partial x}.$$

Equation (3) is a partial differential equation, which, after we
have performed the indicated differentiation, takes the form

$$(4) \qquad M \frac{\partial u}{\partial y} - N \frac{\partial u}{\partial x} = \mu \left(\frac{\partial N}{\partial x} - \frac{\partial M}{\partial y} \right)$$

and is a linear partial differential of the first order. The integrating factor μ can thus be obtained from a particular solution
of the system

$$\text{(5)} \qquad \frac{dx}{-N} = \frac{dy}{M} = \frac{d\mu}{\mu\left(\dfrac{\partial N}{\partial x} - \dfrac{\partial M}{\partial y}\right)}.$$

Illustration. Find an integrating factor for

$$(y - x^2 y^2)dx + x\, dy = 0.$$

Solution. We have

$$M = y - x^2 y^2, \quad \frac{\partial M}{\partial y} = 1 - 2x^2 y,$$

$$N = x, \qquad \frac{\partial N}{\partial x} = 1.$$

The system (5) is

$$\frac{dx}{-x} = \frac{dy}{y - x^2 y^2} = \frac{d\mu}{\mu(2x^2 y)}$$

and we desire the solution for μ. Let us find λ_1, μ_1, ν_1, such that the sum of the denominators is zero and use method III of Section 86. We find

$$\lambda_1 = \frac{1}{x}, \; \mu_1 = \frac{1}{y}, \; \nu_1 = \frac{1}{2\mu}.$$

Then

$$\frac{1}{x}(-x) + \frac{1}{y}(y - x^2 y^2) + \frac{1}{2\mu}(2\mu x^2 y) = -1 + 1 - x^2 y + x^2 y = 0,$$

and we have

$$\frac{dx}{x} + \frac{dy}{y} + \frac{d\mu}{2\mu} = 0$$

or

$$\mu = cx^{-2}y^{-2}$$

and letting $c = 1$, a particular solution and integrating factor is

$$\mu = x^{-2}y^{-2}.$$

88. The General First Order Equation.

A method for finding the complete solution of a general first order partial differential equation was developed by Lagrange and Charpit and is often called the *Lagrange-Charpit method.* Consider a general equation of the form

$$\text{(1)} \qquad f(x,y,z,p,q) = 0$$

in which p, q, and z are functions of the independent variables x and y and p and q are defined by

(2) $$p = \frac{\partial z}{\partial x}, \; q = \frac{\partial z}{\partial y}$$

and we have

(3) $$\frac{\partial p}{\partial y} = \frac{\partial q}{\partial x}.$$

The total differential of z is therefore given by

(4) $$dz = p \, dx + q \, dy.$$

The method consists of finding a relation

(5) $$\varphi(x,y,z,p,q,c) = 0$$

and solving equations (1) and (5) simultaneously for p and q. Furthermore, the values of p and q must be such that when they are substituted into the total differential (4), it must be integrable. The problem then is to find the relation $\varphi(x,y,z,p,q,c)$ where c is an arbitrary constant. Let us differentiate equations (1) and (5) with respect to x and y to obtain

(6) $$\begin{cases} \dfrac{\partial f}{\partial x} + \dfrac{\partial f}{\partial z} p + \dfrac{\partial f}{\partial p} \dfrac{\partial p}{\partial x} + \dfrac{\partial f}{\partial q} \dfrac{\partial q}{\partial x} = 0, \\[2mm] \dfrac{\partial f}{\partial y} + \dfrac{\partial f}{\partial z} q + \dfrac{\partial f}{\partial p} \dfrac{\partial p}{\partial y} + \dfrac{\partial f}{\partial q} \dfrac{\partial q}{\partial y} = 0, \\[2mm] \dfrac{\partial \varphi}{\partial x} + \dfrac{\partial \varphi}{\partial z} p + \dfrac{\partial \varphi}{\partial p} \dfrac{\partial p}{\partial x} + \dfrac{\partial \varphi}{\partial q} \dfrac{\partial q}{\partial x} = 0, \\[2mm] \dfrac{\partial \varphi}{\partial y} + \dfrac{\partial \varphi}{\partial z} q + \dfrac{\partial \varphi}{\partial p} \dfrac{\partial p}{\partial y} + \dfrac{\partial \varphi}{\partial q} \dfrac{\partial q}{\partial y} = 0. \end{cases}$$

We shall now eliminate p_x, p_y, q_x, and q_y from these four equations by multiplying the first equation by $-\varphi_p$, the second by $-\varphi_q$, the third by f_p, and the fourth by f_q and adding results, remembering that $p_y = q_x$, to obtain

(7) $$\frac{\partial f}{\partial p} \frac{\partial \varphi}{\partial y} + \frac{\partial f}{\partial q} \frac{\partial \varphi}{\partial y} - \left(\frac{\partial f}{\partial x} + p \frac{\partial f}{\partial z} \right) \frac{\partial \varphi}{\partial p} - \left(\frac{\partial f}{\partial y} + q \frac{\partial f}{\partial z} \right) \frac{\partial \varphi}{\partial q}$$
$$+ \left(\frac{\partial f}{\partial p} p + \frac{\partial f}{\partial q} q \right) \frac{\partial \varphi}{\partial z} = 0.$$

This is a first order linear equation in the variables x, y, z, p, q, and we may apply the method of Lagrange (Section 86). Thus we desire to find a simple form of φ which satisfies the system of ordinary differential equations

$$(8) \quad \frac{dx}{f_p} = \frac{dy}{f_q} = \frac{dp}{-(f_x + pf_z)} = \frac{dq}{-(f_y + qf_z)} = \frac{dz}{pf_p + qf_q}.$$

Illustration. Solve

$$p^2 = 2xq.$$

Solution. For this problem we have

$$f = p^2 - 2xq = 0,$$

$f_x = -2q$	$f_p = 2p$
$f_y = 0$	$f_q = -2x$
$f_z = 0$	

and equation (8) becomes

$$\frac{dx}{2p} = \frac{dy}{-2x} = \frac{dp}{2q} = \frac{dq}{0} = \frac{dz}{2p^2 - 2xq}.$$

The fourth fraction states that

$$dq = 0 \quad \text{or} \quad q = c,$$

which is indeed a simple form of φ. A substitution into the given equation yields

$$p^2 = 2cx;$$

the total differential becomes

$$dz = \sqrt{2cx}\, dx + c\, dy$$

and

$$z = \tfrac{2}{3}\sqrt{2c}\, x^{3/2} + cy + k$$

is the complete solution.

It should be noted that there is no unique complete solution to the given partial differential equation, as other forms for different choices of the function φ will also satisfy the original equation.

Illustration. Solve

$$q = p^2 x.$$

Solution. For this problem we have

$f \equiv q - p^2 x = 0$	$f_x = -p^2$
$f_p = -2px$	$f_y = 0$
$f_q = 1$	$f_z = 0$

and equation (8) becomes

$$\frac{dx}{-2px} = \frac{dy}{1} = \frac{dp}{p^2} = \frac{dq}{0} = \frac{dz}{q - 2p^2x}.$$

Again we have $q = c$ for a choice of φ, which yields

$$p = c^{\frac{1}{2}}x^{-\frac{1}{2}}$$

and

$$dz = c^{\frac{1}{2}}x^{-\frac{1}{2}}\,dx + c\,dy.$$

The solution is

$$z = 2c^{\frac{1}{2}}x^{\frac{1}{2}} + cy + k.$$

However, we could also consider the second and third fractions

$$\frac{dy}{1} = \frac{dp}{p^2}$$

to obtain

$$p = (c - y)^{-1} \quad \text{and} \quad q = x(c - y)^{-2}.$$

The total differential becomes

$$dz = (c - y)^{-1}\,dx + x(c - y)^{-2}\,dy$$

and an integration yields

$$z + k = \frac{x}{c - y}$$

or

$$x = (c - y)(z + k),$$

which is also a complete solution of the given partial differential equation.

89. Exercise XX.

1. Find the partial differential equations whose integrals are
   (a) $z = ax + y$,
   (b) $z = ax + bxy$,
   (c) $z = \frac{1}{2}a^2x^2 + a^2y + bxy + c$.

2. Solve:

   (a) $\dfrac{\partial z}{\partial y} = ax + 2y$.

   (b) $q = y^2$.

   (c) $p = xy + y^2$.

(d) $\dfrac{\partial^2 z}{\partial y^2} + \dfrac{\partial z}{\partial y} = 4y^3$.

(e) $\dfrac{\partial^2 z}{\partial x^2} = 12x^2 + 2y$.

3. Solve:

(a) $(y - z)p + (z - x)q = x - y$.

(b) $ap + bq = c$.

(c) $xp + yq = z$.

(d) $(1 + y)p + (1 + x)q = 1 + z$.

(e) $yzp + xzq + 2xy = 0$.

4. Solve:

(a) $pq = k$.

(b) $p + q = x$.

(c) $q^2 = z + xp$.

(d) $xp + yq + pq = 0$.

(e) $yp^2 - xq^2 = 0$.

5. In solving $f(z,p,q) = 0$ we may use $\varphi = p - cq$. Use this fact to solve:

(a) $z^2(p^2 + q^2 + 1) = a^2$.

(b) $zp^2 = q$.

(c) $p^2 + q^2 = z$.

XIII

PARTIAL DIFFERENTIAL EQUATIONS OF HIGHER ORDER

90. Definitions. We shall limit our attention to partial differential equations which are *linear* in the dependent variable and all its derivatives. The general type may be written in the form

$$(1) \qquad \sum_{i=0,\,j=0}^{n,\,n} P_{ij}(x,y) \frac{\partial^{i+j}z}{\partial x^i \partial y^j} = f(x,y)$$

with $\qquad i+j \leq n$ and $\dfrac{\partial^0 z}{\partial x^0 \partial y^0} = z.$

The coefficients $P_{ij}(x,y)$ are functions of the independent variables x and y, which, of course, include constants. A specific example would be the equation

$$ax \frac{\partial^2 z}{\partial x^2} + by \frac{\partial^2 z}{\partial x \partial y} + \frac{\partial z}{\partial x} = e^x.$$

If the derivatives are all of the same order, i.e., if $i+j = n$ in all terms, then the equation is said to be **homogeneous**. The equation

$$\frac{\partial^2 z}{\partial x^2} - \frac{\partial^2 z}{\partial x \partial y} + a^2 \frac{\partial^2 z}{\partial y^2} = \sin x$$

is an example of a second order homogeneous partial differential equation.

The treatment of these partial differential equations will be very similar to that for ordinary linear differential equations. Let us define the operators

$$(2) \qquad D \equiv \frac{\partial}{\partial x} \quad \text{and} \quad D^* \equiv \frac{\partial}{\partial y}.$$

Then equation (1) can be written in the form

$$(3) \qquad F(D,D^*)z = f(x,y),$$

where $F(D,D^*)$ is a function of the operators, (2), and the coefficients P_{ij}. As in the case of the ordinary differential equations we shall first consider the solution to the equation

$$F(D,D^*)z = 0$$

and call this the **complementary function.** The *general integral* will again be the sum of the complementary function and a *particular integral* satisfying equation (1).

The following two properties are useful.

I. $$F(D,D^*)e^{hx+ky} = F(h,k)e^{hx+ky}$$

since

$$D(e^{hx+ky}) = he^{hx+ky}$$

and

$$D^*(e^{hx+ky}) = ke^{hx+ky}.$$

II. If $z_i = f_i$, $(i = 1, \cdots, n)$ are solutions of the nth order equation $F(D,D^*)z = 0$,

then

$$z = f_1 + f_2 + \cdots + f_n$$

is the general solution.

91. Homogeneous Equation with Constant Coefficients.

Consider the homogeneous linear partial differential equation

$$(1) \quad F(D,D^*)z = a_0 \frac{\partial^n z}{\partial x^n} + a_1 \frac{\partial^n z}{\partial x^{n-1} \partial y} + \cdots + a_n \frac{\partial^n z}{\partial y^n} = 0$$

where a_i, $(i = 0, \cdots, n)$, are constants. Let φ be a function of $y + mx$; then

$$\frac{\partial^n \varphi}{\partial x^r \partial y^s} = m^r \varphi^{(r+s)}(y + mx)$$

where

$$\varphi^{(r+s)}(y + mx) \equiv \frac{d^{r+s}\varphi(y + mx)}{[d(y + mx)]^{r+s}}$$

and $r + s = n$. Now if

$$(2) \quad z = \varphi(y + mx)$$

satisfies equation (1), it will be a solution. After obtaining the partial derivatives of z and substituting into (1) we have

$$\varphi^{(n)}(y + mx)[a_0 m^n + a_1 m^{n-1} + \cdots + a_n] = 0,$$

which will be satisfied if

(3) $F(m,1) = a_0 m^n + a_1 m^{n-1} + \cdots + a_n = 0.$

Equation (3) is called the auxiliary equation and has n roots $m_1, m_2, \cdots, m_n$. If these roots are all real and distinct, then

(4) $z = \varphi_1(y + m_1 x) + \varphi_2(y + m_2 x) + \cdots + \varphi_n(y + m_n x)$

is the general solution of (1).

Illustration. Solve

$$\frac{\partial^2 z}{\partial x^2} - a \frac{\partial^2 z}{\partial x \partial y} - 6a^2 \frac{\partial^2 z}{\partial y^2} = 0.$$

Solution. The auxiliary equation is

$$F(m,1) = m^2 - am - 6a^2 = 0,$$

which has the roots $m = 3a, -2a$. Hence the general solution is

$$z = \varphi(y + 3ax) + \psi(y - 2ax).$$

If the roots of the auxiliary equation are not distinct, we employ the same technique as we did for ordinary differential equations. Thus, suppose that m_1 is an r-fold root of equation (3); then

$$z_r = \varphi_0(y + m_1 x) + x\varphi_1(y + m_1 x) + \cdots + x^{r-1}\varphi_{r-1}(y + m_1 x)$$

is a solution of the given differential equation.

Illustration. Solve

$$\frac{\partial^2 z}{\partial x^2} - 2a \frac{\partial^2 z}{\partial x \partial y} + a^2 \frac{\partial^2 z}{\partial y^2} = 0.$$

Solution. The auxiliary equation is

$$m^2 - 2am + a^2 = 0,$$

which has the roots $m = a, a$. The general solution is

$$z = \varphi(y + ax) + x\psi(y + ax).$$

If the auxiliary equation contains complex roots, they will occur in conjugate pairs since we are considering only real coefficients of the differential equation. Let the complex roots be $\alpha + i\beta$ and $\alpha - i\beta$; then the corresponding complementary function will be $\varphi(y + \alpha x + i\beta x) + \psi(y + \alpha x - i\beta x)$. From the theory of complex variables we will accept the fact that if φ_1 and ψ_1 are real functions, and we let

$$\varphi = \varphi_1 + i\psi_1 \quad \text{and} \quad \psi = \varphi_1 - i\psi_1,$$

then

$$z = \varphi_1(y + \alpha x + i\beta x) + \varphi_1(y + \alpha x - i\beta x) \\ + i[\psi_1(y + \alpha x + i\beta x) - \psi_1(y + \alpha x - i\beta x)]$$

is real, and we shall let this be the complementary function of the solution to the differential equation.

Illustration. Solve

$$\frac{\partial^4 z}{\partial x^4} - 6\frac{\partial^4 z}{\partial x^3 \partial y} + 14\frac{\partial^4 z}{\partial x^2 \partial y^2} - 16\frac{\partial^4 z}{\partial x \partial y^3} + 8\frac{\partial^4 z}{\partial y^4} = 0.$$

Solution. The auxiliary equation is

$$m^4 - 6m^3 + 14m^2 - 16m + 8 = 0$$

with roots $m = 2, 2, 1 \pm i$. Hence the general solution is

$$z = \varphi_0(y + 2x) + x\psi_0(y + 2x) + \varphi_1(y + x + ix) \\ + \varphi_1(y + x - ix) + i[\psi_1(y + x + ix) - \psi_1(y + x - ix)].$$

92. Nonhomogeneous Linear Equation with Constant Coefficients.

Let us consider the general linear equation

$$(1) \qquad\qquad F(D,D^*)z = 0$$

in which the coefficients in $F(D,D^*)$ are constants. Substitution of

$$(2) \qquad\qquad z = ce^{ax+by}$$

into (1) yields

$$(3) \qquad\qquad F(a,b)ce^{ax+by} = 0$$

and $F(a,b) = 0$ is the general auxiliary equation. If we can find values of a and b for which the auxiliary equation is satisfied, then (2) is a solution of equation (1). Since this is one equation in two variables, there exist an infinite number of ordered pairs (a,b) which will satisfy the auxiliary equation. If $F(a,b) = 0$ is an nth degree equation, we can solve for n roots of a in terms of b to obtain

$$a_1 = \varphi_1(b), \ a_2 = \varphi_2(b), \cdots, \ a_n = \varphi_n(b).$$

Then the general solution of the partial differential equation is

(4)
$$z = \sum_{i=1}^{n} c_i e^{\varphi_i(b)x + by}$$

where c_i are arbitrary constants and b is any arbitrary value consistent in each term.

Occasionally it is possible to factor $F(a,b)$ into linear factors. If such a linear factor is found, say

$$a - \alpha b - \beta,$$

we can solve for a and obtain the specific expression

$$a = \alpha b + \beta$$

so that one solution will have the form

$$z = \sum c_i e^{b_i(\alpha x + y) + \beta x} = e^{\beta x} \sum c_i e^{b_i(\alpha x + y)}$$

for arbitrary values of b_i. The last expression is an arbitrary function of $\alpha x + y$, and we can write

$$\sum c_i e^{b_i(\alpha x + y)} = \varphi(\alpha x + y)$$

so that another form of the solution will be

(5)
$$z = e^{\beta x} \varphi(\alpha x + y).$$

Illustration. Solve

$$(D^2 + 2DD^* + D^{*2} - D - D^*)z = 0.$$

Solution. The auxiliary equation is

$$F(a,b) = a^2 + 2ab + b^2 - a - b = 0,$$

which can be factored into

$$(a + b)(a + b - 1) = 0.$$

Thus

$$a = -b + 0 \quad \text{and} \quad a = -b + 1$$

so that we have $\alpha_1 = -1$, $\beta_1 = 0$ and $\alpha_2 = -1$, $\beta_2 = 1$. The solution in the form of equation (5) is

$$z = e^{0x}\varphi(-x + y) + e^x\psi(-x + y)$$
$$= \varphi(y - x) + e^x\psi(y - x).$$

If a linear factor is repeated, we have the same situation as for repeated roots in the homogeneous equation, and the solution will take the form

(6)
$$z = e^{\beta x}[\varphi_1(\alpha x + y) + x\varphi_2(\alpha x + y)]$$
for a 2-fold linear factor.

Illustration. Solve
$$(D - D^* - 1)^3 z = 0.$$

Solution. The auxiliary equation is
$$(a - b - 1)^3 = 0$$
so that
$$a = b + 1$$
is a 3-fold solution of a in terms of b, with $\alpha = 1$ and $\beta = 1$. The general solution is therefore
$$z = e^x[\varphi_1(y + x) + x\varphi_2(y + x) + x^2\varphi_3(y + x)].$$

93. Complete Linear Equation. If the right-hand side is not equal to zero, we have the complete linear equation
(1)
$$F(D,D^*)z = f(x,y).$$
The solution can be obtained in two parts as was done for ordinary differential equations, namely,
(2)
$$z = z_c + z_p$$
where z_c is the integral of $F(D,D^*)z = 0$ and z_p is any particular integral of equation (1).

The particular integral may be found by the method of undetermined coefficients. We shall limit ourselves to two common forms of $f(x,y)$.

I. *Exponential.* $f(x,y) = ce^{ax+by}$. Assume the form
$$z_p = Ae^{ax+by}.$$
Then
$$F(D,D^*)z_p = AF(a,b)e^{ax+by} = ce^{ax+by}$$
and we can solve for A to obtain
$$A = \frac{c}{F(a,b)}.$$

II. *Trigonometric.* $f(x,y) = c_1 \sin (ax + by) + c_2 \cos (ax + by)$. Assume the form
$$z_p = A \sin (ax + by) + B \cos (ax + by)$$

and substitute into $F(D,D^*)z = f(x,y)$. The values for A and B are now found by equating the coefficients of like terms.

Illustration. Solve

$$(D^2 - 2DD^* + D^{*2} - D + D^*)z = 2e^{2x+3y} - \sin(x+2y).$$

Solution. The auxiliary equation is

$$(a^2 - 2ab + b^2 - a + b) = (a - b)(a - b - 1) = 0$$

and the complementary function is

$$z_c = \varphi_1(y + x) + e^x\varphi_2(y + x).$$

The part of z_p corresponding to $2e^{2x+3y}$ is

$$z_p = \frac{2}{F(2,3)}e^{2x+3y} = \frac{2}{(2-3)(2-3-1)}e^{2x+3y} = e^{2x+3y}.$$

For the trigonometric part let

$$\begin{aligned}
z_p &= A\sin(x+2y) + B\cos(x+2y), \\
Dz_p &= A\cos(x+2y) - B\sin(x+2y), \\
D^2z_p &= -A\sin(x+2y) - B\cos(x+2y), \\
D^*z_p &= 2A\cos(x+2y) - 2B\sin(x+2y), \\
D^{*2}z_p &= -4A\sin(x+2y) - 4B\cos(x+2y), \\
DD^*z_p &= -2A\sin(x+2y) - 2B\cos(x+2y).
\end{aligned}$$

A substitution of these values into the differential equation yields

$$-(A + B)\sin(x+2y) + (A - B)\cos(x+2y) = -\sin(x+2y)$$

so that

$$A + B = 1 \quad \text{and} \quad A - B = 0.$$

or

$$A = \tfrac{1}{2} \quad \text{and} \quad B = \tfrac{1}{2}.$$

Hence the particular integral is

$$z_p = \tfrac{1}{2}\sin(x+2y) + \tfrac{1}{2}\cos(x+2y).$$

The complete solution is given by

$$\begin{aligned}
z = \varphi_1(y + x) + e^x\varphi_2(y + x) + e^{2x+3y} \\
+ \tfrac{1}{2}\sin(x+2y) + \tfrac{1}{2}\cos(x+2y).
\end{aligned}$$

If the form of the particular solution is contained in the complementary function, we need to multiply the particular integral by powers of the independent variable as we did in the case of ordinary differential equations.

Illustration. Solve

$$(D^2 - 3DD^* + 2D^{*2} - 2D + 3D^* + 1)z = 4e^x.$$

Solution. The auxiliary equation is

$$a^2 - 3ab + 2b^2 - 2a + 3b + 1 = (a - 2b - 1)(a - b - 1) = 0.$$

Hence the complementary function is

$$z = e^x[\varphi_1(x + y) + \varphi_2(2x + y)].$$

To find the particular integral we would normally assume

$$z_p = Ae^x$$

but, since e^x is contained in the complementary function, we might assume

$$z_p = Axe^x$$

and obtain

$$Dz_p = Ae^x(1 + x), \quad D^2z_p = Ae^x(2 + x),$$
$$D^*z_p = D^{*2}z_p = DD^*z_p = 0.$$

A substitution into the given equation yields

$$Ae^x[2 + x - 2 - 2x + x] = 0 \; Ae^x,$$

which should equal the right-hand side of the given equation. This impossible situation indicates that there is a combination of

$$\varphi_1(x + y) \quad \text{and} \quad \varphi_2(2x + y)$$

which gives

$$\varphi_1 + \varphi_2 = x,$$

and a little study shows that if

$$\varphi_1(x + y) = -x - y, \quad \varphi_2(2x + y) = 2x + y,$$

we have

$$\varphi_1 + \varphi_2 = -x - y + 2x + y = x.$$

Consequently, we must assume

$$z_p = Ax^2e^x$$

so that

$$Dz_p = Ae^x(x^2 + 2x), \quad D^2z_p = Ae^x(x^2 + 4x + 2),$$
$$D^*z_p = D^{*2}z_p = DD^*z_p = 0,$$

and

$$Ae^x(x^2 + 4x + 2 - 2x^2 - 4x + x^2) = Ae^x(2) = 4e^x.$$

The result is $A = 2$, and the particular integral is

$$z_p = 2x^2e^x.$$

The complete solution is

$$z = e^x\big[\varphi_1(x + y) + \varphi_2(2x + y) + 2x^2\big].$$

If it can readily be determined that forms of φ_1 and φ_2 exist which will result in the assumed form of the particular integral, this fact should be noted before substituting into the given differential equation. However, frequently, the investigation of φ_1 and φ_2 is more time-consuming than the substitution.

94. A Boundary Value Problem. The consideration of physical problems often involves not only the general solution but also that solution which satisfies specified conditions. These conditions may be stated as restrictions at the beginning of the situation (initial values) or at some other points (boundary values). Let us consider an elastic string which is held fixed and then snapped from this equilibrium position. If we restrict the resulting motion to the (x,y)-plane, it may be described by the one-dimensional wave equation

$$(1) \qquad \frac{\partial^2 y}{\partial t^2} = k^2 \frac{\partial^2 y}{\partial x^2}$$

where the parameter k is a constant which depends upon the physical properties of the string. We desire to find a function, $y = f(x,t)$ which remains finite as $t \to \infty$, is zero when $t = 0$, and is zero when $x = 0$. The solution with arbitrary constants can be found by the method of Section 93. Thus let

$$(2) \qquad y = ce^{ax+bt}$$

to obtain the auxiliary equation

$$b^2 - k^2a^2 = 0$$

or

$$b = \pm ka$$

so that

$$(3) \qquad y = e^{ax}(c_1 e^{kat} + c_2 e^{-kat}),$$

where c_1, c_2, and a are arbitrary constants, is a solution. We can also show that

$$(4) \qquad y = e^{-ax}(c_3 e^{kat} + c_4 e^{-kat})$$

is a solution. Consequently

$$(5) \qquad y = e^{ax}(c_1 e^{kat} + c_2 e^{-kat}) + e^{-ax}(c_3 e^{kat} + c_4 e^{-kat})$$

is a solution.

We now impose the boundary conditions. First, the condition that y must remain finite as $t \to \infty$ can be met if we let a be imaginary; i.e., $a = i\alpha$. Then

$$y = e^{i\alpha x}(c_1 e^{i\alpha kt} + c_2 e^{-i\alpha kt}) + e^{-i\alpha x}(c_3 e^{i\alpha kt} + c_4 e^{-i\alpha kt})$$

or (see Chapter VI, Section 46)

$$y = e^{i\alpha x}(A_1 \cos \alpha kt + B_1 \sin \alpha kt) + e^{-i\alpha x}(A_2 \cos \alpha kt + B_2 \sin \alpha kt).$$

By again considering the properties of $e^{\pm i\alpha x}$ we can change this solution to the form

$$y = A \cos \alpha x \cos \alpha kt + B \sin \alpha x \cos \alpha kt$$
$$+ C \sin \alpha x \sin \alpha kt + D \cos \alpha x \sin \alpha kt$$

where A, B, C, D and α are arbitrary constants. Let us now apply the remaining boundary conditions, i.e., $y = 0$ at $t = 0$ and $y = 0$ at $x = 0$;

$$t = 0: \qquad 0 = A \cos \alpha x + B \sin \alpha x.$$
$$x = 0: \qquad 0 = A \cos \alpha kt + D \sin \alpha kt.$$

Consequently, $A = B = D = 0$ and the solution takes the form

$$(6) \qquad y = C \sin \alpha x \sin \alpha kt$$

where C and α are arbitrary constants. The boundary conditions evidently are not sufficient to yield a solution free of arbitrary constants, and additional restrictions must be imposed to determine C and α. Consequently, a sum of terms of the form given by equation (6) will also be a solution.

95. Monge's Method.
A technique for finding solutions of the equation

$$(1) \qquad Rr + Ss + Tt = V,$$

where R, S, T, and V are functions of x, y, z, p, and q in the two independent variables x and y, was developed by Gaspard Monge and is known as *Monge's method*. We recall the definitions of p, q, r, s, and t (Section 82) and write

$$(2) \qquad\qquad dz = p\,dx + q\,dy,$$

$$(3) \qquad\qquad \begin{cases} dp = r\,dx + s\,dy, \\ dq = s\,dx + t\,dy. \end{cases}$$

By use of (3) we solve for r and t to obtain

$$r = \frac{dp}{dx} - s\frac{dy}{dx} \quad \text{and} \quad t = \frac{dq}{dy} - s\frac{dx}{dy}$$

and a substitution into (1) yields

$$(4) \qquad s\left(R\frac{dy}{dx} - S + T\frac{dx}{dy}\right) = R\frac{dp}{dx} + T\frac{dq}{dy} - V.$$

This equation will be satisfied if

$$(5) \qquad \begin{cases} R\,dy^2 - S\,dx\,dy + T\,dx^2 = 0, \\ R\,dy\,dp + T\,dx\,dq - V\,dx\,dy = 0, \end{cases}$$

simultaneously. Equations (2) and (5) are three total differential equations in five variables x, y, z, p, q. Since ordinarily four equations are required, we can find integrals for this system only in special cases. We first solve

$$R\,dy^2 - S\,dx\,dy + T\,dx^2 = 0$$

for $\dfrac{dy}{dx}$ and then

(a) substitute one solution into the other two equations to obtain a first order partial differential equation which may be integrated to find the required solution; or

(b) use both solutions to obtain two first order partial differential equations, solve these for p and q, and substitute into

$$dz = p\,dx + q\,dy,$$

and integrate to obtain the required solution.

Illustration 1. Solve

$$r + 2s + t = 0.$$

Solution. In this problem we have

$$R = 1,\ S = 2,\ T = 1,\ V = 0,$$

and equations (5) have the form

$$\begin{cases} dy^2 - 2\,dx\,dy + dx^2 = 0, \\ dy\,dp + dx\,dq = 0. \end{cases}$$

The first equation factors into

$$(dy - dx)^2 = 0$$

from which we get

$$dy = dx \quad \text{and} \quad y - x = c_1.$$

A substitution into the second equation yields

$$dx(dp + dq) = 0$$

and after an integration we have

$$p + q = c_2.$$

This is a first order linear equation which we can solve by Lagrange's method (Section 86),

$$\frac{dx}{1} = \frac{dy}{1} = \frac{dz}{c_2},$$

to get

$$z = c_2 x + c_3,$$

and replacing c_2 and c_3 by arbitrary functions of $c_1 = y - x$ we obtain the solution

$$z = x\varphi_1(y - x) + \varphi_2(y - x).$$

Illustration 2. Solve the wave equation

$$r - a^2 t = 0.$$

Solution. In this problem we have

$$R = 1,\ S = 0,\ T = -a^2,\ V = 0,$$

so that equations (5) have the form

$$\begin{cases} dy^2 - a^2\,dx^2 = 0, \\ dy\,dp - a^2\,dx\,dq = 0. \end{cases}$$

The first equation factors into

$$(dy - a\,dx)(dy + a\,dx) = 0.$$

Considering the first factor, we have

$$dy = a\,dx \quad \text{and} \quad y - ax = c_1,$$

which when combined with the second equation yields

$$a\,dp - a^2\,dq = 0 \quad \text{or} \quad p - aq = c_2 = \varphi(y - ax).$$

The second factor yields

$$dy = -a\,dx \quad \text{and} \quad y + ax = c_3,$$

which when substituted into the second equation give

$$dp + a\,dq = 0 \quad \text{or} \quad p + aq = c_4 = \psi(y + ax).$$

We now solve the system

$$p - aq = \varphi(y - ax),$$
$$p + aq = \psi(y + ax)$$

for p and q to obtain

$$\begin{cases} p = \tfrac{1}{2}[\varphi(y - ax) + \psi(y + ax)], \\ q = \dfrac{1}{2a}[\psi(y + ax) - \varphi(y - ax)]. \end{cases}$$

These values of p and q are now substituted into the equation

$$dz = p\,dx + q\,dy$$

to give

$$dz = \frac{1}{2}\big[\varphi(y - ax) + \psi(y + ax)\big]dx + \frac{1}{2a}\big[\psi(y + ax) - \varphi(y - ax)\big]dy$$

$$= \frac{1}{2a}\,\psi(y + ax)(dy + a\,dx) - \frac{1}{2a}\,\varphi(y - ax)(dy - a\,dx)$$

$$= f_1(u)du - f_2(v)dv.$$

We can integrate this equation to obtain the solution

$$z = F_1(y + ax) - F_2(y - ax) + k$$

where

$$F_1(y + ax) = \frac{1}{2a}\int \psi(y + ax)(dy + a\,dx),$$

$$F_2(y - ax) = \frac{1}{2a}\int \varphi(y - ax)(dy - a\,dx).$$

96. Exercise XXI. Solve the following partial differential equations.

1. $(D^2 - DD^* - 12D^{*2})z = 0.$
2. $(D^4 - 2D^3D^* - 21D^2D^{*2} + 22DD^{*3} + 40D^{*4})z = 0.$

3. $(D^3 - 9D^2D^* - 24DD^{*2} + 216D^{*3})z = 0.$

4. $(D^3 + 8D^2D^* + 13DD^{*2} + 6D^{*3})z = 0.$

5. $(6D^3 - 11D^2D^* + 6DD^{*2} - D^{*3})z = 0.$

6. $(D^2 - D^{*2} + D - D^*)z = 0.$

7. $(2D^2 - 5DD^* + 3D^{*2} + 2D^* - 8)z = 0.$ (Hint: add and subtract $4a + 4b$ in $F(a,b) = 0$.)

8. $(D^2 - DD^* - D + D^*)z = 4e^{2x+y} + \cos (3x - y).$

9. $r - s - 6t = 0.$

10. $ps - qr = 0.$

3. $(D^2 - 9D^2) - 21(D^2)^2 - 21(D^2)^2 - 21(D^2)^2\beta = 0$.
4. $(D^4 + 8(D)^2 + 13(D^2)^2 + (D^2)^2\beta = 0$.
5. $5(D^2 + 11)D^2 + 6(D^2)^2\beta = 0$.
6. $(D^2 - D^2 + D^2 - D^2)\beta = 0$.

XIV

ELEMENTARY SCIENTIFIC ANALYSES

97. Introduction. In the application of mathematics to scientific problems various concepts become tools. It has long been recognized that the subject of differential equations contains some of the most powerful tools. However, in the investigations of scientific problems the emphasis should be placed upon the solution of the problems and not upon the techniques. Considerable knowledge of the basic laws of nature is necessary to build the appropriate mathematical model. Assumptions and simplifications should always be clearly stated, and the limitations of the conclusions should be specified.

If the original problem is a comparatively complicated one, it is often desirable to study a related problem whose description approximates that of the original problem, but whose solution is more readily obtained. This gives a qualitative concept of the behavior of the solution and may be used as a check when solving the more sophisticated problem.

With the completion of a course in elementary differential equations and courses of the corresponding level in physics and engineering, the student has reached a certain maturity, which should permit him to analyze elementary scientific problems. We shall devote this chapter to the illustration of procedures in the analysis of scientific problems and at the same time present some applications of differential equations. Two problems are presented; one is concerned with pursuit courses and the second with ballistic trajectories. The manner of presentation of the second problem is based on some work by Robert V. Esperti.

Problem I.   Pursuit Courses*

98. Statement of the Problem. The problem of determining the equation of a curve of pursuit is a classical problem in mathe-

---

* For a more detailed discussion of pursuit courses see K. L. Nielsen and J. F. Heyda, *The Mathematical Theory of Airborne Fire Control* (Washington: U.S. Government Printing Service, 1951), Chapter 3.

matics. Historically it dates back to the time of Leonardo da Vinci. One classical statement of the problem was to determine a dog's course as the dog runs toward its master who is walking along a straight path. The military aspects of the problem were brought into prominence in connection with aircraft combat wherein one aircraft is attacked by another possessing guns capable of being fired in a fixed direction only. In order for the one aircraft to keep the other under continuous fire, it must fly some kind of pursuit course. The problem appears again with the invention of homing missiles which continuously change heading under radio, optical, or acoustic guidance unwillingly supplied by the target.

Let us consider the combat between two airplanes with the fighter airplane attacking the target airplane. If the fighter pilot flies his airplane in such a way that his guns are always pointed directly at the target, he is said to fly a *pure pursuit course*. If the fighter flies so that his guns are always directed at a point ahead of the target by the required amount to secure a hit, then he is said to fly a *deviated pursuit course* (also a *lead pursuit course*). There are other types of pursuit courses, but we shall limit ourselves to these two.

In analyzing pursuit courses, there is still another method of classification; namely, the distinction between the actual space course traversed by the combating aircraft and the path of one aircraft relative to the other.

99. The Space Course. If we consider the target to fly a straight and level course, the fighter's motion lies in a geometric plane with the target's course and this plane is called the *plane of action*. We need then to consider only an (x,y)-coordinate system. Let (x_F, y_F) and (x_T, y_T) be the coordinates of the fighter and target, respectively, at any time t. See Fig. 32, p. 216. In a pure pursuit course the fighter is pointing directly at the target so that the equation of the tangent line to the fighter's path must be satisfied by the target's coordinates. Thus we have

$$(1) \qquad\qquad y_T - y_F = m(x_T - x_F)$$

where m is the slope of the tangent, so that

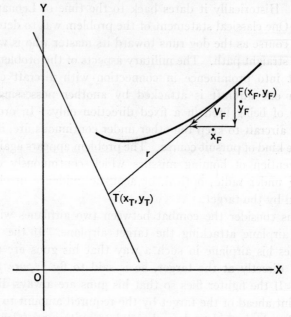

Fig. 32

$$m = \frac{dy_F}{dx_F} = \frac{\dot{y}_F}{\dot{x}_F} \tag{2}$$

and

$$y_T - y_F = \frac{\dot{y}_F}{\dot{x}_F}(x_T - x_F). \tag{3}$$

Referring to the velocity diagram of Fig. 32 we see that

$$\dot{x}_F^2 + \dot{y}_F^2 = V_F^2. \tag{4}$$

Solve equation (3) for $\dot{y}_F$ and substitute into (4) to obtain

$$\dot{x}_F^2\left[1 + \left(\frac{y_T - y_F}{x_T - x_F}\right)^2\right] = V_F^2 \tag{5}$$

or, upon simplifying,

$$\dot{x}_F^2 = V_F^2\frac{(x_T - x_F)^2}{r^2} \tag{6}$$

where

$$r^2 = (x_T - x_F)^2 + (y_T - y_F)^2. \tag{7}$$

The quantity r is the *range* between the target and the fighter at any time t. Equation (6) yields an expression for the time derivative of the fighter's x-coordinate. We can also solve equation (3) for $\dot{x}_F$ and obtain an expression for the time derivative of the fighter's y-coordinate. Thus we have the system of differential equations,

(8)
$$\begin{cases} \dot{x}_F = \dfrac{V_F}{r}\,(x_T - x_F), \\[2mm] \dot{y}_F = \dfrac{V_F}{r}\,(y_T - y_F), \end{cases}$$

which describes the motion of the fighter in terms of coordinates of the target, the fighter's velocity, and the range. The right-hand sides of both equations are thus functions of time, t, the independent variable. For certain restricted cases, these differential equations may be solved explicitly; however, in general, it will be necessary to solve this system numerically.

Let us consider the special case which has the target moving along the positive y-axis at a constant velocity, V_T, and initial coordinates $(0,0)$ at $t = 0$. Let the fighter fly at a constant speed,

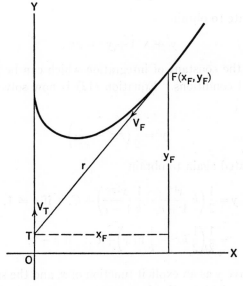

Fig. 33

V_F, and have initial coordinates (x_0, y_0); we shall drop the subscript F from the fighter's coordinates. See Fig. 33. For this case we have

$$x_T = 0 \quad \text{and} \quad y_T = V_T t$$

so that equation (1) becomes

$$V_T t - y = -\frac{dy}{dx} x$$

or

(9) $$y = V_T t + y'x.$$

We can eliminate the variable t by using the arc length along the fighter's path $s = V_F t$, and letting $c = V_T / V_F$ we obtain

(10) $$y = cs + y'x.$$

Differentiate equation (10) to obtain

(11) $$xy'' = c\sqrt{1 + y'^2}$$

since $s' = -\sqrt{1 + y'^2}$. We can now separate the variables

$$\frac{y''}{\sqrt{1 + y'^2}} = \frac{c}{x}$$

and integrate to obtain

(12) $$y' + \sqrt{1 + y'^2} = kx^c,$$

where k is the constant of integration which can be determined from initial conditions. Equation (12) is now solved for y' to give

$$y' = \frac{1}{2}\left(kx^c - \frac{1}{kx^c}\right)$$

and integrated again to obtain

(13) $$y = \frac{1}{2}\left(k\,\frac{x^{1+c}}{1+c} - \frac{1}{k}\,\frac{x^{1-c}}{1-c}\right) + C, \quad \text{if } c \neq 1,$$

$$= \frac{1}{2}\left(\frac{1}{2}\,kx^2 - \frac{1}{k}\ln x\right) + C, \quad \text{if } c = 1.$$

Thus we have y as an explicit function of x, and the space course of the fighter is determined.

100. The Relative Course. The relative course is the one that is seen by an observer who has stationed himself in one of the airplanes and is viewing the other. Let us place the observer at the target and consider the relative course of the pursuer. This relative course is best described in terms of a polar coordinate system which has its origin at the observer. Let us therefore choose a system which measures the angle θ from the stern end of the longitudinal axis of the target aircraft. See Fig. 34. We

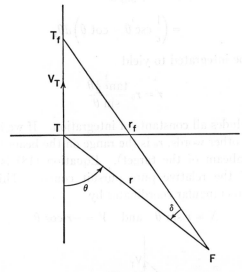

Fig. 34

shall consider a deviated pursuit course and let the deviation be measured by the angle, δ, at which the fighter aircraft is flying away from the direct line to the target. If $\delta = 0$, we have a pure pursuit course, and if δ is a constant, we have a *fixed lead pursuit*.

The polar radius r is also the present range at any time t. From the vector diagram of Fig. 34 we have the rate of change of r,

$$(14) \qquad \dot{r} = -V_F \cos \delta + V_T \cos \theta$$

and the transverse component of relative velocity,

$$(15) \qquad r\dot{\theta} = V_F \sin \delta - V_T \sin \theta.$$

If we divide equation (14) by equation (15), we obtain

(16) $$\frac{dr}{r} = \frac{-V_F \cos\delta + V_T \cos\theta}{V_F \sin\delta - V_T \sin\theta}\, d\theta$$

$$= \frac{-\cos\delta + c\cos\theta}{\sin\delta - c\sin\theta}\, d\theta$$

where again $c = V_T/V_F$. This equation is integrable for various deviation functions. If $\delta = 0$, i.e., pure pursuit, we have

(17) $$\frac{dr}{r} = \frac{-1 + c\cos\theta}{-c\sin\theta}\, d\theta$$

$$= \left(\frac{1}{c}\csc\theta - \cot\theta\right) d\theta,$$

which can be integrated to yield

(18) $$r = r_0 \frac{\tan^{\frac{1}{c}} \frac{1}{2}\theta}{\sin\theta}$$

where r_0 includes all constants of integration. If we let $\theta = 90°$, $r = r_0$ or, in other words, r_0 is the range on the beam (the fighter is directly abeam of the target). Equation (18) is the polar equation of the relative pure pursuit course. This may be changed to rectangular coordinates by

$$X = r \sin\theta \quad \text{and} \quad Y = -r \cos\theta.$$

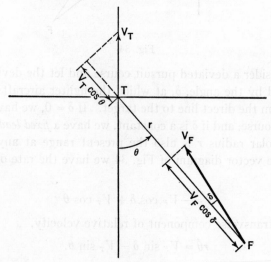

Fig. 35

In aerial combat the deviation function for a variable lead pursuit may be determined from the ballistic triangle which we show in Fig. 35 and where t_f is the time of flight of the bullet over the future range r_f and $\bar{u}$ is the average speed of the bullet. Thus we have

$$TT_f = V_T t_f \quad \text{and} \quad r_f = \bar{u} t_f.$$

The law of sines applied to triangle FTT_f yields

(19)
$$\sin \delta = \frac{TT_f}{r_f} \sin \theta = \frac{V_T t_f}{\bar{u} t_f} \sin \theta$$
$$= c_1 \sin \theta$$

where $c_1 = V_T / \bar{u}$. We shall assume this ratio to be a constant, which is not precisely true since $\bar{u}$ is a function of the range. However, it is a usable approximation. Equation (16) now becomes

(20)
$$\frac{dr}{r} = \frac{1}{c - c_1} (\sqrt{\csc^2 \theta - c_1^2} - c \cot \theta) d\theta.$$

This equation may be integrated; however, the first term on the right-hand side requires some algebraic gymnastics. Introduce a new variable, z, such that

(21)
$$z \cos \delta = c_1 \cos \theta.$$

Then by equation (19) we have the following relations (it is left for the student to check each):

$$d\delta = z\, d\theta,$$
$$dz \cos \delta = (z^2 - 1) c_1 \sin \theta \, d\theta,$$
$$d\theta = \frac{1}{z^2 - 1} \frac{\cos \delta}{c_1 \sin \theta} dz = \frac{1}{z^2 - 1} \frac{\sqrt{1 - c_1^2}}{\sqrt{c_1^2 - z^2}} dz.$$

We then have

$$\int \sqrt{\csc^2 \theta - c_1^2} \, d\theta = (c_1^2 - 1) c_1 \int \frac{dz}{(c_1^2 - z^2)(1 - z^2)},$$

and the solution to the equation (20) is

(22)
$$r = r_0 \left\{ \left[\left(\frac{\cos \delta - \cos \theta}{\cos \delta + \cos \theta} \right) \left(\frac{\cos \delta + c_1 \cos \theta}{\cos \delta - c_1 \cos \theta} \right)^{c_1} \right]^{\frac{1}{2}} \frac{1}{\sin^c \theta} \right\}^{1/c_2}$$

where $c_2 = c - c_1$ and r_0 is again the constant of integration.

During World War II the deviation, δ, was in general small, and the useful approximation of $\cos \delta = 1$ together with equation (19) made equation (16) the simple expression

(23) $$\frac{dr}{r} = \frac{1}{c - c_1} (\csc \theta - c \cot \theta)d\theta$$

which can be integrated to yield

(24) $$r^{c-c_1} = r_0{}^{c-c_1} \left(\frac{\tan \frac{1}{2}\theta}{\sin^c \theta} \right).$$

Problem II. Ballistic Trajectories

101. Statement of the Problem. It is desired to study the free fall motion of a body under the influence of a gravitational field of a single spherical body. This motion is often referred to as the **ballistic trajectory.** It is extremely important in the study of missiles, rockets, space flights, and other related subjects. The precise description of the motion involves empirical data and complicated differential equations. Consequently, we shall limit ourselves to a related but somewhat easier problem. First, we shall make the following *assumptions:*

(a) The body in question behaves as a particle (no aerodynamic forces are involved), and its mass is negligible compared to the mass of the earth.

(b) The earth is an isolated spherical body, not rotating with respect to inertial space, whose density is a function only of the distance from the center.

(c) The analysis is based upon the laws of Newtonian mechanics, including the inverse square law of gravitational attraction.

Desired results. The analysis should result in formulas from which we can calculate the elements of the trajectory if we are given initial or boundary conditions.

102. Definitions and Nomenclature. The next logical step in the analysis is to define rigorously the notation, symbols, and terminology which will be used. At this time we also adopt certain mathematical conventions and should make use of geometrical drawings to clarify the concepts.

Let us choose the configuration shown in Fig. 36, and let this figure define the direction of the x and y axes, the direction of measurement of the angles, and certain crucial points. Note that we have chosen the x-axis to pass through the *apogee*, the point of greatest distance from the earth in an elliptic orbit.

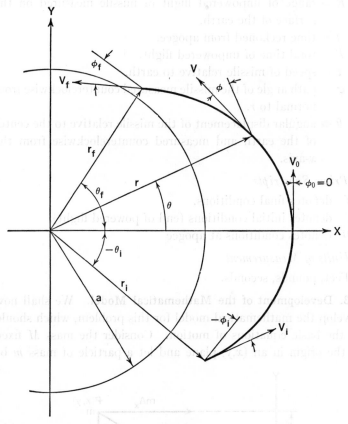

Fig. 36

To add a little glamor to our problem, let us call the body a missile so that the problem becomes a study of its unpowered flight, that is, its flight after the fuel has been spent.

Prime Symbols.

$a \equiv$ radius of the earth $\doteq 2.08555 \times 10^7$ ft.

$c \equiv GM \doteq 1.4080 \times 10^{16}$ ft.^{3} sec.$^{-2}$

$G \equiv$ universal constant of gravitation.

$h \equiv$ altitude of missile referred to the surface of the earth.

$m \equiv$ mass of the missile.

$M \equiv$ mass of the earth.

$r \equiv$ distance from center of earth to missile $= a + h$.

$R \equiv$ range of unpowered flight of missile measured on the surface of the earth.

$t \equiv$ time reckoned from apogee.

$T \equiv$ total time of unpowered flight.

$v \equiv$ speed of missile relative to earth.

$\varphi \equiv$ path angle of the missile measured counterclockwise from normal to r.

$\theta \equiv$ angular displacement of the missile relative to the center of the earth and measured counterclockwise from the x-axis.

Prime Subscripts.

f denotes final conditions.

i denotes initial conditions (end of powered flight).

0 denotes conditions at apogee.

Units of Measurement.

Feet, pounds, seconds.

103. Development of the Mathematical Model. We shall now develop the mathematical model for this problem, which should be the basic equations of motion. Consider the mass M fixed at the origin in an (x,y)-plane and let a particle of mass m be

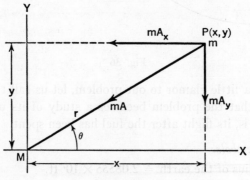

Fig. 37

situated at a point, P, in this plane. The rectangular coordinates of P are (x,y) and the polar coordinates are (r,θ). We display the configuration in Fig. 37.

According to Newtonian mechanics the mutual attraction between the two masses is given by the inverse square law,

$$(1) \qquad\qquad F_{Mm} = G\,\frac{Mm}{r^2}\,\frac{\mathbf{r}}{r}$$

in which F is the *force vector* and r is the *distance vector*. Now since we assume that m is negligible in comparison to M, the force exerted on m is given by

$$(2) \qquad\qquad F_m = m\mathbf{A}$$

where A is the acceleration imparted to m relative to the (x,y)-coordinate system. Since equations (1) and (2) are equivalent expressions of the same force, we have

$$(3) \qquad\quad F_{Mm} = F_m \quad\text{or}\quad \frac{cm}{r^2}\,\frac{\mathbf{r}}{r} = m\mathbf{A},$$

where $c = GM$ and the vector A is anti-parallel to r. Consequently, the scalar of A is given by

$$(4) \qquad\qquad A = -\,\frac{c}{r^2}.$$

From Fig. 37 we see that the components of the acceleration are given by*

$$(5) \qquad \begin{cases} A_x = \ddot{x} = A\,\cos\theta = -\dfrac{c}{r^2}\cos\theta, \\[2mm] A_y = \ddot{y} = A\,\sin\theta = -\dfrac{c}{r^2}\sin\theta. \end{cases}$$

Equations (5) are expressions which display a mixture of rectangular and polar coordinates. Let us, therefore, obtain these expressions first in rectangular coordinates alone and then in polar coordinates alone. This is accomplished by the elementary transformations:

$$(6) \qquad \begin{cases} x = r\,\cos\theta, \\ y = r\,\sin\theta, \\ r^2 = x^2 + y^2. \end{cases}$$

---

* Remember that $\ddot{x} = \dfrac{d^2x}{dt^2}$.

To obtain the equations in rectangular coordinates we solve for
$\sin \theta$, $\cos \theta$, and r and then substitute into equations (5) to
obtain

(7) $\begin{cases} \ddot{x} = -cx(x^2+y^2)^{-\frac{3}{2}}, \\ \ddot{y} = -cy(x^2+y^2)^{-\frac{3}{2}}. \end{cases}$

This is a system of second order ordinary differential equations
describing the motion of the particle of mass m in terms of its
rectangular coordinates (x,y).

To obtain the equations in polar coordinates, differentiate
the transformation equations (6) twice with respect to t. The
results are

(8) $\begin{cases} \ddot{x} = \ddot{r} \cos \theta - 2\dot{r}\dot{\theta} \sin \theta - r\ddot{\theta} \sin \theta - r\dot{\theta}^2 \cos \theta, \\ \ddot{y} = \ddot{r} \sin \theta + 2\dot{r}\dot{\theta} \cos \theta + r\ddot{\theta} \cos \theta - r\dot{\theta}^2 \sin \theta. \end{cases}$

A substitution of equations (8) into equations (5) yields

(9) $\begin{cases} \ddot{r} \cos \theta - 2\dot{r}\dot{\theta} \sin \theta - r\ddot{\theta} \sin \theta - r\dot{\theta}^2 \cos \theta = -cr^{-2} \cos \theta, \\ \ddot{r} \sin \theta + 2\dot{r}\dot{\theta} \cos \theta + r\ddot{\theta} \cos \theta - r\dot{\theta}^2 \sin \theta = -cr^{-2} \sin \theta. \end{cases}$

These equations can be simplified. Multiply the first equation
by $\cos \theta$, the second equation by $\sin \theta$ and add; the result is

$$\ddot{r} - r\dot{\theta}^2 = -cr^{-2}.$$

Multiply the first equation by $\sin \theta$, the second equation by $\cos \theta$
and subtract the first equation from the second to obtain

$$4\dot{r}\dot{\theta} + 2r\ddot{\theta} = 0.$$

Thus the two equations

(10) $\begin{cases} \ddot{r} - r\dot{\theta}^2 = -cr^{-2}, \\ 2\dot{r}\dot{\theta} + r\ddot{\theta} = 0 \end{cases}$

describe the motion of the particle m in polar coordinates, the
description of the acceleration being along the line joining M
and m and normal to this line.

Equations (7) or equations (10) form the mathematical model
for our problem. Either set describes the motion of the particle
m with respect to M in the plane of action. Other known mathematical formulas may become parts of our model; for example,
the speed of the particle is given by

$$v = \sqrt{\dot{x}^2 + \dot{y}^2}, \text{ in rectangular coordinates,}$$

or

$$v = \sqrt{\dot{r}^2 + r^2\dot{\theta}^2}, \text{ in polar coordinates.}$$

However, these known expressions are considered as basic knowledge and usually are not listed as part of the mathematical model.

104. Solution of the Mathematical Model. We shall now turn to the solution of the mathematical model. It is, of course, necessary to determine in what form or forms the solution should appear. We desire to obtain formulas which describe the properties of the trajectories and from which we can calculate certain elements having given sufficient conditions. We shall first obtain a geometric solution, that is, one which is free of the independent variable t. This solution will give us a geometric picture of the path of the particle m.

The mathematical model which is more easily solved by the techniques developed in our study of differential equations is the one given by equations (10),

$$\begin{cases} \ddot{r} - r\dot{\theta}^2 = -cr^{-2}, \\ 2\dot{r}\dot{\theta} + r\ddot{\theta} = 0. \end{cases}$$

This is a system of second order differential equations, and we should solve it to obtain r as a function of t, $r(t)$, and θ as a function of t, $\theta(t)$. An elimination of t would then result in r as a function of θ. However, this particular system can be solved in an easier manner.

If we multiply the second equation by the integrating factor, r, it becomes an exact differential

$$2r\dot{r}\dot{\theta} + r^2\ddot{\theta} = \frac{d}{dt}(r^2\dot{\theta}) = 0$$

and an integration yields

(11) $$r^2\dot{\theta} = k_1 = \text{constant}.$$

Solve equation (11) for $\dot{\theta}$ and substitute into the first equation of (10) to obtain

(12) $$\ddot{r} - \frac{k_1^2}{r^3} = -\frac{c}{r^2}.$$

Since

$$\ddot{r} = \frac{d\dot{r}}{dt} = \frac{d\dot{r}}{dr}\frac{dr}{dt} = \frac{d\dot{r}}{dr}\dot{r},$$

we can change equation (12) to the form,

$$\dot{r}\,d\dot{r} = \left(\frac{k_1^2}{r^3} - \frac{c}{r^2}\right) dr,$$

in which the variables are separated, and an integration yields

(13) $$\tfrac{1}{2}\dot{r}^2 = -\tfrac{1}{2}k_1^2 r^{-2} + cr^{-1} + K_1.$$

We shall choose the arbitrary constant,

$$K_1 = \tfrac{1}{2}(k_2^2 - c^2)k_1^{-2},$$

to simplify the notation of the final solution.   The solution for $\dot{r}$ is

$$\dot{r} = \frac{\pm \sqrt{(k_2^2 - c^2)r^2 + 2k_1^2 cr - k_1^4}}{k_1 r}.$$

Since $\dot{\theta} = k_1 r^{-2}$, the *quotient*

$$\frac{\dot{r}}{\dot{\theta}} = \frac{dr}{d\theta} = \pm \frac{r}{k_1^2}\sqrt{(k_2^2 - c^2)r^2 + 2k_1^2 cr - k_1^4}$$

yields a differential equation in which the variables are separable,

(14) $$\frac{k_1^2\,dr}{r\sqrt{(k_2^2 - c^2)r^2 + 2k_1^2 cr - k_1^4}} = d\theta.$$

The integral of the left-hand side can be found in a table of integrals in the form

$$\int \frac{dx}{x\sqrt{A + Bx + Cx^2}} = \frac{1}{\sqrt{-A}} \text{ arc sin} \left(\frac{Bx + 2A}{x\sqrt{B^2 - 4AC}}\right) + K_2$$

and for our problem

$$A = -k_1^4,\ B = 2k_1^2 c,\ C = k_2^2 - c^2$$

so that

$$\sqrt{-A} = \sqrt{-(-k_1^4)} = k_1^2,$$
$$\sqrt{B^2 - 4AC} = \sqrt{4k_1^4 c^2 + 4k_1^4(k_2^2 - c^2)} = 2k_1^2 k_2,$$

and the solution of (14) is

$$\frac{k_1^2}{k_1^2} \text{ arc sin} \frac{2k_1^2 cr - 2k_1^4}{r2k_1^2 k_2} = \theta + K_3$$

where K_3 is another arbitrary constant of integration.   Simplifying we have

$$cr - k_1^2 = k_2 r \sin (\theta + K_3)$$

or

$$r[c - k_2 \sin (\theta + K_3)] = k_1^2$$

and solving for r:

$$(15) \qquad r = \frac{k_1^2}{c - k_2 \cos (\theta + k_3)}$$

where k_3 is a new constant based on

$$\sin (\theta + K_3) = \cos \left(\theta + K_3 + \frac{\pi}{2}\right) = \cos (\theta + k_3).$$

Equation (15) is the geometric solution of the system of differential equations (10) and gives r as a function of θ. The equation is the familiar polar form of a conic with one focus at the origin. There are three arbitrary constants, k_1, k_2, k_3, involved in this equation, and we shall now evaluate them in terms of chosen conditions. Let the axis of symmetry of the conic be along the ray $\theta = 0$ so that $k_3 = 0$, and let us denote values at $\theta = 0$ by the subscript 0. Differentiate equation (15) with respect to t and evaluate the derivative at $\theta = 0$ to obtain, since $\sin 0^0 = 0$,

$$(16) \qquad \dot{r}_0 = \frac{k_1^2 k_2 \sin \theta}{[c - k_2 \cos \theta]^2}\bigg|_{\theta=0} = 0.$$

Since then

$$V_0 = \sqrt{\dot{r}_0^2 + r_0^2 \dot{\theta}_0^2} = r_0 \dot{\theta}_0,$$

we have by equation (11)

$$(17) \qquad k_1 = r_0^2 \dot{\theta}_0 = r_0(r_0 \dot{\theta}) = r_0 V_0.$$

The value for k_2 can now be found by letting $\theta = 0$ in equation (15)

$$r_0 = \frac{k_1^2}{c - k_2} = \frac{r_0^2 V_0^2}{c - k_2}$$

whence

$$(18) \qquad k_2 = c - r_0 V_0^2.$$

Before giving the result of substituting these values for k_1, k_2, and k_3 into the solution (15), let us define a dimensionless quantity which greatly simplifies the expression, namely,

$$(19) \qquad p = 1 - \frac{r_0 V_0^2}{c}.$$

Then the solution becomes

(20)
$$r = \frac{(1 - p)r_0}{1 - p \cos \theta}.$$

We recall from analytic geometry that the eccentricity of the conic is the coefficient of the $\cos \theta$ term, $(-p)$, and determines the character of the conic. This leads us to the interesting geometric characteristics of the ballistic trajectories:

Ellipse:
$$\begin{cases} \text{apogee at } \theta = 0: \quad 0 < p < 1 \text{ or} \quad 0 < V_0 < \sqrt{\dfrac{c_0}{r_0}}, \\[2mm] \text{circular path:} \qquad p = 0 \qquad \text{or} \qquad V_0 = \sqrt{\dfrac{c}{r_0}}, \\[2mm] \text{perigee at } \theta = 0: \; -1 < p < 0 \text{ or} \sqrt{\dfrac{c}{r_0}} < V_0 < \sqrt{\dfrac{2c}{r_0}}. \end{cases}$$

Parabola: $p = -1$ or $V_0 = \sqrt{\dfrac{2c}{r_0}}$.

Hyperbola: $p < -1$ or $V_0 > \sqrt{\dfrac{2c}{r_0}}$.

Some typical cases are shown in Figure 38.

We shall now turn our attention to a solution which will involve the variable t. Let us begin with the equation

(21)
$$\dot{r} = \frac{\pm \sqrt{(k_2^2 - c^2)r^2 + 2k_1^2 cr - k_1^4}}{k_1 r}$$

and replace k_1 and k_2 by their values in terms of c, r_0, and V_0. We shall also make use of

(22)
$$c(1 - p) = r_0 V_0^2$$

which is easily obtained from formula (19). For convenience of substitution we list these values:

$$k_2 = c - r_0 V_0^2 = cp,$$
$$k_2^2 - c^2 = c^2(p^2 - 1) = -c^2(1 - p)(1 + p) = -cr_0 V_0^2(1 + p)$$
$$= -\frac{c}{n} k_1^2,$$

with

(23)
$$n = \frac{r_0}{1 + p}.$$

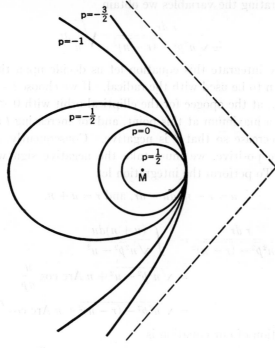

Fig. 38

Then

$$(\sqrt{k_2^2 - c^2}\,r^2 + 2k_1^2 cr - k_1^4 = \sqrt{-\frac{c}{n}k_1^2 r^2 + 2k_1^2 cr - k_1^4}$$

$$= k_1\sqrt{\frac{c}{n}}\sqrt{-r^2 + 2nr - nr_0^2 V_0^2 c^{-1}}.$$

Now

$$nr_0^2 V_0^2 c^{-1} = nr_0(1-p) = n[n(1+p)](1-p) = n^2(1-p^2)$$

so that the last radical becomes

$$\sqrt{-r^2 + 2nr - n^2(1-p^2)} = \sqrt{n^2 p^2 - (r-n)^2}.$$

A substitution into the right-hand side of equation (21) yields

$$\frac{dr}{dt} = \pm\frac{1}{r}\sqrt{\frac{c}{n}}\sqrt{n^2 p^2 - (r-n)^2}$$

and separating the variables we obtain

$$\frac{r\,dr}{\pm\sqrt{n^2p^2 - (r-n)^2}} = \sqrt{\frac{c}{n}}\,dt.$$

Before we integrate this equation let us decide upon the value of the sign to be used with the radical. If we choose $t = 0$ when $\theta = 0$, i.e., at the apogee for the elliptical orbit with $0 < p < 1$, then r is a maximum at this point, and for increasing t and θ, r should decrease so that $\dot{r}$ is negative. Consequently, since k_1 and r are positive, we must take the negative sign with the radical. To perform the integration let

$$u = r - n,\ du = dr,\ \text{and}\ r = u + n.$$

Then

$$-\int \frac{r\,dr}{\sqrt{n^2p^2 - (r-n)^2}} = -\int \frac{(u+n)du}{\sqrt{n^2p^2 - u^2}}$$

$$= \sqrt{n^2p^2 - u^2} + n\,\text{Arc cos}\,\frac{u}{np}$$

$$= \sqrt{n^2p^2 - (r-n)^2} + n\,\text{Arc cos}\,\frac{r-n}{np}.$$

The solution of our equation is

$$(24)\qquad \sqrt{n^2p^2 - (r-n)^2} + n\,\text{Arc cos}\,\frac{r-n}{np} = \sqrt{\frac{c}{n}}\,t + \tau$$

where τ is the constant of integration. To determine τ we consider the values at $t = 0$, and since we let $\theta = 0$ at that time, we have $r(t = 0) = r_0$ to be consistent with our previous definitions. Consequently, at $t = 0$

$$r - n = r_0 - \frac{r_0}{1+p} = r_0\left(\frac{1+p-1}{1+p}\right) = \frac{r_0}{1+p}\,(p) = np$$

and, since Arc cos $1 = 0$, we have $\tau = 0$. We can now solve equation (24) for t:

$$(25)\qquad \boxed{\,t = \sqrt{\frac{n}{c}}\left[\sqrt{n^2p^2 - (r-n)^2} + n\,\text{Arc cos}\,\frac{r-n}{np}\right]\,}$$

and we have t given as a function of r. We can also get t as a function of θ by replacing r by the right-hand side of equation (20). Thus

$$r - n = \frac{(1-p)r_0}{1 - p \cos \theta} - n = pn \left[\frac{\cos \theta - p}{1 - p \cos \theta} \right],$$

$$\sqrt{n^2 p^2 - (r-n)^2} = \frac{np}{1 - p \cos \theta} \sqrt{(1 - p \cos \theta)^2 - (\cos \theta - p)^2}$$

$$= \frac{np}{1 - p \cos \theta} \left(\sqrt{1 - p^2} \sin \theta \right),$$

and

$$\text{Arc cos} \frac{r-n}{np} = \text{Arc cos} \frac{\cos \theta - p}{1 - p \cos \theta} = \text{Arc sin} \frac{\sqrt{1 - p^2} \sin \theta}{1 - p \cos \theta}$$

so that

(26)
$$\boxed{ t = \frac{n^{\frac{3}{2}}}{c^{\frac{1}{2}}} \left[\frac{p \sqrt{1 - p^2} \sin \theta}{1 - p \cos \theta} + \text{Arc sin} \frac{\sqrt{1 - p^2} \sin \theta}{1 - p \cos \theta} \right] . }$$

By our choice of conditions at $t = 0$ we note that the time t will be negative for values of $\theta < 0$, and thus in using equation (26) we must take the negative of the right-hand side when θ is negative.

We continue our pursuit of the desired results by determining the *velocity vector;* that is, we desire to know the speed, V, and the trajectory path angle, φ. The magnitude of the speed can be found from

$$V = \sqrt{\dot{r}^2 + r^2 \dot{\theta}^2}.$$

Let us first differentiate formula (20) with respect to t and obtain

$$\dot{r} = -(1-p)r_0 \frac{p \dot{\theta} \sin \theta}{(1 - p \cos \theta)^2}.$$

From equation (11) we have

(27)
$$\dot{\theta} = \frac{k_1}{r^2} = \frac{r_0 V_0}{r^2}$$

so that

$$r^2 \dot{\theta}^2 = r^2 \left[\frac{r_0 V_0}{r^2} \right]^2 = \frac{r_0^2 V_0^2}{r^2}$$

$$= \frac{V_0^2 (1 - p \cos \theta)^2}{(1 - p)^2}$$

and

(28)
$$\dot{r} = -\left[\frac{(1-p)r_0 p \sin \theta}{(1-p \cos \theta)^2}\right]\left[\frac{r_0 V_0 (1 - p \cos \theta)^2}{(1-p)^2 r_0^2}\right]$$
$$= -\frac{V_0 p \sin \theta}{1-p}.$$

A substitution of these values yields
$$V = \sqrt{\frac{V_0^2 p^2 \sin^2 \theta}{(1-p)^2} + \frac{V_0^2 (1 - p \cos \theta)^2}{(1-p)^2}}$$

or

(29)
$$\boxed{V = \frac{V_0}{1-p} \sqrt{1 - 2p \cos \theta + p^2}}\,.$$

To obtain the path angle, φ, we need a velocity diagram. From our basic conventions (Fig. 36) we draw Fig. 39, and by the geometry, we have

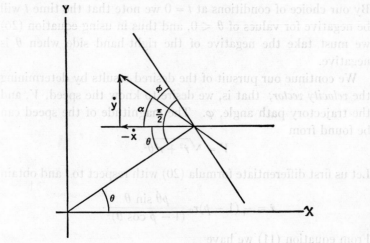

Fig. 39

$$\varphi + \theta = \frac{\pi}{2} - \alpha$$

so that

$$\tan(\varphi + \theta) = \tan\left(\frac{\pi}{2} - \alpha\right) = \cot \alpha.$$

Now

$$\alpha = \operatorname{arc\,cot}\left(\frac{-\ddot{x}}{\dot{y}}\right)$$

so that

$$\cot \alpha = \cot \operatorname{arc} \cot \left(\frac{-\dot{x}}{\dot{y}}\right) = -\frac{\dot{x}}{\dot{y}},$$

and

$$-\frac{\dot{x}}{\dot{y}} = \tan (\varphi + \theta) = \frac{\tan \varphi + \tan \theta}{1 - \tan \varphi \tan \theta}.$$

Let us solve this equation for $\tan \varphi$ to obtain

$$\tan \varphi = \frac{\dfrac{\dot{x}}{\dot{y}} + \tan \theta}{\dfrac{\dot{x}}{\dot{y}} \tan \theta - 1}.$$

By differentiating the first two of equations (6) with respect to t we obtain

$$\frac{\dot{x}}{\dot{y}} = \frac{\dot{r} \cos \theta - r\dot{\theta} \sin \theta}{\dot{r} \sin \theta + r\dot{\theta} \cos \theta}.$$

Making use of equations (27) and (28) we can, after a little algebraic gymnastics, arrive at the delightful result

$$\frac{\dot{x}}{\dot{y}} = \frac{\sin \theta}{p - \cos \theta}.$$

Consequently, we obtain

(30)
$$\boxed{\tan \varphi = \frac{p \sin \theta}{1 - p \cos \theta}.}$$

Equations (29) and (30) determine the magnitude and direction of the velocity vector in terms of θ. We may use equation (20) to eliminate θ and obtain expressions for V and φ in terms of r. For this purpose it is convenient to use $\cos \varphi$ instead of $\tan \varphi$ so that we have

$$\cos \varphi = \frac{1 - p \cos \theta}{\pm \sqrt{1 - 2p \cos \theta + p^2}}$$

and from equation (20)

$$p \cos \theta = 1 - (1 - p)\rho,$$

where

$$\rho = \frac{r_0}{r},$$

we obtain

(31)
$$V = V_0 \sqrt{\frac{2\rho - (1 + p)}{1 - p}}$$

and

(32)
$$\cos \varphi = \frac{\rho\sqrt{1 - p}}{\sqrt{2\rho - (1 + p)}}.$$

We have now described the trajectory in terms of the conditions at $\theta = 0$. These conditions were chosen in order to make the mathematical solutions more elegant. Unfortunately, these conditions usually are not known or seldom specified. The common practice is to state the conditions at the end of the powered portion of the flight. Normally, the objective of the powered flight analysis is to determine the necessary specifications to attain a certain attitude at the "time of burnout." Since we have chosen the unpowered part of the trajectory as our problem, we shall consider these conditions to be the *initial* conditions and to be known.

105. Trajectory in Terms of Initial Conditions. We proceed to extend our analysis to the determination of the trajectory in terms of the initial conditions r_i, V_i, and φ_i. In the development of this section we shall omit many of the algebraic manipulations. This is frequently done in the publication of scientific analyses, and since the student should learn to read such publications, let this section serve a double purpose of instruction in the scientific analysis itself and the reading of scientific papers. In order to comprehend the discussion, the student should supply the missing steps by performing the indicated mathematical operations.

The first step is to obtain r_0 and V_0 in terms of the initial conditions. From Fig. 36 we can deduce that, in our convention, the component of V_i normal to the radius vector, r_i, is given by

(33)
$$V_i \cos \varphi_i = r_i \dot{\theta}_i,$$

and since, by equations (11) and (17),

$$r^2\dot{\theta} = r_0 V_0,$$

then, at the point (r_i, θ_i), we have

(34) $$\dot{\theta}_i = \frac{r_0 V_0}{r_i^2}.$$

Equations (33) and (34) combine to yield

(35) $$r_0 V_0 = r_i V_i \cos \varphi_i = w_i,$$

in which we also define the new constant w_i. Equations (35) and (19) can be solved simultaneously to yield

(36) $$\begin{cases} V_0 = \dfrac{c}{w_i}\,(1 - p), \\[2mm] r_0 = \dfrac{w_i^2}{c(1 - p)}. \end{cases}$$

However, we have not as yet solved for r_0 and V_0 since p is a function of these quantities. We are indeed treacherously close to the fallacious circular argument. We shall be saved if we can obtain p as a function of the initial conditions. At the point of initial conditions, equation (31) has the form (after squaring)

(37) $$V_i^2 = V_0^2 \left[\frac{2\rho_i - (1 + p)}{1 - p} \right]$$

where $\rho_i = \dfrac{r_0}{r_i}$. We shall solve equation (37) for p. Substituting for V_0 by the use of (36) we have

$$V_i^2 = \left(\frac{c}{w_i}\right)^2 \left[2\,\frac{r_0}{r_i}\,(1 - p) - (1 - p^2) \right].$$

Substituting for r_0 by the use of (36) we have

$$V_i^2 = \frac{2c}{r_i} - \left(\frac{c}{w_i}\right)^2 (1 - p^2)$$

which simplifies to

$$c^2 p^2 = c^2 - \frac{2c}{r_i}\,w_i^2 + V_i^2 w_i^2$$

or

$$p^2 = 1 - r_i^2 V_i^2 \cos^2 \varphi_i \left(\frac{2}{cr_i} - \frac{V_i^2}{c^2} \right)$$

$$= 1 - \frac{r_i V_i^2}{c} \left(2 - \frac{r_i V_i^2}{c} \right) \cos^2 \varphi_i$$

$$= 1 - K_i(2 - K_i) \cos^2 \varphi_i$$

where

$$K_i = \frac{r_i V_i^2}{c}.$$

Consequently,

(38) $$p = \sqrt{1 - K_i(2 - K_i) \cos^2 \varphi_i}$$

expresses p in terms of the initial conditions, and with this value
of p it can be said that equations (36) express V_0 and r_0 in terms
of the initial conditions.

We shall now turn to the task of expressing the elements of
the trajectory in terms of the initial conditions by substituting
the values for r_0 and V_0 from equations (36) into equations (20),
(26), (29), and (30). Remember that p is now obtained from
equation (38). From equation (20) we have immediately

(39) $$r = \frac{w_i^2}{c(1 - p \cos \theta)}.$$

In equation (26) we need only be concerned with

$$n^{\frac{3}{2}} c^{-\frac{1}{2}} = \left(\frac{r_0}{1+p} \right)^{\frac{3}{2}} c^{-\frac{1}{2}} = c^{-\frac{1}{2}} \left[\frac{w_i^2}{c(1 - p^2)} \right]^{\frac{3}{2}}$$

$$= c \left(\frac{r_i}{2c - r_i V_i^2} \right)^{\frac{3}{2}} = c^{-\frac{1}{2}} \left(\frac{r_i}{2 - K_i} \right)^{\frac{3}{2}} = q,$$

and we have

(40) $$t = q \left[\frac{p\sqrt{1 - p^2} \sin \theta}{1 - p \cos \theta} + \text{Arc sin} \frac{\sqrt{1 - p^2} \sin \theta}{1 - p \cos \theta} \right]$$

where q is defined by

$$q = c^{-\frac{1}{2}} r_i^{\frac{3}{2}} (2 - K_i)^{-\frac{3}{2}}.$$

Equation (29) becomes

(41)
$$V = \frac{c}{w_i} \sqrt{1 - 2p \cos \theta + p^2}$$

and equation (30) retains its form with the proper understanding of p.

Equation (30) permits a direct substitution into equation (40) to give another formula for t.

(42)
$$t = q\left[p\sqrt{1 - p^2} \tan \varphi + \text{Arc sin } p^{-1}\sqrt{1 - p^2} \tan \varphi\right]$$

There are two other elements of the trajectory which are of interest for missiles, namely, the range, R, and the time of flight, T. We shall consider the range to be the great circle arc length subtended by the rays along r_i and r_f and define, by elementary trigonometry,

(43)
$$R = a(\theta_f - \theta_i)$$

The time of flight will be defined by

(44)
$$T = t_f - t_i$$

where t_f and t_i are found from formula (42) by evaluation at $\varphi = \varphi_f$ and $\varphi = \varphi_i$.

106. A Numerical Example.

In order to clarify our thinking, it is always advantageous to solve a numerical example. Let us therefore determine the elements of the trajectory which is specified by the initial conditions:

$h_i = 500,000$ ft.	$\varphi_i = -25°$
$V_i = 24,000$ ft./sec.	$h_f = 0$

The inclusion of $h_f = 0$ specifies that we shall consider the trajectory until impact with the surface of the earth. Let it be required to find values for

$$h_0, \ V_0, \ V_f, \ \varphi_f, \ R, \text{ and } T.$$

The solution is summarized as follows:

Given Constants.

$a = 2.08555 \times 10^7$		$V_i = 2.4000 \times 10^4$	
$c = 1.4080 \times 10^{16}$		$h_i = 5.00000 \times 10^5$	
$\cos \varphi_i = 0.90631$		$\tan \varphi_i = -0.46631$	

Symbol	Formula	Value
	Initial Values and Auxiliary Constants	
r_i	$a + h_i$	2.13555×10^7
w_i	$r_i V_i \cos \varphi_i$	4.64513×10^{11}
K_i	$c^{-1} r_i V_i^2$	0.873634
p	$\sqrt{1 - K_i(2 - K_i) \cos^2 \varphi_i}$	0.437856
θ_i	$\cos \theta_i = \dfrac{cr_i - w_i^2}{pcr_i}$	-0.86983
q	$c^{-\frac{1}{2}} \left(\dfrac{r_i}{2 - K_i} \right)^{\frac{3}{2}}$	695.735
P	$p\sqrt{1 - p^2}$	0.393651
Q	$p^{-1}\sqrt{1 - p^2}$	2.053289
γ_i	Arc sin $(Q \tan \varphi_i)$	-1.2781
t_i	$q(P \tan \varphi_i + \gamma_i)$	-1016.93 sec.
	Apogee Values	
V_0	$c(1 - p)w_i^{-1}$	17039 ft./sec.
r_0	$w_i V_0^{-1}$	2.72613×10^7
h_0	$r_0 - a$	0.64058×10^7
	Impact Values	
r_f	$a + h_f$	2.08555×10^7
θ_f	$\cos \theta_f = \dfrac{cr_f - w_i^2}{pcr_f}$	0.92019
V_f	$V_f = \dfrac{c}{w_i} \sqrt{1 - 2p \cos \theta_f + p^2}$	24650 ft./sec.
φ_f	$\tan \varphi_f = \dfrac{p \sin \theta_f}{1 - p \cos \theta_f}$	0.442755
γ_f	Arc sin $(Q \tan \varphi_f)$	1.340378
t_f	$q(P \tan \varphi_f + \gamma_f)$	1062.4 sec.
R	$a(\theta_f - \theta_i)$	3.73318×10^7
T	$t_f - t_i$	2079.3 sec.

The units of measurement are feet, seconds, and radians.   In terms of more familiar units for these magnitudes, we have

$h_i = 94.7$ miles	$\varphi_i = -25°$
$h_0 = 1213.2$ miles	$\theta_i = -49.8°$
$R = 7070.4$ miles	$\varphi_f = 25.4°$
$T = 34$ min. 39.3 sec.	$\theta_f = 52.7°$

107. Exercise XXII.   It is always desirable to minimize the total energy necessary to attain a given range.   This is a crucial problem in the determination of the propulsive forces necessary for flight.   If we assume that the altitude at the end of the powered flight is known, i.e.,

$$r_i = a + h_i$$

is specified, then it is possible to calculate the optimum values of φ_i and V_i in order to travel a desired range.   The formulas are derived by a consideration of the extremum of the range, R; i.e.,

$$\frac{\partial R}{\partial \varphi_i} = 0,$$

and good approximations can be obtained from series expansions. They are

$$\varphi_i(\text{opt}) \doteq -\left[\frac{\pi}{4} - \frac{\psi}{2} - \frac{\delta}{4}\cot\psi + \frac{\delta^2}{8}\cot\psi\right],$$

$$V_i(\text{min}) \doteq \sqrt{\frac{2c\sigma}{r_i(1+\sigma)}}\left[1 - \frac{1}{4\sigma}\delta - \frac{1+2\sigma}{32\sigma^2}\delta^2\right]$$

where

$$\psi = \frac{R}{2a},\ \delta = \frac{h_i - h_f}{a + h_f},\ \sigma = \sin\psi,\ r_i = a + h_i.$$

Find the optimum values of φ_i and V_i if $h_i = 600,000$ ft., $h_f = 0$, and $R = 6000$ nautical miles.   (1 nautical mile = 6076.1155 feet.) [Hint: $\psi = .87403, \delta = .02877$, radical in formula for $V_i = 23868$.]

EXAMINATIONS

In the pursuit of knowledge it is advantageous to measure one's progress. In academic training this is usually done by "taking an examination." It can also be accomplished by attempting to solve "original problems." One way to review for an examination is to take a pre-examination, or to solve similar problems. One of the most troublesome things in elementary differential equations is to recognize the equation as a member of a particular class of equations to which a specific technique can be applied. We have therefore prepared a set of examinations which follow the order of the book but which attempt to "mix up" the categories of differential equations.

Examination I.

1. Find the general solution for each of the following:
   (a) $x^2\, dy + y^2\, dx = x^2 y\, dy - xy^2\, dx$.
   (b) $(2x + y^{-1})dx + (y^{-1} - xy^{-2})dy = 0$.

2. Determine the integral curves passing through the given points.
   (a) $y^2\, dx + x^2\, dy = xy\, dy$; $(1,1)$.
   (b) $(x^2 + 3)\dfrac{dy}{dx} + 2xy + 5x^2 = 0$; $(2,1)$.

3. Find the general solution and sketch the particular solution obtained by letting the constant be zero.
$$xy^2\, dx = y\, dx - x\, dy.$$

4. In a simple series circuit without capacitance
$$L = \tfrac{1}{2}\text{ henry, } R = 15 \text{ ohms, } E = 4 \sin 2t.$$
   Find $i(t)$ if $i = 0$ when $t = 0$.

5. A body of mass m is falling vertically in space so that it is pulled toward the earth by the gravitational force and is being retarded by a force which is proportional to the square of the distance traveled; let the constant of proportionality be equal to 3.

(a) Find the velocity, v, as a function of the distance, x, if the body starts from rest.

(b) Find the velocity after the body has fallen 100 feet if its mass is $10,000/32$ slugs ($g = 32$ ft./sec.^{2}).

Examination II.

1. Find the general solution of
   (a) $D^2y + 6Dy + 9y = 0$.
   (b) $(k^2D^2 + 2kD + k^2 + 1)y = 0$.
2. Find the general solution of
   (a) $(D^2 + 4D + 4)y = x^{-2}e^{-2x}$.
   (b) $(D^2 + D)y = \sin 2x$.
3. Prove that if $g_i(t)$ are solutions of
   (1) $\ddot{x} + a\dot{x} + bx = f_i(t)$ for $i = 1, \cdots, n$, then
   (2) $x = g_1(t) + \cdots + g_n(t)$ is a solution of
   (3) $\ddot{x} + a\dot{x} + bx = f_1(t) + \cdots + f_n(t)$.
4. Given the following equation of motion:

$$\ddot{x} + 2\dot{x} + 2x = 0.$$

Describe the motion as to character, damping, period, frequency, and logarithmic decrement.

5. Find the general solution of
   (a) $xy'' + y' = 16x^3$.
   (b) $y'' = xe^x$.

Examination III.

1. Find the general solution of
   (a) $(D^3 - 7D^2 + 12D)y = 0$. $\qquad \left(D = \dfrac{d}{dx}\right)$.
   (b) $(D^2 + 4D + 13)y = 0$.
2. Find the general solution of

$$(D^3 - D^2)y = 3x + xe^x, \qquad \left(D = \dfrac{d}{dx}\right).$$

3. Find three functions $x(t)$, $y(t)$, and $z(t)$ satisfying
   $Dy - 3z = 5$,
   $y - Dz - x = 3 - 2t$, $\qquad \left(D = \dfrac{d}{dt}\right)$.
   $z + Dx = -1$.
4. Find the particular solution which satisfies the initial conditions:
   $(D - 1)^3y = x^{-3}e^x$; $y = Dy = D^2y = 0$ when $x = 1$.

Examination IV.

1. Find the series solution of

$$y'' + xy' - 2y = 0$$

if $y = 1$, $y' = 0$ for $x = 0$.

2. (a) Let $y = x^n(a_0 + a_1x + a_2x^2 + a_3x^3 + \cdots)$ be a solution of

$$x^2y'' + xy' + (x^2 - n^2)y = 0$$

with $a_0 \neq 0$. Determine the explicit forms of a_i ($i = 1, 2, 3, 4, 5, 6$) in terms of a_0.

   (b) Write the function $y(x)$ for $n = \frac{1}{2}$.

3. Find the orthogonal trajectories of the family of curves given by $x^2 + y^2 = 25$.

4. Find the family of curves having an intercept of the tangent on the y-axis equal to 2.

Examination V.

1. Solve $\dfrac{\partial z}{\partial x} = x^2$.

2. Solve $(1 - y)p + (1 - x)q = 1 - z$.

3. Solve $p + q = y$.

4. Solve $zq^2 = p$.

Examination VI.

1. Solve $(D^2 - DD^* - 6D^{*2})z = 0$.

2. Solve $(D^2 + DD^* + D + D^*)z = e^{x+y}$.

3. Solve $p + q = z$.

4. Solve $r - t = 0$.

Examination VII.   (Final.)

1. Find the orthogonal trajectories of the particular integral of

$$3(y - 5x^2)dx + x\,dy = 0$$

which passes through the point (1,1).

2. Find the complete solution of

$$(2D^2 - 2D + 1)y = \tfrac{5}{4} \cos \tfrac{1}{2}x.$$

3. (a) Show that a logical definition of $e^{\alpha+i\beta}$ is given by

$$e^{\alpha+i\beta} = e^\alpha (\cos \beta + i \sin \beta).$$

   (b) Prove that $e^{\ln x} = x$.

   (c) Prove that $e^{ax}f(D)y = f(D - a)\left[e^{ax}y\right]$.

4. Find the series solution about $x = 0$ of
$$(1 + x^2)y'' - 8xy' + 20y = 0.$$

5. Find two functions $x(t)$ and $y(t)$ which satisfy
$$\begin{cases} (D + 1)y - (D - 1)x = t, \\ (D - 1)y + (D + 1)x = 0. \end{cases}$$

6. (a) Solve $zp + q^2 = 0$.
   (b) Solve $(D^2 - 4DD^* + 3D^{*2} - 4D + 8D^* + 4)z = 0$.
   [Hint: $f(a,b) = a^2 - ab - 2a - 3ab + 3b^2 + 6b - 2a + 2b + 4$.]

7. A body of mass m is propelled by a thrust, T, and retarded by a drag, D, so as to maintain a constant velocity
$$v = \sqrt{\dot{x}^2 + \dot{y}^2}.$$

If its motion is confined to a vertical (x,y)-plane so that the gravity force, g, is acting in the negative y direction, find the differential equations of motion. Remember that $\tan \alpha = \dfrac{\dot{y}}{\dot{x}}$.

Solve the differential equations, assuming $\dfrac{T - D}{m} = k$, a constant.

ANSWERS TO THE EXERCISES

Exercise I.

1. (a) $\dfrac{b^2 x}{a^2 y}$. 　　　(b) $e^{ax} \sin nx$. 　　　(c) $4x - 1 + \dfrac{6}{x}$.

　　(d) $-\dfrac{2Ax + By + D}{Bx + 2Cy + E}$. 　　(e) $x^{-1} + x^{-\frac{3}{2}}(x-1) \arctan \sqrt{x}$.

2. (a) $\frac{1}{3} e^{3x}(x^3 - x^2 + \frac{2}{3}x - \frac{2}{9}) + c$.

　　(b) $\dfrac{e^{2x}}{2 + 2a^2}\left[\sin 2ax - a \cos 2ax\right] + c$.

　　(c) $2 \sin x^2 - (2x^2 - \frac{3}{2}) \cos x^2 + c$.

3. (a) 2. 　　　(b) 28. 　　　(c) $\frac{1}{2}(e^{3x} - e^x)$.

4. Function is not continuous in the whole interval; it is defined and continuous for $-1 \leq x < 0,\, 0 < x \leq 3$ and is not defined at $x = 0$.

5. $e^{ix} = \left(1 - \dfrac{x^2}{2!} + \dfrac{x^4}{4!} - \cdots\right) + i\left(x - \dfrac{x^3}{3!} + \dfrac{x^5}{5!} - \cdots\right)$.

8. 145 ft., 5 sec. 　　**9.** 40 mi.

10. 8.05 ft./sec., 20.125 ft.

Exercise II.

1. (a) First order, first degree.

　　(b) First order, third degree.

　　(c) Second order, third degree.

　　(d) Third order, fourth degree.

　　(e) Third order, first degree.

3. (a) $y' = 3x^2$. 　　　(b) $y'' - y + x = 0$.

　　(c) $y' = \dfrac{y}{x \ln x}$. 　　(d) $x - yy' = 0$.

　　(e) $D_x^4 y = 0$.

Exercise III.

1. (a) $x^2 - y^2 = c$. 　　　(b) $2x^3 - y^4 = c$.

　　(c) $\dfrac{1}{8} \ln \dfrac{x^2 - 4}{x^2} + \dfrac{2}{\sqrt{3}} \arctan \dfrac{2y + 1}{\sqrt{3}} = c$.

　　(d) $\rho \sin \theta = c$. 　　(e) $2y = 2x - x^{-2} + c$.

2. (a) $x^2 + y^2 = 5$.   (b) $\rho = \sec\theta$.

    (c) $1 + e^x = 2(1 + e^3)\cos y$.

Exercise IV.

1. (a) $x + y = c$.   (b) $cx^2 = y + \sqrt{x^2 + y^2}$.

    (c) $y^3 = cx^3 - x^3 \ln x^3$.   (d) $2y - x\sin\dfrac{2y}{x} + 4x\ln x = cx$.

    (e) $y^2 + 7xy + x^2 = c(y + 3x)$.

2. (a) $y\ln y = x$.   (b) $y^2 - xy + x^2 = 3(y + x)$.

Exercise V.

1. (a) $20x^3 + 75x^2y^2 - 12y^5 = c$.

    (b) $ax^3 + 3bx^2y + 3cy^2x + y^3 = k$.

    (c) $\tan x \tan y = k$.   (d) $x^3 + 3xye^{2y} = k$.

    (e) $(x + 1)\sin y - \cos x = k$.

2. (a) $4x^2 - 4xy + 5y^2 + 6x + 14y - 50 = 0$.

    (b) $x^2 \sin y + x^2 + 3y \sin x = \frac{1}{4}\pi^2$.

    (c) $ye^{2x} - 3x^2e^{2y} - 2e^y + 5 = 0$.

Exercise VI.

1. (a) $2y = xy^2 + cx$.   (b) $\ln\dfrac{y}{x} = \dfrac{1}{3}x^3 + c$.

    (c) $\ln xy = \arctan\dfrac{y}{x} + c$.   (d) $x^3y^2 + x^4y^3 = k$.

    (e) $\arcsin\dfrac{y}{x} = \dfrac{1}{2}x^2 + c$.

2. (a) $xy = x^3 - 6$.   (b) $x + y = x^2(x - y)$.

    (c) $xy^3 - 2xy + 1 = 0$.

Exercise VII.

2. (a) $32y = 8x^2 - 4x + 1 + ce^{-4x}$.

    (b) $y = (x^2 + c)e^{\cos x}$.

    (c) $yx = 2x^2 + 2x\sin 2x + \cos 2x + c$.

    (d) $y = \frac{1}{13}(2\sin 3x - 3\cos 3x) + ce^{-2x}$.

    (e) $x + \ln y = e^y \displaystyle\int \frac{e^{-y}}{y}\,dy$.

Exercise VIII.

1. $2y - 2x + 5\ln(2x + 2y + 1) = c$.

2. $5x - 7\ln(3x - 5y + \frac{31}{5}) = c$.

3. $4 \ln (x + y - 1) = \dfrac{x + 5}{x + y - 1} + c.$

4. $5 \ln (2x - 2y - 1) = 2x + 6y + c.$

5. $\ln \sqrt{y^2 + xy + x^2 - 3y - 3x + 3} + \dfrac{2}{\sqrt{3}} \arctan \dfrac{2y + x - 3}{\sqrt{3}(x - 1)} = c.$

Exercise IX.

1. $x^2 y^2 = 2x^4 + c.$

2. $2(x^2 + y^2)^2 - y^2 = cy^2(x^2 + y^2)^2.$

3. $y + xe^{y/x} = c.$

4. $y^2 = (2x + c) \cos^2 x.$

5. $x^2 + x^2 y^2 = cy^2.$

Exercise X.

1. $y = 1 + ce^{-x^2}.$

2. $y^{16} = 2(2x - 1)^7 (2x + 1)^5 e^{4x}.$

3. $\sin x + \cos y = ce^{-x}.$

4. $xy(x \cos x - \sin x + c) = 1.$

5. $q = CE(1 - e^{-t/RC}).$

6. $x(xy + 1) = cx^2 y^2 e^{xy}.$

7. $x^3 - x^2 y + y^4 = 5.$

8. $y^2 + xy + x^2 = c(y + 3x).$

9. $(x + y + 2)^3 (x - y) = c.$

10. $3x + 2y + 7 \ln (x + y - 3) = c.$

Exercise XI.

1. $y = \pm \sqrt{3x} + c.$ **2.** $y = (2 \pm \sqrt{2})x + c.$

3. $y = -x + c; \quad y^3 + 3x^3 \ln x + 3cx^3 = 0.$

4. $y = cx + c^2; \quad x^2 + 4y = 0.$

5. $4(x + c)^3 = 27(y - c)^2; \quad x + y = 1.$

6. $2ay - akx^2 + ck^3 = 0; \quad y = \dfrac{1}{3} \sqrt{\dfrac{a}{3c}}\, x^3.$

7. $(y - cx)^2 = c^3.$

8. $x^3 + (c - y^{\frac{3}{2}})^2 = 0.$

9. $(x^2 + y^2 - 4c)^3 + 27cy^4 = 0.$

10. $y(c^2 x - 1) + c = 0; \quad 4xy^2 + 1 = 0.$

11. $(y - c)^2 = cx; \quad x + 4y = 0.$

12. $(y - cx^2)(2y - 3x^2 - c) = 0; \quad x - 2y = 0.$

13. $y = cx - c^2 + 1; \quad 4y = x^2 + 4.$

14. $(y - c)(xy - c) = 0.$

15. $(y - cx)^2 = c.$

16. $4y = (x + c)^2; \quad y = 0.$

17. $(y - x + c)(y + x + c) = 0; \quad x = 0.$

18. $(2y + x + c)(2y - x + c)(\ln y + x + c) = 0.$

19. $y = cx + \ln c; \quad xe^{y+1} + 1 = 0.$

20. $y = x \pm 2c\sqrt{x} + c^2; \quad y = 0.$

Exercise XII.

1. (a) $y^2 = 6x + 10.$ (b) $y = 2e^{2x}.$

  (c) $(x + c)^2 + y^2 = 9.$ (d) $\rho \cos (\theta + c) = 2.$

  (e) $1 = \rho(c - \theta).$

2. (a) $(y - c)^3 = x^2; \quad x = 0,$ s.s., cuspidal locus.

  (b) $(x + c)^3 = (y - c)^2; \quad 4 = 27(x + y),$ s.s.; $x + y = 0,$ cuspidal locus.

  (c) $y = c(c - x)^2; \quad 27y = 4x^3,$ s.s.; $y = 0,$ s.s., tac-locus.

3. (a) $y^2 = ce^{-x/a}.$ (b) Members of $xy = c.$

  (c) $\rho = c \sin \theta.$

  (d) Members of $\rho^2(1 - \cos \theta) \sin \theta = c.$

  (e) $y^2 - x^2 = c^2.$

Exercise XIII.

1. $y = c_1e^{5x} + c_2e^{7x}.$ **2.** $y = c_1 + c_2e^{2x}.$

3. $y = (c_1 + c_2x)e^{5x/3}.$

4. $y = e^{2x/3} \left(c_1 \sin \dfrac{\sqrt{2}}{3} x + c_2 \cos \dfrac{\sqrt{2}}{3} x \right).$

5. $y = c_1e^x + c_2e^{-x} + c_3e^{2x} + c_4e^{4x}.$

6. $y = c_1e^{2x} + c_2 \sin \sqrt{3}x + c_3 \cos \sqrt{3}x.$

7. $y = (c_1 + c_2x)e^{2x} + c_3 \sin x + c_4 \cos x.$

8. $y = e^{2x}[(c_1 + c_2x) \sin 3x + (c_3 + c_4x) \cos 3x].$

9. $y = (c_1 + c_2x + c_3x^2)e^x - 2x^2 - 9x + 2.$

10. $y = c_1e^{-x} + c_2e^{3x} + 2xe^{-x} + x - \frac{2}{3}.$

11. $y = c_1 \sin 2x + c_2 \cos 2x - \frac{1}{2} \cos 2x \ln (\tan 2x + \sec 2x).$

12. $y = c_1 + (x^6 - 6x^5 + 30x^4 - 120x^3 + 360x^2 - 720x + c_2)e^x.$

Exercise XIV.

1. (a) $e^{3x}.$ (b) $7 \sin 2x - 4 \cos 2x.$

  (c) $-18 + 12x - 15x^2.$ (d) $-(2x + 5x^2)e^x.$

2. (a) $x^3.$ (b) $0.$ (c) $2e^{-ax}.$ (d) $6xe^x.$ (e) $xe^{ax}.$

  (f) $-(x^4 + 4x^3 + 12x^2 + 24x + 24).$

(g) $(4 \cos x - 5 \sin x)e^{2x}$.

(h) $8e^{-x} \sin 2x$. (i) $3e^{-x}(3x^2 - 6x + 2)$.

(j) $\frac{1}{4}x^2 e^x$.

Exercise XV.

1. $y = (c_1 + c_2 x + \frac{1}{6}x^3)e^{2x}$.

2. $y = (c_1 + x) \sin 2x + c_2 \cos 2x$.

3. $y = c_1 e^{3x} + c_2 x e^{3x} + c_3 + \frac{1}{4}e^x + \frac{1}{36}x^4 + \frac{2}{27}x^3 + \frac{1}{9}x^2 + \frac{8}{81}x$.

4. $y = (c_1 + c_2 x + \frac{1}{12}x^4)e^{-ax}$.

5. $y = c_1 + (c_2 + c_3 x + c_4 x^2 - \frac{1}{6}x^3 + \frac{1}{24}x^4)e^x$.

6. $y = (c_1 + c_2 x)e^{-3x} - e^{-2x} \cos x$.

7. $y = c_1 + (c_2 + c_3 x)e^{-x} + \frac{1}{2}e^{-x} (\sin x + \cos x)$.

Exercise XVI.

1. $v = 20(1 - e^{-0.0025t})$; $v_\infty = 20$ ft./sec. $= 13.63$ mi./hr.

2. $x = 1736500(1 - e^{-.01t})$, $y = 10169800(1 - e^{-.01t}) - 100gt$,
   $x_{10} = 31.3$ mi., $y_{10} = 177.2$ mi.

3. $x = \frac{1}{2} \cos 8t + \frac{1}{2}$; Period $\equiv \dfrac{\pi}{4}$; Frequency $\equiv \dfrac{4}{\pi}$.

4. $i = \dfrac{E}{\beta L} e^{-\alpha t} \sin \beta t$, $q = \dfrac{EC}{\beta} \left[\beta - e^{-\alpha t}(\beta \cos \beta t + \alpha \sin \beta t)\right]$,

   $\alpha = \dfrac{R}{2L}$, $\beta = \sqrt{\dfrac{1}{LC} - \dfrac{R^2}{4L^2}}$.

5. 177.7 lbs.

6. $i_1 = \dfrac{E_0}{\omega L} (1 - \cos \omega t)$, $i_3 = \dfrac{E_0}{R} \sin \omega t$, $q = CE_0 \sin \omega t$,

   $i_4 = CE_0 \omega \cos \omega t$,

   $i = E_0 \left[\dfrac{1}{\omega L} + \dfrac{1}{R} \sin \omega t + \left(C\omega - \dfrac{1}{\omega L}\right) \cos \omega t\right]$.

7. 320 ft. 8. $2\pi \sqrt{\dfrac{l}{g}}$, $\dfrac{1}{2\pi} \sqrt{\dfrac{g}{l}}$.

9. $y = \dfrac{1}{EI} \left[\frac{1}{5}x^5 - \frac{2}{3}L^2 x^3 + \frac{7}{15}L^4 x\right]$.

10. $c = \dfrac{c_0}{1 - e^{2mL}} \left[e^{mx} - e^{2mL}e^{-mx}\right]$ where $m = \sqrt{\dfrac{k}{r}}$.

Exercise XVII.

1. $y = c_1 e^{t/2} + c_2 e^{-t} + t + 2$, $x = -c_1 e^{t/2} + 2c_2 e^{-t} - t - 2$.

2. $z = c_1 e^{2t} + c_2 e^{-2t} - 2$, $y = \frac{3}{2}c_1 e^{2t} - \frac{3}{2}c_2 e^{-2t} - t + c_3$,
   $x = -\frac{1}{2}c_1 e^{2t} + \frac{1}{2}c_2 e^{-2t} + t + c_3 - 3$.

3. $y = e^t + c_1 t + c_2$, $x = \frac{5}{2}e^t + c_4 e^{-t} + c_1 t + c_2$.

5. $x = \frac{1}{5}e^{2t} - \frac{8}{15}e^{-3t} + \frac{1}{3}$, $y = \frac{3}{10}e^{2t} + \frac{8}{15}e^{-3t} - \frac{5}{6}$,
$z = -e^{-t} - \frac{1}{5}e^{2t} - \frac{4}{5}e^{-3t} + 2$.

6. $x^2 - y^2 = c_1$, $y + x = c_2 z$.

7. $y^2 + z^2 + x^2 = c_1^2$, $yz = c_2 + x^3$.

8. $z = c_1 x$, $x^2 - y^2 + z^2 = cx$.

9. $x = c_1 + c_2 e^{-4t}$, $y = 3c_1 - c_2 e^{-4t}$.

10. $x = c_1 e^{-t} + c_2 e^{4t}$, $y = \frac{3}{2}c_2 e^{4t} - c_1 e^{-t}$.

11. $x = c_1 e^{2t} + c_2 e^{-2t} + 1$, $y = 2t - c_1 e^{2t} + c_2 e^{-2t}$.

12. $x = (c_1 + c_2 t - \frac{1}{4}t^2)e^t + c_3 e^{-t}$, $y = (c_2 + \frac{1}{2} - \frac{1}{2}t)e^t + (2c_3 - 1)e^{-t}$.

Exercise XVIII.

1. $y = \cos x$.

2. (a) $y = c_0 +$
$$c_1\left(x - \frac{3}{2}x^2 + \frac{1}{2}x^3 + \frac{3}{4!}x^4 + \cdots + \frac{3 \cdot 3 \cdot 5 \cdots (2k-3)}{(k+2)!}x^{k+2}\right).$$

(b) $y = c_0\left(1 + 3x^2 - x^4 + x^6 + \sum_{k=4}^{\infty}(-1)^{k+1}\frac{9 \cdot 13 \cdots (4k-7)}{7 \cdot 9 \cdots (2k-1)}x^{2k}\right)$
$\quad + c_1 x\left(1 + \frac{1}{2}x^2 - \frac{3}{8}x^4 - \frac{3}{8}\sum_{k=3}^{\infty}(-1)^{k+1}\frac{7 \cdot 11 \cdots (4k-5)}{6 \cdot 8 \cdots 2k}x^{2k}\right)$.

(c) $y_1 = c_0\left(1 - x - \sum_{k=2}^{\infty}\frac{k!}{1 \cdot 3 \cdot 5 \cdots (2k-3)}x^k\right)$.
$\quad y_2 = b_0 x^{\frac{3}{2}}\left(1 + \sum_{k=1}^{\infty}\frac{5 \cdot 7 \cdot 9 \cdots (2k+3)}{4^k k!}x^k\right)$.

(d) $y_1 = x^2 + \sum_{k=1}^{\infty}(-1)^k\frac{(k+1)(k+2)}{k!\,2}x^{k+2}$.
$\quad y_2 = y_1(\ln x - \frac{3}{2})$
$\quad\quad + \sum_{k=1}^{\infty}(-1)^k\frac{(k+1)(k+2)}{k!\,2}\left(\frac{1}{k+1} + \frac{1}{k+2} - H_K\right)x^{k+2}$.

(e) $y = c_0 x^{-1}\left[\sum_{k=0}^{\infty}(-1)^k\frac{1}{k!}x^k\right] + b_0 x^2\left(1 + \sum_{k=1}^{\infty}\frac{6}{(k+3)!}x^k\right)$.

(f) $y = c - c^2 x + \frac{1 + 2c^3}{2}x^2 - \frac{c + 3c^4}{3}x^3 + \frac{5c^2 + 12c^5}{4}x^4 - \cdots$.

(g) $y = Ax + Bx^{-3}$.

3. $y = Au + Bv$, where

$$u = x^n \left[1 - \frac{x^2}{4(1+n)} + \frac{x^4}{4^2(2!)(1+n)(2+n)} \right.$$
$$\left. + (-1)^k \frac{x^{2k}}{4^k(k!)(1+n)(2+n)\cdots(k+n)} + \cdots \right],$$

$$v = x^{-n} \left[1 - \frac{x^2}{4(1-n)} + \frac{x^4}{4^2(2!)(1-n)(2-n)} \right.$$
$$\left. + (-1)^k \frac{x^{2k}}{4^k(k!)(1-n)(2-n)\cdots(k-n)} + \cdots \right].$$

Exercise XIX.

1. (a) $y = 1 + x + .25x^4 + .20x^5 + .03125x^8 + .022222x^9$
$\qquad\qquad + .002604x^{12} + .001709x^{13} + \cdots$.

(b) $y = -2[x + .333333x^3 + .066667x^5 + .009523x^7$
$\qquad\qquad + .001058x^9 + .000096x^{11} + \cdots]$.

2.

x	0	.2	.4	.6	.8	1.0
y	1	.9813	.9316	.8606	.7792	.6988

x	0	1	2	3	4	6
y	1	.6988	.6746	1.8688	4.1030	7.2398

3. $y(x) = \frac{1}{2}x^2 + \frac{1}{6}x^3 + \frac{1}{720}x^6 + \cdots, \quad y(.1) = .006667$.

Exercise XX.

1. (a) $z = px + y, \ q = 1$.

(b) $z = px$.

(c) $t = 0, \ r = 6, \ p - qx = s(y - x^2)$.

2. (a) $z = axy + y^2 + \varphi(x)$.

(b) $z = \frac{1}{3}y^3 + \varphi(x)$.

(c) $z = \frac{1}{2}x^2y + xy^2 + \varphi(y)$.

(d) $z = y^4 - 4y^3 + 12y^2 - 24y + 24 + \psi_1(x) + \psi_2(x)e^{-y}$.

(e) $z = x^4 + x^2y + \psi_1(y)x + \psi_2(y)$.

3. (a) $x^2 + y^2 + z^2 = c_1^2, \ x + y + z = c_2$.

(b) $bx = ay + k_1, \ cy = bz + k_2;$ or $bz = cy + \varphi(bx - ay)$.

(c) $x = c_1y, \ z = c_2y;$ or $z = y\varphi\left(\dfrac{x}{y}\right)$.

(d) $x(2 + x) = 2y + y^2 + c_1, \ c_4 + x + y = c_3z$.

(e) $x^2 + y^2 + z^2 = c_1^2, \ x^2 - y^2 = c_2^2$.

4. (a) $z = cx + \dfrac{k}{c} y + b.$

(b) $z = \frac{1}{2}x^2 - cx + cy + b.$

(c) $2z(c^2 - x) = (cy + b)^2, \; x^2z + bx = cxy - c^2.$

(d) $2cz + c^2x^2 + y^2 + 2cxy = k.$

(e) $z = k(x^{\frac{3}{2}} + y^{\frac{3}{2}})^{\frac{2}{3}} + b.$

5. (a) $(c^2 + 1)(a^2 - z^2) = (cx + y + b)^2.$

(b) $c^2z^2 = 2cx + 2y + b.$

(c) $2\sqrt{z} = kx + \sqrt{1 - k^2}\,y + b$, with $k = (1 + c)^{-\frac{1}{2}}$ in $q = cp.$

Exercise XXI.

1. $z = \varphi(y + 4x) + \psi(y - 3x).$

2. $z = \varphi_1(y + 2x) + \varphi_2(y - x) + \varphi_3(y - 4x) + \varphi_4(y + 5x).$

3. $z = \varphi_1(y + 9x) + \varphi_2(y + 2\sqrt{6}x) + \varphi_3(y - 2\sqrt{6}x).$

4. $z = \varphi_1(y - x) + x\varphi_2(y - x) + \varphi_3(y - 6x).$

5. $z = \varphi_1(y + x) + \varphi_2(y + \frac{1}{2}x) + \varphi_3(y + \frac{1}{3}x).$

6. $z = \varphi(y + x) + e^{-x}\psi(y - x).$

7. $z = e^{-2x}\varphi(y + \frac{3}{2}x) + e^{2x}\psi(y + x).$

8. $z = \varphi_1(y + x) + e^x\varphi_2(y) + 4e^{2x+y} - \frac{1}{2}\sin{(3x - y)}$
$$- \frac{3}{2}\cos{(3x - y)}.$$

9. $z = \frac{1}{5}f_1(y + 3x) - \frac{1}{5}f_2(y - 2x).$

10. $y = c_1, \; x = c_4z$; therefore $x = \varphi_1(y) + \varphi_2(z).$

Exercise XXII.

1. $\varphi_1 = -19.6°, \; V_i = 23641$ ft./sec.

Examination I.

1. (a) $x + y = xy \ln{\dfrac{cx}{y}}.$ **(b)** $x^2 + \dfrac{x}{y} + \ln y = k.$

2. (a) $y = x + x \ln y.$ **(b)** $3y(x^2 + 3) + 5x^3 = 61.$

3. $yx^2 = 2x + c; \; xy = 2.$

4. $i = \frac{4}{226}(15 \sin 2t - \cos 2t + e^{-30t}).$

5. (a) $v^2 = 2gx - \dfrac{2}{m}x^3.$ **(b)** $v = 0.$

Examination II.

1. (a) $y = c_1e^{-3x} + c_2xe^{-3x}.$

(b) $y = e^{-x/k}(c_1 \cos x + c_2 \sin x).$

2. (a) $y = e^{-2x}(c_1 + c_2x - \ln x).$

(b) $y = c_1 + c_2e^{-x} - \frac{1}{5}\sin 2x - \frac{1}{10}\cos 2x.$

4. $x = e^{-t}(c_1 \cos t + c_2 \sin t)$; oscillatory; undercritically damped; period $\equiv 2\pi$; frequency $\equiv \dfrac{1}{2\pi}$; log. dec. $\equiv -2\pi$.

5. (a) $y = x^4 + c_1 \ln x + c_2$.
   (b) $y = e^x(x - 2) + c_1 x + c_2$.

Examination III.

1. (a) $y = c_1 + c_2 e^{4x} + c_3 e^{3x}$.
   (b) $y = e^{-2x}(c_1 \cos 3x + c_2 \sin 3x)$.

2. $y = c_1 + c_2 x + e^x(c_3 - 2x + \frac{1}{2}x^2) - \frac{3}{2}x^2 - \frac{1}{2}x^3$.

3. $z = c_1 e^{2t} + c_2 e^{-2t} - 2$, $y = \frac{3}{2}c_1 e^{2t} - \frac{3}{2}c_2 e^{-2t} - t + c_3$,
   $x = -\frac{1}{2}c_1 e^{2t} + \frac{1}{2}c_2 e^{-2t} + t + c_3 - 3$.

4. $y = e^x(\frac{1}{2}\ln x + \frac{1}{4}x^2 - x + \frac{3}{4})$.

Examination IV.

1. $y = 1 + x^2$.

2. (a) $y(x) = a_0 x^n \left(1 - \dfrac{x^2}{4(n+1)}\right.$
   $\left. + \dfrac{x^4}{32(n+1)(n+2)} - \dfrac{x^6}{(12)(32)(n+1)(n+2)(n+3)} + \cdots \right)$.
   (b) $y(x) = a_0 x^{-\frac{1}{2}} \sin x$.

3. $y = kx$.

4. $y = 2 + cx$.

Examination V.

1. $z = \frac{1}{3}x^3 + \varphi(y)$.

2. $2x - x^2 = 2y - y^2 + c_1$; $c_2 - x - y = c_3 z$.

3. $z = cx + \frac{1}{2}y - cy + b$.

4. $z^2 = 2c^2 x + 2cy + b$.

Examination VI.

1. $z = \varphi_1(3x + y) + \varphi_2(y - 2x)$.

2. $z = \varphi_1(y - x) + e^{-x}\varphi_2(y) + \frac{1}{4}e^{x+y}$.

3. $\ln z = x + \varphi(y - x)$.

4. $z = \displaystyle\int \psi(y + x)(dy + dx) - \int \varphi(y - x)(dy - dx)$.

Examination VII.

1. $30y = -\ln(x^5 + 1) + c$.

2. $y = \left(\dfrac{1}{2} + c_1 e^{x/2}\right)\cos\dfrac{x}{2} + \left(c_2 e^{x/2} - 1\right)\sin\dfrac{x}{2}$.

4. $y = c_0(1 - 10x^2 + 5x^4) + c_1(x - 2x^3 + \frac{1}{5}x^5)$.

5. $y = c_1 \sin t + c_2 \cos t + \frac{1}{2}t + \frac{1}{2}$,

$x = c_2 \sin t - c_1 \cos t + \frac{1}{2}t - \frac{1}{2}$.

6. (a) $z = be^{-c(cx+y)}$

(b) $z = e^{2x}[\varphi_1(x + y) + \varphi_2(3x + y)]$.

7. $\begin{cases} v\ddot{x} - k\dot{x} = 0, \\ v\ddot{y} - k\dot{y} + vg = 0; \end{cases}$

$x = c_1 + c_2 e^{kt/v}$,

$y = c_1 e^{(\alpha+\beta)t} + c_2 e^{(\alpha-\beta)t}, \; \alpha = \dfrac{k}{2v}, \; \beta = \dfrac{\sqrt{k^2 - 4v^2 g}}{2v}$.

INDEX

INDEX

INDEX